An Introduction to
the Properties of
Engineering Materials

An Introduction to the Properties of Engineering Materials

by **K. J. PASCOE,** M.A., A.INST.P.

University Lecturer in Engineering and Fellow of
St. John's College, Cambridge

BLACKIE AND SON LIMITED

LONDON AND GLASGOW

BLACKIE & SON LIMITED
5 FITZHARDINGE STREET
PORTMAN SQUARE
LONDON · W.I
BISHOPBRIGGS, GLASGOW

BLACKIE & SON
(INDIA) LIMITED
103-5 FORT STREET
BOMBAY

First published 1961
Reprinted 1962, 1963, 1966

PRINTED IN GREAT BRITAIN BY BLACKIE & SON LIMITED · GLASGOW

PREFACE

IN RECENT YEARS the teaching of materials to engineering students has undergone a revolution. The descriptive course of metallurgy has given way to a study of aspects of solid-state physics which will lead to an understanding of the mechanical and physical properties of the materials which the engineer uses, non-metallic as well as metallic materials being considered.

This book is based on a course which has been found suitable for University Engineering students to give them an introduction to the fundamentals of the structure of materials. It is not comprehensive, mainly metals and mechanical properties are considered, but is of an extent that could be covered in a course of about sixty to eighty lectures.

The course starts with the physics of the atom and the nature of the various types of inter-atomic bonding. The assembly of atoms or molecules is considered by way of gases, liquids, and solids. Sufficient crystallography is discussed to facilitate an understanding of the mechanical behaviour of metal crystals. The band theory of solids is not included, but the basic concepts which form a preliminary to the theory—energy levels of electrons in an atom, Pauli's exclusion principle, etc.—are dealt with.

The inherent weaknesses of single crystals are explained in terms of dislocations, and the various methods of strengthening discussed.

So far, the topics covered are mainly fundamental physics. The next part of the book is more technological in nature.

The mechanical testing of metals and the relationship of test results to engineering design form the subject matter of two chapters. The heat treatment of steels is considered at some length. The importance that should be paid to corrosion problems and to the metallurgical factors in welding are emphasized.

A final chapter introduces some nuclear physics and shows that yet other properties have to be considered when selecting materials for use in nuclear-engineering projects.

Throughout the book, actual materials are quoted by way of example only, no exhaustive list of any class of material being given.

In a work of this kind, it is not convenient to restrict the units used to one system. For the pure science sections, the M.K.S. system of units has been adopted, while in the applied sections, common British industrial usage has been adhered to.

My thanks are due to many colleagues and friends who have given me help and encouragement in writing this book, in particular to Mr. M. G. Cooper for discussions on Chapter 18.

K. J. PASCOE

Cambridge,
   March, 1961.

CONTENTS

Chapter 15 | Alloy Steels

Chapter 16 | Corrosion

Chapter 17 | Welding

Chapter 18 | The Nucleus

ACKNOWLEDGMENTS

The publishers gratefully acknowledge permission to use, and help with, the following illustrations:

Figs. 3.2 and 3.4, J. K. Roberts, HEAT AND THERMODYNAMICS, Blackie.

Fig. 5.5, Macmillan & Co. Ltd.

Figs. 5.7 and 10.3, Dr. C. F. Tipper: G. H. Elam, DISTORTION OF METAL CRYSTALS, Oxford University Press.

Fig. 8.1, Dr. E. Gregory, METALLURGY, Blackie.

Fig. 10.4, A. F. Brown and the Institute of Metals.

Figs. 10.13 and 10.14, A. H. Cottrell, THEORETICAL STRUCTURAL METALLURGY, Edward Arnold & Co. Ltd.

Figs. 10.15 and 10.16, Sir Lawrence Bragg, Dr. J. F. Nye and the Royal Society.

Fig. 10.18, Dr. A. R Verma and the Royal Society.

Figs. 10.21 and 11.2, Messrs. Whelan, Hirsch, Horne and Bollmann, and the Royal Society.

Fig. 12.14, Dr. D. Tabor, THE HARDNESS OF METALS, Oxford University Press.

Fig. 13.11, Dr. W. A. Wood, PROCEEDINGS OF THE INTERNATIONAL CONFERENCE ON FATIGUE OF METALS, Institution of Mechanical Engineers.

Fig. 13.12, P. J. E. Forsyth, PROCEEDINGS OF THE INTERNATIONAL CONFERENCE ON FATIGUE OF METALS, Institution of Mechanical Engineers.

Fig. 13.20, Messrs. Woodward, Gunn and Forrest, PROCEEDINGS OF THE INTERNATIONAL CONFERENCE ON FATIGUE OF METALS, Institution of Mechanical Engineers.

Fig. 14.6, TRANSFORMATION CHARACTERISTICS OF DIRECT-HARDENING NICKEL-ALLOY STEELS, International Nickel Co. (Mond) Ltd.

Figs. 15.6 and 15.7, Messrs. Irvine, Pickering, Heselwood and Atkins, and the Iron and Steel Institute.

Fig. 18.2, S. Glasstone and M. C. Edlund, THE ELEMENTS OF NUCLEAR REACTOR THEORY, Macmillan.

The publishers also acknowledge permission for the use of the following figures which are based on diagrams or data in the works detailed:

Figs. 10.9, 10.11, 11.6, Boas, AN INTRODUCTION TO THE PHYSICS OF METALS AND ALLOYS, Melbourne University Press.

Fig. 11.7, Tin Research Institute.

Fig. 11.8, Seitz, PHYSICS OF METALS, McGraw-Hill.

Fig. 11.9, Rollason, METALLURGY FOR ENGINEERS, Edward Arnold.

Figs. 13.25, 13.26, THE NIMONIC ALLOYS: DESIGN DATA, Henry Wiggin & Co. Ltd.

Figs. 14.12, 14.13, 14.19, Clark and Varney, PHYSICAL METALLURGY FOR ENGINEERS, Van Nostrand.

Figs. 14.8, 14.10, 14.22, 14.23, 15.4, TRANSFORMATION CHARACTERISTICS OF DIRECT-HARDENING NICKEL-ALLOY STEELS, International Nickel Co. (Mond) Ltd.

Figs. 14.16, 15.5, THE MECHANICAL PROPERTIES OF NICKEL ALLOY STEELS, International Nickel Co. (Mond) Ltd.

Figs. 14.20, 14.24, METALS HANDBOOK, American Society of Metals.

Fig. 15.2, Heyer, ENGINEERING PHYSICAL METALLURGY, Van Nostrand.

Figs 15.8, A.1 to A.14, and Table 6.1, METALS REFERENCE BOOK, second edition edited by Smithells, Butterworth.

Fig. 16.5, CORROSION-RESISTANT MATERIALS IN MARINE ENGINEERING, International Nickel Co. (Mond) Ltd.

Fig. 17.1, Bruckner, WELDING METALLURGY, Pitman.

The author gratefully acknowledges permission given by the Syndics of the Cambridge University Press to reproduce certain questions from Examination papers.
The sources of these questions are indicated as follows:

[MST]   Mechanical Science Tripos.
[P]   Preliminary Examination in Mechanical Sciences.
[S]   Examination in Engineering Studies.

CHAPTER I

Introduction

1.1. The fundamental nature of material properties

The primary jobs of the engineer are the design, construction, and maintenance of structures, machinery, etc. In his function as a designer, he makes use of the principles of thermodynamics, electricity, and the statics and dynamics of solids and fluids, but he is always limited finally by the materials at his disposal.

For example, the maximum distance that can be spanned by a cable is dependent upon the strength/weight ratio of the material used. Also the efficiency of gas turbines increases with the temperatures attained, but the top temperature usable is limited by the availability of materials with sufficient strength at that temperature. For some applications, more than one property may be needed, such as high strength, associated with good electrical conductivity and corrosion resistance. As will be seen in Chapter 18, the nuclear-power engineer has to consider properties that are of no concern in other engineering fields. Although the range of materials is very wide and countless variations of properties are available, the ideal material for a particular application, having a combination of optimum values for various properties, does not always exist and a compromise is necessary. Economics may also play a part, so that a cheaper, though less suitable, material may be used where the capital saving may more than compensate for higher maintenance costs or a shorter life.

The properties of any class of available material can always be obtained by reference to appropriate catalogues and handbooks, and the design engineer can carry out his work merely by reference to these sources of information and to experience. He can, however, attain a much better appreciation of properties of materials and the possibilities that may be afforded by use of a different type of material or by development along certain lines if he has an understanding of the fundamentals which govern the properties.

The aim of this book is to introduce the reader to the relationships between these fundamentals and the properties. As the properties of any material depend upon the structure of the atom and the manner in which the atoms are arranged, it is necessary for a suitable course to begin with the structure of the atom and then pass on to a consideration of the

1

behaviour of atoms in large numbers, firstly as gases and then as liquids and solids.

Of materials used by the engineer, the non-metallic building materials—concrete, stone, and brick—represent the greatest tonnage. Following them come metals, with steel ranking first, and it is mainly with these that this book is concerned. The majority of the contents may properly be called physical metallurgy, but much of the fundamental behaviour discussed is also applicable to non-metallic materials.

The reader is not expected to memorize values of the mechanical properties of the individual metals and alloys, as those data are always available from handbooks. For this reason, catalogues of data which would be of direct use to the designer are not given, and where values are quoted they are by way of illustration only.

CHAPTER 2

Atomic Structure

2.1. Classification of the elements

One of the more immediately obvious methods of subdivision of the elements is the distinction between metals and non-metals. The distinction is based on both physical and chemical properties, some of the distinguishing properties for a metal being as follows:

> Ductility, that is, ability to be bent or otherwise deformed.
> High conductivity for heat and electricity.
> Capability of taking a polish, giving metallic lustre.
> Ease of alloying, alloys differing from other forms of chemical combination in that there is no law of constant proportions.
> Chemically, the oxides are basic and salts are formed with acids.

For most elements, the classification as metal or non-metal is obvious, but the two classes merge into one another, some metals possessing both metallic and non-metallic properties. Arsenic, for example, possesses many of the physical properties of a metal, but chemically it is much more like a non-metal. Such elements are called *metalloids*.

A list of all the elements arranged in alphabetical order is given in Table 2.1, together with their chemical symbols, atomic weights, atomic numbers, melting-points, boiling-points and data concerning their structure.

Newlands (1864) pointed out that if the elements were tabulated in order of increasing atomic weight, the properties of the first seven elements re-appeared in the second seven. He named this the *law of octaves*. Mendelejeff (1869) developed a more elaborate and systematic representation of this which is known as his *periodic law*. The periodic table in the general arrangement proposed by Mendelejeff, but including all naturally occurring elements (several of which were not known in Mendelejeff's time) is shown in Table 2.2.

The elements fall into 7 periods and 9 groups. The first period contains only the lightest element—hydrogen. The second and third periods contain 8 elements each, the fourth and fifth periods contain 18 elements each, there are 32 in the sixth period, and the seventh is incomplete.

In the second and subsequent periods, the first element is a chemically

TABLE 2.1—SOME PHYSICAL PROPERTIES OF THE ELEMENTS

Element	Symbol	Atomic number	Atomic weight [1]	M.P. °C [2]	B.P. °C [2]	Crystal structure [3]	Lattice constants [4] a	b	c
Actinium	Ac	89	227	1050		f.c.c.	5·311		
Aluminium	Al	13	26·98	660	2400	f.c.c.	4·0496		
Americium	Am	95	[243]	850					
Antimony	Sb	51	121·76	630	1440	r.	4·5076 α = 57° 6·5′		
Argon	A	18	39·944	−189	−186	f.c.c.	5·42 (at −233° C)		
Arsenic	As	33	74·91	814[5]		r.	4·139 α = 54° 7·5′		
Astatine	At	85	[210]						
Barium	Ba	56	137·36	710	1770	b.c.c.	5·025		
Berkelium	Bk	97	[247]						
Beryllium	Be	4	9·013	1280	2450	c.p.h.	2·2856		3·5843
Bismuth	Bi	83	209·00	271	1530	r.	4·7450 α = 57°14·2′		
Boron	B	5	10·82	2300	2550	t.	8·73		5·03
Bromine	Br	35	79·916	−7	58	orth.	4·48	6·67	8·72
								(at −150° C)	
Cadmium	Cd	48	112·41	321	767	c.p.h.	2·9793		5·618
Caesium	Cs	55	132·91	29	713	b.c.c.	6·16		
Calcium	Ca	20	40·08	850	1440	f.c.c.	5·582		
Californium	Cf	98	[249]						
Carbon (graphite)	C	6	12·011	3500	3900	hex.	2·4612		6·7079
Cerium	Ce	58	140·13	804	2900	f.c.c.	5·1615		
Chlorine	Cl	17	35·457	−101	−34	t.	8·56 (at −185° C)		6·12
Chromium	Cr	24	52·01	1900	2600	b.c.c.	2·8850		
Cobalt	Co	27	58·94	1492	2900	c.p.h.	2·5053		4·0886
Copper	Cu	29	63·54	1083	2550	f.c.c.	3·6150		
Curium	Cm	96	[245]						
Dysprosium	Dy	66	162·51	1500	2600	c.p.h.	3·5903		5·6475
Einsteinium	E	99	[254]						
Erbium	Er	68	167·3	1525	2600	c.p.h.	3·5588		5·5874
Europium	Eu	63	152·0	900	1400	b.c.c.	4·606		
Fermium	Fm	100	[253]						
Fluorine	F	9	19·00	−220	−188				
Francium	Fr	87	[223]						
Gadolinium	Gd	64	157·26	1320	2700	c.p.h.	3·6360		5·7826
Gallium	Ga	31	69·72	30	2250	orth.	4·524	4·523	7·661
Germanium	Ge	32	72·60	958	2880	d.	5·6575		
Gold	Au	79	197·0	1063	2660	f.c.c.	4·0786		
Hafnium	Hf	72	178·5	2000	5100	c.p.h.	3·1969		5·0583
Helium	He	2	4·003	−270	−269	c.p.h.(?)	3·57 (at −271·5° C)		5·83
Holmium	Ho	67	164·94	1500	2700	c.p.h.	3·5773		5·6158
Hydrogen	H	1	1·0080	−259	−253	hex.	3·75 (at −271° C)		6·12
Indium	In	49	114·82	156	2000	f.c.t.	3·2515		4·9459
Iodine	I	53	126·91	114	183	orth.	4·792	7·271	9·773
Iridium	Ir	77	192·2	2443	5300	f.c.c.	3·8394		
Iron	Fe	26	55·85	1539	2900	b.c.c.	2·8663		

(1) A value given in brackets [ ] denotes the mass number of the isotope of longest known half-life, which is not necessarily the most important isotope in atomic-energy work.

(2) Melting and boiling-points are given to the nearest degree. Except for the noble metals, most values above about 1500° C are not known accurately.

(3) The structure given is that at room temperature, except for elements which are not solid at that temperature. Many elements have other structures at higher temperature. Structures are denoted as follows:

b.c.c.	body-centred cubic
b.c.t.	body-centred tetragonal
c.p.h.	close-packed hexagonal
cub.	cubic
d.	diamond structure, two interpenetrating f.c.c. lattices
f.c.c.	face-centred cubic
f.c.orth.	face-centred orthorhombic
f.c.t.	face-centred tetragonal
hex.	hexagonal
monoc.	monoclinic
orth.	orthorhombic
r.	rhombohedral
t.	tetragonal

(4) Lattice constants are given for 20° C unless otherwise stated. The values are in Ångström units (1 Ångström unit, Å = 10^{-10}m).

(5) Value at 36 atmospheres pressure. Arsenic sublimes at 610° C at a pressure of one atmosphere.

TABLE 2.1—(*Continued*)—SOME PHYSICAL PROPERTIES OF THE ELEMENTS

Element	Symbol	Atomic number	Atomic weight [1]	M.P. °C [2]	B.P. °C [2]	Crystal structure [3]	Lattice constants [4] a	b	c
Krypton	Kr	36	83·80	−157	−153	f.c.c.	5·68 (at −191° C)		
Lanthanum	La	57	138·92	920	4200	c.p.h.	3·761		6·061
Lead	Pb	82	207·21	327	1750	f.c.c.	4·9505		
Lithium	Li	3	6·940	180	1330	b.c.c.	3·5089		
Lutetium	Lu	71	174·99	1700	1900	c.p.h.	3·5031		5·5509
Magnesium	Mg	12	24·32	650	1100	c.p.h.	3·2094		5·2103
Manganese	Mn	25	54·94	1250	2100	cub.	8·912		
Mendelevium	Mv	101	[256]						
Mercury	Hg	80	200·61	−39	357	r.	3·005 $\alpha = 70° 31·7'$ (at −46° C)		
Molybdenum	Mo	42	95·95	2620	4600	b.c.c.	3·1468		
Neodymium	Nd	60	144·27	1024	3170	c.p.h.	3·6579		5·899
Neon	Ne	10	20·183	−249	−246	f.c.c.	4·52 (at −268° C)		
Neptunium	Np	93	[237]	640					
Nickel	Ni	28	58·71	1453	2820	f.c.c.	3·5241		
Niobium (Columbium)	Nb (Cb)	41	92·91	2420	5100	b.c.c.	3·3007		
Nitrogen	N	7	14·008	−210	−196	hex.	4·03 (at −234° C)		6·59
Nobelium	No	102	[253]						
Osmium	Os	76	190·2	2700	4600	c.p.h.	2·7314		4·3197
Oxygen	O	8	16·0000	−219	−183	cub.	6·83 (at −225° C)		
Palladium	Pd	46	106·4	1552	3200	f.c.c.	3·8898		
Phosphorus	P	15	30·975	44	280	cub.	7·17 (at− 35° C)		
Platinum	Pt	78	195·09	1769	3800	f.c.c.	3·9231		
Plutonium	Pu	94	[244]						
Polonium	Po	84	210	254	960	r.	3·36 $\alpha = 98° 13'$		
Potassium	K	19	39·100	63	760	b.c.c.	5·333		
Praseodymium	Pr	59	140·92	935	3000	c.p.h.	3·6725		5·917
Promethium	Pm	61	[145]						
Protactinium	Pa	91	231	3000					
Radium	Ra	88	226·05	700	1140				
Radon	Rn	86	222	−71	−62				
Rhenium	Re	75	186·22	3170	5900	c.p.h.	2·760		4·458
Rhodium	Rh	45	102·91	1960	3900	f.c.c.	3·8031		
Rubidium	Rb	37	85·48	39	710	b.c.c.	5·70		
Ruthenium	Ru	44	101·1	2400	3900	c.p.h.	2·7058		4·2819
Samarium	Sm	62	150·35	1052	1600				
Scandium	Sc	21	44·96	1400	2500	f.c.c.	4·533		
Selenium	Se	34	78·96	217	685	hex.	4·3640		4·9594
Silicon	Si	14	28·09	1410	2480	d.	5·4305		
Silver	Ag	47	107·880	961	2180	f.c.c.	4·0862		
Sodium	Na	11	22·991	98	883	b.c.c.	4·2906		
Strontium	Sr	38	87·63	770	1460	f.c.c.	6·075		
Sulphur	S	16	32·066	119	445	f.c.orth.	10·437	12·845	24·369
Tantalum	Ta	73	180·95	3000	6000	b.c.c.	3·3058		
Technetium (Masurium)	Tc (Ma)	43	[99]	2700					
Tellurium	Te	52	127·61	450	997	hex.	4·4565		5·9268
Terbium	Tb	65	158·93	1450	2500	c.p.h.	3·6010		5·6936
Thallium	Tl	81	204·39	304	1460	c.p.h.	3·4560		5·5248
Thorium	Th	90	232·05	1700	4200	f.c.c.	5·0843		
Thulium	Tm	69	168·94	1600	2100	c.p.h.	3·5375		5·5546
Tin	Sn	50	118·70	232	2606	b.c.t.	5·8313		3·1812
Titanium	Ti	22	47·90	1680	3300	c.p.h.	2·9504		4·6833
Tungsten	W	74	183·86	3380	5700	b.c.c.	3·1652		
Uranium	U	92	238·07	1133	3800	orth.	2·858	5·877	4·945
Vanadium	V	23	50·95	1920	3400	b.c.c.	3·0282		
Xenon	Xe	54	131·3	−112	−108	f.c.c.	6·24 (at −185° C)		
Ytterbium	Yb	70	173·04	824	1500	f.c.c.	5·486		
Yttrium	Y	39	88·92	1500	3000	c.p.h.	3·6474		5·7306
Zinc	Zn	30	65·38	419	907	c.p.h.	2·6649		4·9468
Zirconium	Zr	40	91·22	1850	4400	c.p.h.	3·2312		5·1476

TABLE 2.2—THE PERIODIC TABLE OF THE ELEMENTS (AFTER MENDELEJEFF)

Period	Group 0	Group I A	Group I B	Group II A	Group II B	Group III A	Group III B	Group IV A	Group IV B	Group V A	Group V B	Group VI A	Group VI B	Group VII A	Group VII B	Group VIII
1		H														
2	He	Li		Be			B		C		N		O		F	
3	Ne	Na		Mg			Al		Si		P		S		Cl	
4	A	K	Cu	Ca	Zn	Sc	Ga	Ti	Ge	V	As	Cr	Se	Mn	Br	Fe Co Ni
5	Kr	Rb	Ag	Sr	Cd	Y	In	Zr	Sn	Nb	Sb	Mo	Te	Ma	I	Ru Rh Pd
6	Xe	Cs	Au	Ba	Hg	La and rare earths	Tl	Hf	Pb	Ta	Bi	W	Po	Re	—	Os Ir Pt
7	Rn	—		Ra		Ac		Th		Pa		U				

6

neutral inert gas, and the remaining elements show a gradual transition from the strongly electropositive alkali metals (lithium, sodium, etc.) to the strongly electronegative halogens (fluorine, chlorine, etc.).

In each group, the elements show a similarity in properties. The elements of each group in the fourth and subsequent periods are divided into two sub-groups, the elements of one sub-group more closely resembling the elements of that group in the second and third periods than do those of the other sub-group. For example, in Group I, potassium (K), rubidium (Rb) and caesium (Cs) have a greater resemblance to lithium (Li) and sodium (Na) than do copper (Cu), silver (Ag) and gold (Au). The properties of the elements in Group VIII are intermediate between those of Group VII A elements and Group I B elements. Thus iron (Fe), cobalt (Co), and nickel (Ni) show a gradual transition of properties between manganese and copper.

Lothar Meyer (1869) pointed out that many of the physical properties of the elements are also periodic functions of atomic weight. A curve of atomic volume (atomic weight/specific gravity) plotted against atomic weight (fig. 2.1) shows a periodicity, similar elements occupying similar positions on the curve. It will be seen from fig. 2.2 that melting-point is also a periodic function of atomic weight and gives a similar sort of curve. Some other physical properties that show a periodicity when plotted against atomic weight are specific gravity, hardness, thermal and electrical conductivities. One property that is not periodic is specific heat, which is considered more fully in Chapter 9.

2.2. Valency

The valency of an element is the number of atoms of hydrogen with which it will combine or which it will replace.

Valencies, in general, rise from 0 in Group 0 to 4 in Group IV and either fall again to 1 or increase to 7 in Group VII. Thus elements of Groups V, VI, and VII may exhibit two valencies which total to 8. Table 2.3 shows examples of compounds formed by representative elements of each group which illustrate these valency values.

TABLE 2.3

Group	0	I	II	III	IV	V	VI	VII
Valency	0	1	2	3	4	5 / 3	6 / 2	7 / 1
Element	He	Li	Be	B	C	N	S	Cl
Compound	—	LiH Li_2O	BeO	B_2O_3	CH_4 CO_2	NH_3 N_2O_5	H_2S SO_3	HCl Cl_2O_7

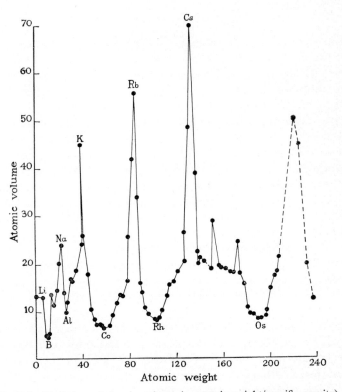

Fig. 2.1.—Variation of atomic volume (= atomic weight/specific gravity) of elements with atomic weight

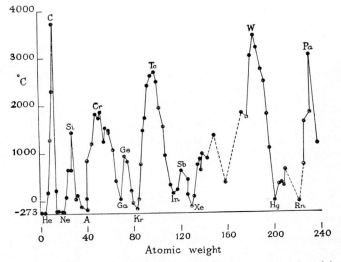

Fig. 2.2.—Variation of melting-points of the elements with atomic weight.

8

When the periodic table was first put forward, it was necessary to leave gaps so that similar elements should fall in similar groups. It was possible to predict the properties of the elements that would fill these gaps, and the predictions were confirmed when the elements were actually discovered.

The similarities and dissimilarities of the elements must depend upon differences in the atoms of the various elements. An explanation is therefore dependent upon a prior knowledge of the structure of the atom.

2.3. Atomic number

The atom consists of a central positively-charged nucleus around which circulate a number of electrons, sufficient to give electrical neutrality to the atom. The nuclear charge is $+Ze$, where $-e$ is the charge on an electron and Z is an integer. Z is thus the number of orbiting electrons and is known as the *atomic number*, each element having a different atomic number.

In general, the atomic weight increases as the atomic number increases. There are a few exceptions, for which it was found necessary in arranging the elements in the periodic table to reverse the order as given by the atomic weight to make the properties of the elements fit.

Thus the arrangement of elements in order of increasing atomic number also gives the periodic table. A more modern layout for the periodic table is shown in fig. 2.3. Each period is represented by a vertical line of elements, and elements in different periods with similar chemical and physical properties are linked by cross lines.

After the first short period comprising hydrogen (H) and helium (He) follow two periods of eight elements each. Each element in the third period falls alongside an element of the second period with very similar properties. In the fourth period, potassium (K) and calcium (Ca) bear a strong resemblance to sodium (Na) and magnesium (Mg) respectively, and then there are ten more elements before gallium (Ga), which resembles aluminium (Al), and five more elements corresponding to the last five elements of the third period. As was evident in Mendelejeff's periodic table, sodium also shows a weaker resemblance to copper (Cu), magnesium to zinc (Zn), etc. The weaker resemblances are shown by dashed lines in fig. 2.3. The ten elements, scandium (Sc) to zinc, are known as *transition elements*.

The fifth period is also a " long " period with all elements in it resembling the respective ones of the fourth period. The sixth period commences in a similar manner, but at the beginning of the transition elements fifteen *rare earth* elements, from lanthanum (La) to lutetium

(Lu) appear. These resemble yttrium (Y) and each other so closely that they are placed in a single space of the table. After these rare earths or *lanthanides*, this period follows the previous one. The seventh period is incomplete, but as more elements of high atomic number are produced by nuclear reactions, it gradually grows. Ten trans-uranium elements with atomic numbers from 93 to 102 have been identified and are shown in fig. 2.3.

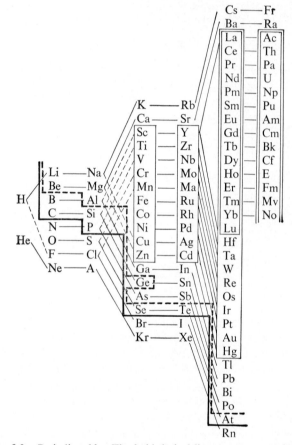

Fig. 2.3.—Periodic table. The bold dashed line separates metals from metalloids; the bold full line separates metalloids from non-metals

The elements following radium (Ra) may belong to a group analogous to the rare earths and are known as the *actinides*.

It should be observed that the numbers in the periods are 2, 8, 8, 18, 18, 32, — —, which are 2×1^2, 2×2^2 twice, 2×3^2 twice and 2×4^2.

Boundaries are marked on fig. 2.3 between metallic, metalloid, and non-metallic elements. Apart from the trans-uranium elements, the numbers in each group are:

metals	70
metalloids	8
non-metals	14

The picture of atomic structure will have to explain not only the cause of metallic properties, but also why there are so many metals.

2.4. The Bohr-Rutherford atom

The idea of an atom comprising a central positively-charged nucleus surrounded by negative charges was proposed by Rutherford in 1911, following the analysis of the results of experiments on the scattering of charged particles. The angular dependence of the scattering of α-particles (see p. 269) when beams of these particles were passed through different materials could be explained only by postulating this central nucleus whose diameter was of the order of 10^{-4} to 10^{-5} of that of an atom.

The negative charges surrounding the nucleus were identified with electrons which had been discovered by J. J. Thomson in 1897. The nucleus must exert an attraction on the electrons, so it is necessary to postulate that they would circulate in orbits in such a manner that the centrifugal force balances the electrostatic attraction. When electric charges move in an orbit, they emit electromagnetic waves, in the manner that oscillations of charge in an aerial can transmit wireless waves. Hence, on classical theory, the electron would be expected to emit electromagnetic radiation of the same frequency as the orbital frequency. This would involve loss of energy and an approach of the electron nearer the nucleus. This, in turn, would mean a change of frequency of the emitted radiation in a continuous manner and also the final collapse of the electron into the nucleus—neither of which is observed to happen. When atoms do emit radiation, it is in the form of fixed frequencies.

In 1913, Bohr proposed a quantum model for the atom, his assumptions being:

(1) The electrons exist only in stable circular orbits of fixed energy, the angular momentum of an electron in an orbit being an integral multiple of $h/2\pi$, where h is Planck's constant.
(2) An electron will emit or absorb energy only when making a transition from one to another possible orbit.

Some years earlier, Planck introduced the idea that light and all other forms of electromagnetic radiation possess energy, the smallest unit of which, a *quantum*, or *photon*, has energy hv, where v is the frequency of

11

the radiation, i.e. $v = c/\lambda$, where c is the velocity of light and λ is the wavelength. h is Planck's constant and has the value 6.62×10^{-34} joule sec.

From values of wavelengths observed in the spectra of the light emitted by hot gases, the values of energy of the photons can be calculated. Bohr's hypothesis was an attempt to find a basis for possible electron orbits, the energy differences between which would account for the observed spectral lines.

2.5. The single-electron system

Consider one electron of mass m moving with velocity v in a circular orbit of radius r around a fixed nucleus which has a charge $+Ze$ (fig. 2.4). Assume that the Coulomb inverse-square law for attraction and repulsion between electrostatic charges is valid for atomic distances. Then the attractive force between the electron and the nucleus is

$$Ze^2/4\pi\varepsilon_0 r^2$$

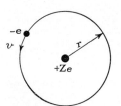

Fig. 2.4.—The Bohr-Rutherford atom with one electron.

where ε_0 is the permittivity of free space. Assuming that Newton's laws of motion apply, then the centrifugal force on the electron is mv^2/r. If the electron remains in its circular orbit, these forces are equal, that is

$$\frac{mv^2}{r} = \frac{Ze^2}{4\pi\varepsilon_0 r^2} \tag{1}$$

or

$$v^2 = \frac{Ze^2}{4\pi\varepsilon_0 m r}$$

Thus for any value of r there is a particular value of v.

The energy of the electron is made up of two parts: its kinetic energy and its potential energy. The kinetic energy is

$$\text{K.E.} = \tfrac{1}{2}mv^2$$

The potential energy of the electron at any position is the work that has to be performed to move it to that position from a position at which the potential energy is taken to be zero. In this case, if the zero position is taken at infinity, the potential energy is the work done on the electron in moving it from infinity to a distance r from the nucleus, i.e.

$$\text{P.E.} = -\frac{Ze^2}{4\pi\varepsilon_0 r} = -mv^2$$

Thus the total energy of the electron when in the orbit of radius r, relative to its energy when at rest at infinity, is

$$\text{K.E.} + \text{P.E.} = \tfrac{1}{2}mv^2 - mv^2$$
$$= -\tfrac{1}{2}mv^2$$

Introducing Bohr's condition that the angular momentum mvr can have certain values only,

$$mvr = \frac{nh}{2\pi} \qquad (2)$$

where n can take the integral values 1, 2, 3, etc. Combining equations (1) and (2),

$$v = \frac{Ze^2}{2nh\varepsilon_0}$$

and the total energy is

$$-\tfrac{1}{2}mv^2 = -\frac{Z^2me^4}{8n^2h^2\varepsilon_0^2}$$

By inserting the numerical values of the constants (Table 2.4), the total energy becomes

$$-2\cdot18\frac{Z^2}{n^2} \times 10^{-18} \quad \text{joules}$$

As n, called the *principal quantum number*, takes the values 1, 2, 3, 4, etc., the energy levels will be in the proportions 1, $\frac{1}{4}$, $\frac{1}{9}$, $\frac{1}{16}$, etc., as represented in fig. 2.5a.

TABLE 2.4—FUNDAMENTAL CONSTANTS AND
CONVERSION CONSTANTS

Electronic charge	e	$1\cdot60202 \times 10^{-19}$ coulomb
Mass of electron	m	$9\cdot1083 \times 10^{-31}$ kg
Mass of proton	M_p	$1\cdot67238 \times 10^{-27}$ kg
Mass of neutron	M_n	$1\cdot67470 \times 10^{-27}$ kg
Avogadro's number	N_0	$6\cdot0249 \times 10^{23}$ atoms (gm mole)$^{-1}$
Planck's constant	h	$6\cdot625 \times 10^{-34}$ joule sec
Boltzmann's constant	k	$1\cdot38048 \times 10^{-23}$ joule deg^{-1}
Atomic mass unit		$1\cdot65977 \times 10^{-27}$ kg
1 Electron volt (1 eV)		$1\cdot60202 \times 10^{-19}$ joule
Velocity of light	c	$2\cdot99793 \times 10^8$ m sec^{-1}
Permittivity of space	ε_0	$8\cdot854 \times 10^{-12}$ farad m^{-1}

As an electron jumps from infinity or an outer orbit to an orbit nearer the nucleus, there will be a decrease in its total energy equal to the difference in its energies in the two orbits.

$$\delta E = 2 \cdot 18 \times 10^{-18} Z^2 \left(\frac{1}{n_1^2} - \frac{1}{n_2^2} \right) \text{joules}$$

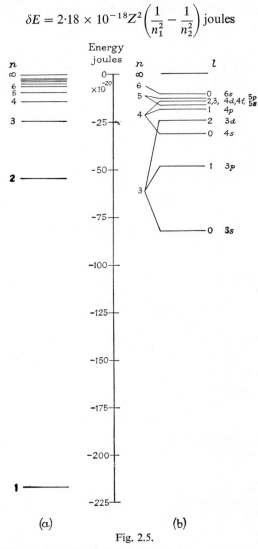

(a)   (b)

Fig. 2.5.

(a) Electron energy levels in hydrogen atom.

(b) Energy levels for valency electron in sodium atom. The energies of the $n = 1$ and $n = 2$ levels are out of the range of the diagram. The $4f$ level moves above the $5p$ level in heavier atoms.

This energy is released as a quantum of electromagnetic radiation of frequency $v = \delta E / h$, or of wavelength $\lambda = c/v = ch/\delta E$.

It is possible to check the values of the wavelengths emitted in the spectra of atomic hydrogen ($Z = 1$) and ionized helium ($Z = 2$), (i.e. a helium nucleus with only one orbiting electron). If either of these is excited, i.e. the electron knocked out of the innermost possible orbit, as for example by moving electrons in a gas discharge tube, then an electron can return to the innermost orbit by a single jump or a series of jumps. The wavelengths of the emitted radiation (which are of such order of magnitude that they fall in the visible and near-visible portion of the spectrum) are found to confirm generally the above formula. Slight differences have led to refinements of the theory.

Firstly, Sommerfeld postulated elliptical as well as circular oibits, the possible orbits again being restricted. This involved the introduction of a second quantum number, commonly known by the symbol *l*.*

Then further work resulted in the introduction of two more quantum numbers, one m_l to allow for the restriction of possible directions of the axes of the electron orbits, and the other m_s to allow for possible values of the spin of the electron.

Bohr's assumption that the angular momentum of the electron should be an integral multiple of $h/2\pi$ gave the right results, but there seemed to be no logical basis for it. A new system of mechanics, called *quantum mechanics* or *wave mechanics*, was developed which dealt satisfactorily with the behaviour of electrons and which led naturally to the quantum numbers of the electrons around a nucleus.

2.6. Wave-particle duality

Classical mechanics assumes that at any definite instant of time, both the position and velocity of a particle can be determined simultaneously. While this is so for large particles, e.g. a golf ball, it is easily shown that it is far from true for small particles of the order of size of an electron. The more accurately one is determined, then the greater the error in any simultaneous determination of the other.

Thus the position of an electron may be determined by observing the reflection of a photon of electromagnetic radiation. A more precise determination requires a photon of shorter wavelength, but this would have a greater energy, and at the impact between photon and electron there would be a larger momentum change of the electron, making any determination of the original velocity less precise.

This is summed up in Heisenberg's *uncertainty principle*, which may be expressed mathematically as follows: the minimum uncertainties δx and δp in determining the simultaneous values of the position x and the

---

* Sommerfeld used a symbol k which is equal to $(l + 1)$.

momentum p of a body are related by

$$\delta x . \delta p = \frac{h}{2\pi}$$

or, alternatively, the minimum uncertainties δE and δt in the energy E and the time t are related by

$$\delta E . \delta t = \frac{h}{2\pi}$$

An electron in motion about an atom is in a stationary state, i.e. the energy will not vary rapidly with time, or δt is large, so that δE can be very small. That is to say, electrons in stationary states would have sharp values of energy.

Quantum mechanics deals with the probability of an electron being at any specified position at any time. From the curves of probability the observable properties of electrons in atoms and molecules can be calculated.

2.7. Wave mechanics

Wave mechanics deals with a wave function ψ which varies with position and whose meaning is that $\psi^2 \delta x$ is the probability of finding the electron in the range between x and $x + \delta x$. Alternatively, ψ^2 can be regarded as the average electrical charge density at x due to the electron. The value of ψ can be calculated from Schrödinger's wave equation, which is a standard equation of the kind that deals with the motion of waves in strings, etc.

De Broglie, in 1924, pointed out that just as electromagnetic radiation had both a wave and a particle nature, so might all matter in general. He derived an appropriate wavelength for particles of matter:

$$\lambda = h/p$$

where λ is the wavelength of the particle and p is its momentum. The wave nature of electrons has been demonstrated by electron diffraction phenomena.

2.8. Electron states in atoms

The various permitted stationary states of motion of an electron in an atom are represented by various patterns of the wave function, each pattern being a possible solution of the wave equation. The quantum numbers n, l, and m_l appear as possible roots of the equation.

The most conspicuous features of the patterns are the nodes, i.e. places where $\psi = 0$ or where the probability of finding an electron is nil. These nodes lie on certain surfaces in the atom which are called *nodal surfaces*. There will be a nodal surface at infinity, since ψ will be zero there. The total number of nodes for a given state of motion is given by n ($= 1, 2, 3$, etc.). In changing from one state of motion to another, the number of nodes must change by an integral number, so that the electrons can only take one or another of a fixed set of energy values.

The nodal surfaces are of two kinds: spherical surfaces concentric with the nucleus, and plane surfaces passing through the nucleus. The number of nodal planes passing through the nucleus is denoted by the second quantum number l, which can take any of the values $0, 1, 2, ...,$ $(n-1)$. The possible orientations of the nodal planes are given by the values of the third quantum number m_l, which can take any integral value from $-l$ to $+l$ including 0.

To define completely the state of an electron, values must be given for each of the four quantum numbers. n is the principal quantum number and is a measure of the energy of the particle. For any given value of n (which must be an integer) the other quantum numbers are restricted to certain values as follows:

Angular momentum quantum number

$$l = 0, 1, 2, ..., (n-1).$$

Magnetic quantum number $m_l = -l, -(l-1), ..., -1, 0, 1, ..., l.$

Spin quantum number $m_s = \pm\frac{1}{2}.$

Thus, for example, if $n = 1$, then $l = 0$, $m_l = 0$, $m_s = \pm\frac{1}{2}$, so that there are only two sets of quantum numbers for an electron of this energy level. If $n = 2$, then either

$$l = 0, \quad m_l = 0, \quad m_s = \pm\frac{1}{2},$$

or $l = 1, \quad m_l = -1, 0 \text{ or } +1, \quad m_s = \pm\frac{1}{2},$

giving 8 sets of quantum numbers.

For $n = 3$ there will be 18, etc.; that is, for a particular value of n there are $2n^2$ possible sets of quantum numbers.

2.9. Many-electron atoms

According to Pauli's exclusion principle, which applies when more than one electron is present, not more than one electron may occupy a state described by any one set of values of the four quantum numbers. In the stable condition the electrons will occupy the states of lowest energy consistent with this principle.

17

Thus for helium, which has two electrons per atom, these electrons will be in the energy level corresponding to $n = 1$. The lithium atom has three electrons, of which two will occupy the $n = 1$ level, and the other one will go into the $n = 2$ level. Beryllium ($Z = 4$) will have two electrons in each of the first two levels, and so on. Each level of energy defined by a different value of n is termed a *shell*.

For the one-electron system, the energy of any possible electron state is governed exclusively by n. When more than one electron is present, the simple analysis previously given does not apply entirely, and the energy depends to a lesser extent upon l as well. Each shell thus has a series of sub-levels. Some of the sub-levels for the valency electron of a sodium atom are shown in fig. 2.5b. It will be seen that for the higher shells, where the difference in energy between successive values of n becomes less, the spread of the sub-levels is sufficient to give overlapping between the levels of different shells.

As it is often convenient to refer to the sub-level of a shell, these have been given the letters *s*, *p*, *d*, and *f*, corresponding to $l = 1, 2, 3,$ and 4 respectively. In any one shell, there could be two *s* electrons, each shell beyond the first can have six *p* electrons, etc. The letters may be preceded by a number denoting the value of n. Thus a boron atom ($Z = 5$) in the stable condition would have two 1*s* electrons, two 2*s* electrons, and one 2*p* electron.

Wave mechanics also leads to the result that, when all shells are full or contain 8 or 18 electrons, a completely symmetrical structure is formed which is extremely stable and will not react chemically.

Thus the inert gases have the electron configurations:

helium	2
neon	2, 8
argon	2, 8, 8, even though the $n = 3$ shell is not full
krypton	2, 8, 18, 8, etc.

2.10. Relationship of chemical behaviour to electron structure

The two 1*s* electrons of lithium are closely bound to the nucleus by the attraction of the $+3e$ charge, but the single 2*s* electron is much farther away from the nucleus and partly screened from its attraction by the negative charges of the two 1*s* electrons. Consequently the lithium atom readily loses this outer electron forming a positively charged *ion* (written as Li^+). This ion has the same electron structure as the inert gas helium and is stable, though unlike helium it has a net positive charge.

Fluorine ($Z = 9$) has two electrons in the first shell and seven in the second shell (two 2*s* and five 2*p* electrons). It is short of one electron to form the stable structure of the neon atom, which has eight electrons in the $n = 2$ shell, and will readily absorb any available electron to give this stable structure. Thus it acquires a resultant negative charge and so becomes a negative ion (F^-).

Hydrogen may either lose an electron to become H^+ or take one up to form H^-.

In the third period of the periodic table, sodium ($Z = 11$) and chlorine ($Z = 17$) are one electron over and one electron short respectively of stable structures, and so behave like lithium and fluorine. Elements near to lithium and sodium in these periods, which have two or three electrons in their outer shells, also lose electrons to form stable positive ions, which carry two or three units of charge respectively. Elements near fluorine and chlorine similarly tend to form negative ions.

It will be seen from fig. 2.5b that the 4s sub-level has less energy than the 3d sub-level. The two elements of atomic number just above argon will thus have electron structures

potassium	2, 8, 8, 1
calcium	2, 8, 8, 2

Since chemical properties are dictated mainly by the number of electrons in the outermost shell, these will be similar to sodium and magnesium. The next ten elements in increasing order of atomic number will be formed by the filling of the 3d level with two electrons in the 4s shell in each case.* These ten elements are the transition elements to which reference was made on p. 9. Following zinc, the period is completed by the filling of the 4p level for the next six elements up to the inert gas krypton.

The next period follows a similar pattern, but the sixth period has added complications. In building up successive elements, the first two electrons go into the 6s level, then one goes into the 5d level, after which the as yet vacant 4f level receives electrons. These electrons are unable to exert much influence on the chemical behaviour, being screened by the $n = 5$ shell. Thus these elements from lanthanum to lutetium (known as the rare-earth metals or lanthanides) are so similar chemically that they are put into a single space in the periodic table. After lutetium, the period completes in the same manner as the previous period.

The seventh period, which is incomplete, appears to follow the same pattern as the sixth.

It will be noticed that the majority of elements (which includes the

---

* This is not quite true, there being two exceptions—chromium and copper which have only one 4s. electron

transition elements) have only a few electrons in the outermost shell. These are the elements that form positive ions, a property typical of metals.

2.11. X-ray spectra

Energies of a high order are required to remove the electrons in the inner shells of the heavier atoms from their orbits—energies such as would be acquired by an electron in traversing a potential difference of a few kilovolts. When an electron is removed in such a manner, the vacancy is filled by another electron jumping in from an outer orbit with a consequent evolution of energy. This is given out as a quantum of electromagnetic radiation, the wavelength being of the order of 1/1000 of that of visible light. This intensely energetic radiation is known as X-rays.

Each element has its characteristic X-ray spectrum, the lines of which are denoted partially by a letter indicating the shell into which the electron jumps. The letters K, L, M, N, O, P, and Q refer to the shells for which $n = 1, 2, 3, ..., 7$ respectively.

2.12. The bonding between atoms

1. *The electrovalent bond*

It has been shown above that, in forming ions, atoms favour structures which have a stable outer shell of electrons. This ion formation is simply the losing or gaining per atom of a number of electrons, and the number will be equal to the valency. Thus sodium and chlorine form monovalent ions by reactions which may be written as:

$$Na \rightarrow Na^+ + e^-$$
$$Cl + e^- \rightarrow Cl^-$$

where e^- represents an electron. The ions can combine by the attractive force between unlike charges, giving an *electrovalent* or *ionic* bond.

$$Na^+ + Cl^- \rightarrow Na^+Cl^-$$

An alternative form of presentation of these reactions is to show the electron structure of the outermost electron shell of each atom as follows:

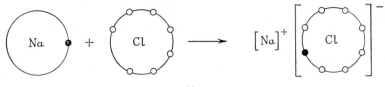

20

In calcium chloride, the $+2e$ charge on the divalent calcium ion is balanced by the charges on two monovalent chlorine ions:

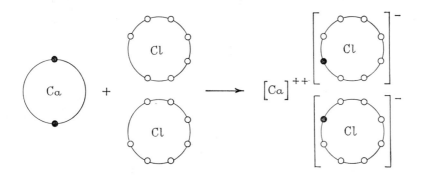

2. The covalent bond

Another way in which atoms can form the inert gas structure is exhibited by a form of bonding between atoms which have nearly eight electrons in their outer shells. Electrons are shared, so that some electrons orbit around both nuclei. An example is found in the chlorine molecule, where two electrons, one from each atom, are shared. The number of atoms in the outer shell of each atom is raised to the stable number of eight. Covalent bonds tend to be very stable.

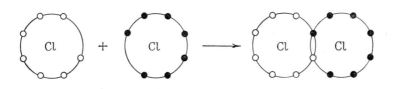

Elements lying between the alkali metals (Li, Na, etc.) at one end of the periodic table and the halogens (F, Cl, etc.) at the other end are less definite in character than these extreme groups. The tendency is for the formation of covalent rather than ionic bonds.

In general, atoms forming positive ions are seldom able to lose more than three electrons, or those forming negative ions to gain more than two. This may be easily understood; for example, although aluminium loses three electrons to form Al^{+++}, this tendency is strongly opposed by the attraction of the triply charged ion for the electrons.

Fully ionic and fully covalent bonding are completely different, but even so only represent extremes, since many bonds are partly ionic and partly covalent in character. An example is found in the compound between hydrogen and chlorine. These elements each form diatomic molecules with covalent bonding. In the HCl molecule, the bonding is covalent, but the shared pair is nearer the chlorine atom than the hydrogen atom.

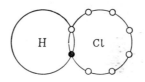

This means that the chlorine atom has a resultant small negative charge and the hydrogen atom has a small positive charge. This constitutes an electric dipole—the electrical equivalent of a bar magnet.

+ ━━━━━━━ −

When dissolved in water, the bonding of most of the hydrogen chloride molecules changes to ionic, dissociation to H^+ and Cl^- ions occurring.

Water is another example of a covalent molecule with a dipole moment. The molecule has a definite shape; the two hydrogen atoms are not on diametrically opposite sides of the oxygen atom, but at a definite angle to one another.

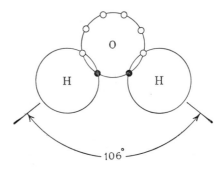

3. *The coordinate bond*

The coordinate bond is formed, like the covalent bond, by the sharing of a pair of electrons, but both of the electrons are provided by one of the atoms. An example is found in the bonding of oxygen to sulphur in the sulphate ion. The sulphur atom has six electrons in its outer shell. By sharing each pair of these with an oxygen atom, three oxygen atoms acquire an outer shell of eight electrons. Two more electrons gained from metal atoms or hydrogen provide the link for the fourth oxygen atom.

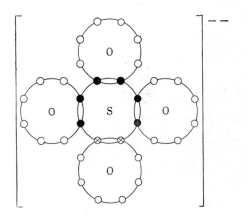

○ electrons from oxygen atoms

● electrons from sulphur atom

⊗ electrons from element
forming positive ion

4. *The metallic bond*

Metals obviously cannot form covalent bonds, as in general each atom has one or two electrons to lose.

Even when uncombined with other elements, metals are ionized. A metal may be described as a *cloud* or *gas* of free electrons in which the positive ions are embedded at the lattice positions, and the mutual repulsion due to their positive charges is balanced by the negative charge of the electron cloud which holds them together. This picture of a metal is called the *free-electron theory* and gives an explanation of the electrical conductivity of metals, as the electrons would be free to move. The thermal conductivity and optical effects can also be explained by it. The free-electron picture is highly simplified and not entirely correct.

By consideration in terms of wave mechanics, the electron density is obtained from the solution of the wave equation for the case where the potential is a function which repeats periodically in three dimensions within the boundaries of the crystal, the potential reaching a maximum at each position occupied by a positive ion. The results show that there is a series of possible energy levels for these valency electrons. In accordance with Pauli's exclusion principle, each level can be occupied by only two electrons (these having opposite spins), and in the stable state those levels of lowest energy will be occupied. The energy distribution that results from this theory can explain several features, such as semiconductors, which the free-electron theory does not.

QUESTIONS

1. What are the valencies of the metal atoms in each of the following compounds: $MgCl_2$, $SnCl_4$, SnO, P_2O_3, PCl_5, SbH_3, $CrSO_4$, $Cr_2(SO_4)_3$, CrO_3, Mn_2O_7.

2. Describe the electron structure of the light atoms up to that of atomic number 19. Discuss the formation of ionic and covalent bonding between atoms in terms of the electron structure. [MST]

3. Describe the atomic structure of helium, aluminium, and bromine. What types of chemical bond can each form? [MST]

4. Derive an expression for the energy levels of a hydrogen atom according to the Bohr-Rutherford theory. Hence calculate the wavelengths of the spectral lines corresponding to electrons jumping from the $n = 2$ to $n = 1$ and $n = 4$ to $n = 3$ levels.

5. Describe the arrangement of electrons in atoms of the alkali metals and the nature of the bond between atoms in crystals of these metals.

How are some of the physical properties typical of metals explained in terms of this structure? [MST]

6. A diffraction experiment shows that a certain beam of electrons exhibits a wavelength of 4 Å. Calculate the velocity of the electrons and their energy in electronvolts. (See footnote, p. 265).

7. Calculate the wavelength of a billiard ball of mass 0·2 kg moving with a velocity of 3 metre/sec.

CHAPTER 3

Aggregations of Atoms—The Fluid States

3.1. Introduction

In general, the engineer does not need to consider atoms as individuals, but is concerned with the properties or behaviour of assemblages of atoms in one or more of the three states of aggregation: gas, liquid and solid. In gases, the spacing of the atoms or molecules is large (except at very high pressures), but in liquids and solids each atom is in close proximity to its neighbours. The state of aggregation in which a particular group of atoms or molecules exists depends on the nature of the attractive forces present and may vary with changes in temperature and pressure. Under any particular set of conditions, the state or states will be such that the energy of the system is a minimum.

It will be more appropriate to consider the nature of the attractive forces after consideration of the behaviour of aggregates of atoms or molecules in the three states.

GASES

3.2. The behaviour of a gas

The more obvious qualitative features of gas behaviour are that it is homogeneous, that it has a large compressibility, that gases diffuse through one another, and that they never settle.

Quantitatively it was found that at low pressures gases obeyed the laws of Boyle and Charles, which may be summarized by the equation

$$pV = R_m T$$

where p and V are the pressure and volume of a mass m of the gas at an absolute temperature T, and R_m is a constant appropriate to the mass m.

Clearly R_m is proportional to m, since at the same pressure and temperature V will be proportional to m. Also Avogadro's hypothesis, which was deduced originally from chemical evidence and since verified in other ways, states that at the same temperature and pressure equal volumes of all gases contain the same number of molecules. This hypothesis is accurate to the extent to which gases obey the simple gas laws.

Gases deviate in practice from these laws, but at sufficiently low temperature and pressure the deviation is negligible. A gas in such a condition that it obeys these laws is known as a *perfect gas.*

3.3. Mole

If M is the molecular weight of a substance, then that quantity the mass of which is numerically equal to M is called a *mole.*

When the unit of mass is a gram, a mole is M grams—a gram mole. When the unit of mass is a pound, a mole is M pounds—a pound mole.

From the definition of the mole, it follows that one mole of any substance contains the same number of molecules. This number is Avogadro's number and its value is

$$N_0 = 6 \cdot 02 \times 10^{23} \text{ molecules per gm mole}$$

$$= 2 \cdot 73 \times 10^{26} \text{ molecules per lb mole.}$$

As a consequence of Avogadro's hypothesis, 1 mole of any gas at a given temperature and pressure always occupies the same volume. At *standard temperature and pressure* (S.T.P.), i.e. at $0°$ C and a pressure of $0 \cdot 76$ m of mercury, the volume of a gram mole is $0 \cdot 0224$ m^3 and of a pound mole is 359 ft^3.

Thus, 1 m^3 at S.T.P. will contain $6 \cdot 02 \times 10^{23}/0 \cdot 0224 = 2 \cdot 7 \times 10^{25}$ molecules.

Hence, if m is taken as the gram mole of any gas, R_m will always have the same value. If p is expressed in newtons/m^2, V in m^3, and T in centigrade degrees absolute

$$R = 8 \cdot 317 \text{ joules/gm mole per degree}$$

$$= 1 \cdot 98 \text{ calories/gm mole per degree.}$$

Although the value of R is of great importance, it has no fundamental significance, since the size of a gram mole is an arbitrary choice depending on the standard unit of mass and the convention that the atomic weight of oxygen be taken as 16.

Hence it is often more convenient to use a more fundamental constant: viz.

$$\frac{R}{N_0} = k = \text{Boltzmann's constant}$$

$$= 1 \cdot 38 \times 10^{-23} \text{ joule/degree.}$$

This may be regarded as the gas constant for a single molecule.

3.4. The kinetic theory of gases

Any theoretical model of a gas must explain the qualitative features listed above, and obey the laws quoted.

We suppose that a gas consists of molecules, which in any one gas are all alike—hence the homogeneity of a gas. The actual volume occupied by the molecules is very small compared with the total volume of the gas—explaining the high compressibility. Since diffusion can occur, the molecules must be in motion. Also we assume that the molecules exert no force on each other except when actually in contact, and that the collisions between molecules and of molecules with the container walls are perfectly elastic. If this were not so, there would be a loss of energy at each collision and the molecules, losing velocity, would gradually settle.

The pressure exerted by a gas is due to the collisions of the molecules with the walls of the container.

3.5. Calculation of the pressure of a perfect gas

Consider a closed cubical vessel of side d containing n molecules of gas, each of mass m.

Let a particular molecule have a velocity c_1, the components of which in the three directions perpendicular to the cube faces are x_1, y_1, z_1.

Then
$$c_1{}^2 = x_1{}^2 + y_1{}^2 + z_1{}^2$$

Consider the two faces perpendicular to the x-direction. At each collision of the molecule, its momentum perpendicular to the face changes from mx_1 to $-mx_1$. The molecule traverses the cube x_1/d times per unit time and hence makes $x_1/2d$ impacts on each face per unit time. Then the rate of change of momentum at each face is

$$2mx_1 \cdot \frac{x_1}{2d} = \frac{mx_1^2}{d}$$

This is the force exerted on each face perpendicular to the x-direction by a single molecule. Owing to collisions, one molecule will not, in general, traverse the cube without changes in velocity. Momentum in each direction will, however, be conserved and the total change of momentum at a face will be unaltered whether there are inter-molecular collisions or not.

Let $\overline{C^2}$ be the *mean-square velocity* such that

$$c_1^2 + c_2^2 + c_3^2 + - - = n\overline{C^2}$$

Then the total force on all sides of the cube is

$$\frac{2nm\overline{C^2}}{d}$$

The area of each face is d^2, and assuming an equal force on each face, the pressure is

$$p = \frac{2nm\overline{C^2}}{d} \cdot \frac{1}{6d^2}$$

$$= \frac{nm\overline{C^2}}{3d^3}$$

But d^3 is the volume V occupied by the gas.
Therefore

$$pV = \tfrac{1}{3}nm\overline{C^2}$$

$$= \tfrac{2}{3} \times \tfrac{1}{2}nm\overline{C^2}$$

$$= \tfrac{2}{3} \times \text{kinetic energy of translational motion of all the molecules in the gas.}$$

If we assume that kinetic energy is proportional to absolute temperature, i.e.

$$\tfrac{2}{3} \times \tfrac{1}{2}nm\overline{C^2} \propto T \quad \text{or} \quad \tfrac{2}{3} \times \tfrac{1}{2}nm\overline{C^2} = RT$$

where R is a constant, then

$$pV = RT$$

This equation combines the experimentally determined laws of Boyle and Charles. Hence the kinetic theory so far developed explains the laws of a perfect gas.

If we have equal volumes of two gases at the same temperature and pressure, then

$$\tfrac{2}{3} \times \tfrac{1}{2}n_1 m_1 \overline{C_1^2} = \tfrac{2}{3} \times \tfrac{1}{2}n_2 m_2 \overline{C_2^2}$$

where n_1 and n_2 are the numbers of molecules, and m_1 and m_2 are their masses for the two gases respectively.

Then if we assume that the average kinetic energies of the molecules of these gases are the same at the same temperature,

$$\tfrac{1}{2}m_1 \overline{C_1^2} = \tfrac{1}{2}m_2 \overline{C_2^2}$$

Hence $n_1 = n_2$, or equal volumes of two gases at the same temperature and pressure contain equal numbers of molecules, which is Avogadro's hypothesis.

3.6. Energy and velocity of molecules

The molecules in a volume of gas will not all have the same velocity. Even if this were possible at any instant, the molecules would immediately get different velocities owing to mutual collisions. Hence $\overline{C^2}$ really does represent an average value of C^2.

Consider a gram mole of gas at S.T.P. Then the pressure is 0·76 m of mercury or $0·76 \times 13{,}600 \times 9·81$ newtons/m^2, since the density of mercury is 13,600 kg/m^3 and the gravitational acceleration is 9·81 m/sec. The temperature is 273° K (Kelvin or Absolute) and the volume is 0·0224 m^3.

The value of the kinetic energy of the gas molecules will be

$$\tfrac{1}{2}nm\overline{C^2} = \tfrac{3}{2}pV$$

$$= \tfrac{3}{2} \times (0·76 \times 13{,}600 \times 9·81) \times 0·0224 \text{ joules/gm mole}$$

$$= 3·4 \times 10^3 \text{ joules/gm mole}$$

or $\qquad 1·08 \times 10^6$ ft Lb/lb mole.

This is called the molecular energy of translation of a gas at S.T.P. and from it we can calculate the root-mean-square speed of the molecules. Now $nm = M$, where M is the molecular weight in grams, so that

$$\overline{C^2} = \frac{2 \times 3·4 \times 10^3}{M} \text{ joules/kg}$$

For hydrogen, $M = 0·002$ kg, giving

$$\sqrt{(\overline{C^2})} = \sqrt{(3·4 \times 10^6)}$$

$$= 1840 \text{ m/sec at } 0°\text{ C}$$

The magnitude of this velocity may be appreciated more readily if expressed as 1·14 miles/sec or 4100 m.p.h.

For carbon dioxide, $M = 0·044$ kg, giving

$$\sqrt{(\overline{C^2})} = \sqrt{\left(\frac{2 \times 3·4 \times 10^3}{0·044}\right)}$$

$$= 393 \text{ m/sec at } 0°\text{ C}$$

Now $\overline{C^2}$ is proportional to absolute temperature. Therefore at 400° K for carbon dioxide

$$\sqrt{(\overline{C^2})} = 393 \times \sqrt{(400/273)} \text{ m/sec}$$

$$= 476 \text{ m/sec}$$

3.7. Maxwellian distribution of velocities

The results of the foregoing theory give the value of $\overline{C^2}$, but do not give any information about the *distribution* of velocities among the molecules. The form of the distribution curve, which will not be derived here, is given by *Maxwell's distribution law*. Of the total number of molecules, the fraction which have velocities lying between c and $(c+\delta c)$ is proportional to

$$\frac{1}{T^{3/2}} c^2 e^{-mc^2/2kT} \delta c$$

The curve of the distribution of velocities has the shape shown in fig. 3.1. The shaded area is proportional to the above expression. An increase of

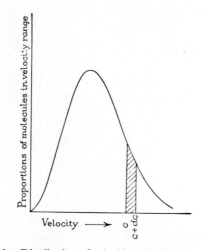

Fig. 3.1.—Distribution of velocities of molecules of a gas

temperature alters the shape of the curve as may be seen from the distribution curves for hydrogen in fig. 3.2.

The mean velocity is found to bear a definite relation to the root-mean-square velocity.

$$\overline{c} = 0.921\sqrt{(\overline{C^2})}$$

The most probable velocity α, i.e. the value of the velocity at the peak of the distribution curve, is given by

$$\alpha = 0.816\sqrt{(\overline{C^2})}$$

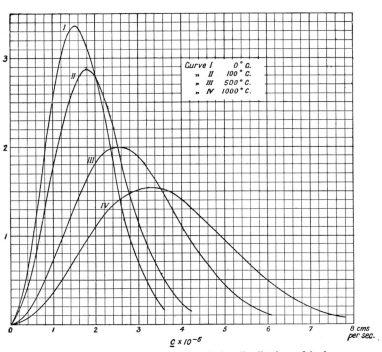

Fig. 3.2.—Effect of temperature on velocity distribution of hydrogen gas molecules. [Roberts]

3.8. Mean free path

The *mean free path* is the average distance that a molecule travels between successive collisions with other molecules.

A simple calculation of its value can be made by assuming all molecules but one to be at rest. Let

$$d = \text{diameter of each molecule}$$

$$n = \text{number of molecules per unit volume.}$$

The moving molecule will collide with any other molecule whose centre lies within a distance d of the path of the centre of the moving molecule. In travelling a distance l, it will collide with all molecules whose centres lie in a cylinder of length l and radius d (fig. 3.3). The number of molecules contained in the volume $\pi d^2 l$ is $\pi d^2 ln$, which is also the number of collisions.

Hence the mean free path λ is given by

$$\lambda = \frac{l}{\pi d^2 ln} = \frac{1}{\pi d^2 n}$$

31

If account is taken of the motion of all the molecules, and the velocities are assumed to be distributed according to Maxwell's distribution law, the mean free path is found to be

$$\lambda = \frac{1}{\sqrt{2\pi d^2 n}}$$

The term *diameter* as applied to a gas molecule does not have any precise significance, so that it is not possible to calculate λ from the above

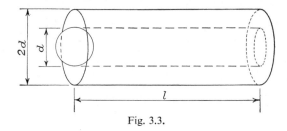

Fig. 3.3.

expression. The mean free path is obviously of importance in connection with any property of a gas which involves transfer. An example is *thermal conductivity*. A simple approximate calculation leads to the expression

$$K = \tfrac{1}{3} nm\bar{c}\lambda C_v$$

where K = thermal conductivity and C_v = specific heat at constant volume (see p. 114). As in the previous calculation, a more refined treatment merely modifies the numerical constant.

K can be measured experimentally and hence λ and d calculated. Some approximate values at 15° C and 1 atmosphere pressure are:

	λ	d
H_2	$16 \cdot 3 \times 10^{-8}$ m.	$2 \cdot 3 \times 10^{-10}$ m.
N_2	$8 \cdot 5$	$3 \cdot 15$
O_2	$9 \cdot 6$	$2 \cdot 96$

3.9. Variation of λ and K with pressure

Since $\lambda = 1/\sqrt{2\pi d^2 n}$ and because n is proportional to pressure at a given temperature,

$$\lambda \propto \frac{1}{p}$$

Therefore at low pressures λ may be quite large.

For example, in a radio valve, where the pressure is of the order of 10^{-9} atmosphere, the mean free path will be about 100 m. This is much greater than the dimensions of the valve, so that in general a molecule traversing the valve will not collide with any other molecules. (Even at this low pressure, there are still $2 \cdot 7 \times 10^{16}$ molecules/m^3.)

Since $K = \frac{1}{3}nmc\lambda C_v$, and because n is proportional to pressure and λ to the reciprocal of pressure, K will be independent of pressure. This is found to be true at fairly high pressures, but not at low ones. Obviously the above expression is no longer valid when the mean free path becomes comparable with the size of the containing vessel.

3.10. Deviations from the gas laws

It was stated on p. 25 that at low pressures gases obeyed the laws summarized in the equation

$$pV = RT$$

At ordinary and high pressures gases depart from these laws to a measurable extent, the amount of departure varying from gas to gas.

Hydrogen, oxygen, and several others show extremely small departure at ordinary temperatures, while carbon dioxide shows considerable departure at ordinary temperatures and high pressures. With dihydrogen oxide (H$_2$O) the departure is considerable at ordinary temperatures and pressures.

The most famous experiments on the deviation from the perfect gas laws are those made by Andrews.

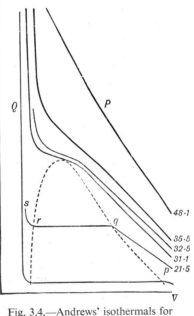

Fig. 3.4.—Andrews' isothermals for carbon dioxide. [Roberts]

He studied the behaviour of carbon dioxide using pressures up to 2000 Lb/in^2 and obtained the results shown in fig. 3.4. Each curve is an *isothermal*, showing the relationship between pressure and volume of a given mass of gas at a constant temperature.

Considering the isothermal for 21·5° C as the pressure is increased from a low value, the volume decreases until the point q on the curve is reached. On further compression, the pressure remains constant while the gas changes to liquid. At point r, the carbon dioxide is all liquid, and beyond this point the gradient is very steep, a large change in pressure producing only a small change in volume.

Liquefaction took place in a similar manner for all temperatures up to 31·1° C, but at higher temperatures no liquefaction occurred, however

33

much the pressure was increased. 31·1° C is called the *critical temperature* for carbon dioxide, and the isothermal for this temperature is the critical isothermal.

Two dotted curves are shown, one drawn through all points such as *q* which represent the volume of gas when in equilibrium with liquid, and the other through points such as *r* which represent the volume of liquid when in equilibrium with gas. These conditions are known as saturated vapour and saturated liquid respectively. These two curves meet at the critical isothermal at a point where the specific volumes of gas and liquid are equal. The pressure and specific volume at this point are known as the *critical pressure* and *critical volume*.

At *P*, the substance would be in the gaseous state, while at *Q* it would be in the liquid state. *P* and *Q* are single-phase regions, while between the two we have a two-phase region. (See p. 68 for the definition of a phase.) It is possible to pass from *P* to *Q* without any discontinuity occurring, by using a series of processes which do not pass through the two-phase region. This is referred to as the *continuity of the liquid and gaseous states*.

All gases show behaviour of a similar type, but the values of the critical temperatures, pressures, and volumes differ widely.

3.11. Van der Waals' equation

In deriving the perfect gas laws on the basis of the kinetic theory, two factors were neglected. These were the attractive forces between the molecules and the volume of the molecules. These factors were considered by Van der Waals, who made the first attempt to modify the simple kinetic theory.

If an approximate value for the molecular " diameter " is taken as $3·33 \times 10^{-10}$ m (see p. 63), then at least $2·7 \times 10^{28}$ molecules could be packed into one cubic metre. At S.T.P. the actual number is $2·7 \times 10^{25}$. Hence the molecules occupy only about 1/1000 of the total space at S.T.P. But when the gas is highly compressed, the volume of the molecules will be an appreciable part of the whole. A molecule thus has less far to go between collisions than would be apparent on simple theory, and hence will make more frequent collisions, putting up the pressure. The effect is the same as if the molecules were of negligible size but contained in a smaller volume.

The equation is written as

$$p(V-b) = RT$$

where *b* is the correction for the volume of the molecules (but not equal to it).

The attraction of the molecules for each other will have the effect of decreasing the volume; that is, it acts like an external pressure, and the volume of the gas depends upon the actual external pressure and the *internal pressure*. The force on a molecule depends upon the number of molecules within a sphere of radius such that the attractive force due to any molecule within that distance is appreciable. This number is proportional to the density or reciprocal of the volume. Also the internal pressure depends upon the number of molecules in a given volume that are subject to the attractive forces, again proportional to the reciprocal of the volume. Therefore the internal pressure term is proportional to $1/V^2$, or equal to a/V^2 where a is a constant. The equation of Van der Waals is thus

$$\left(p + \frac{a}{V^2}\right)(V - b) = RT$$

for a gram mole.

3.12. The properties of Van der Waals' equation

Isothermal curves calculated from this equation are plotted in fig. 3.5. At low temperatures each curve has a maximum and a minimum, while at higher temperatures the curves merely have a point of inflexion and get closer to $pV = RT$ with increasing temperature.

One intermediate curve has a point of inflexion with a horizontal tangent at C. This corresponds to the critical isothermal as found by Andrews, and C is the critical point. The temperature of this critical isothermal, and the pressure and volume at C are denoted by T_c, p_c, and V_c respectively.

Now Van der Waals' equation can be rewritten in the form

$$p = \frac{RT}{V - b} - \frac{a}{V^2}$$

This may be differentiated with respect to volume for an isothermal, giving

$$\frac{\partial p}{\partial V} = -\frac{RT}{(V - b)^2} + \frac{2a}{V^3}$$

which equals 0 when

$$\frac{RT}{(V - b)^2} = \frac{2a}{V^3}$$

or

$$p = \frac{2a}{V^3}(V - b) - \frac{a}{V^2}$$

$$= \frac{a(V - 2b)}{V^3}$$

35

This is the equation of the dotted curve through the maxima and minima in fig. 3.5. For this curve

$$\frac{dp}{dV} = \frac{a}{V^3} - \frac{3a(V-2b)}{V^4}$$

$$= \frac{-2aV+6ab}{V^4}$$

The maximum of this curve is given by the point for which

$$\frac{dp}{dV} = 0$$

that is, when $V_c = 3b$ and $p_c = a/27b^2$.

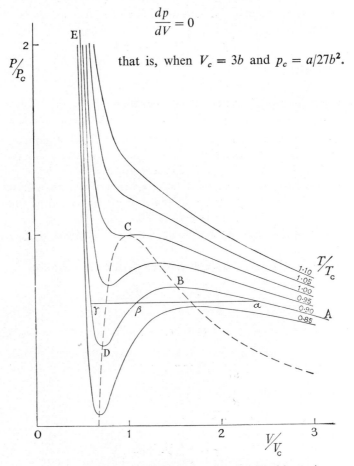

Fig. 3.5.—Isothermals calculated from Van der Waals' equation. The pressure, volume, and temperature are expressed in terms of the values of these variables at the critical point *C*. In this form the curves are independent of the actual values of *a* and *b*.

It then follows that

$$\frac{RT_c}{p_cV_c} = \left(1 + \frac{a}{p_cV_c^2}\right)\left(1 - \frac{b}{V_c}\right)$$

$$= \left(1 + a \cdot \frac{27b^2}{a} \cdot \frac{1}{9b^2}\right)\left(1 - \frac{b}{3b}\right)$$

$$= \frac{8}{3}$$

Also

$$T_c = \frac{8}{3} \cdot \frac{a}{27b^2} \cdot \frac{3b}{R}$$

$$= \frac{8}{27} \cdot \frac{a}{Rb}$$

3.13. Comparison of Van der Waals' equation with experiment

Below the critical isothermal, Van der Waals' equation gives an S-shaped curve *ABDE*, whereas experiment gives *AαβγE*, with discontinuities at α and γ. Here αβγ corresponds to the heterogeneous region of two phases in equilibrium.

The portions αB and γD which correspond to a supercooled vapour and a superheated liquid respectively can be obtained experimentally. *BD* represents an unstable region where increase of pressure causes an increase of volume, and could not be realized in practice.

The equation gives no indication as to where the point α corresponding to the start of liquefaction should be, but by thermodynamic reasoning it can be shown that the horizontal line αβγ should be drawn in such a position that areas αBβ and βDγ are equal.

The values of *a* and *b* deduced from the critical point give isothermal curves that differ somewhat from the experimental ones, so that Van der Waals' equation is not completely correct. It is, however, a good general approximation and has the merit of simplicity. Other equations of state have been suggested, which are improvements on that of Van der Waals, but none give complete agreement with experimental results.

LIQUIDS

3.14. The behaviour of liquids

A liquid, like a gas, is composed of molecules, but with much less free space. The molecules are still freely in motion, having kinetic energy which is dependent upon temperature, but the Van der Waals attractive force has a significant value.

3.15. Surface tension

Whereas molecules in the bulk of the liquid will experience equal Van der Waals attractive forces in all directions, those molecules nearer the surface will have an attractive force towards the bulk of the liquid which is not counterbalanced by any force from outside. This results in a definite force on the surface molecules which causes the liquid to behave as if enclosed in a skin. This force is known as the *surface tension*. The surface tension is measured in terms of the force necessary to separate an element of the surface layer of unit length. In increasing the surface area, work equal to the product of the surface tension and the increase of area has to be done. This is the *surface energy*.

The surface tension decreases with increasing temperature and becomes zero at the critical temperature (where vapour and liquid are indistinguishable). The surface tension of water is about 0·070 and that of alcohol about 0·025 newtons/metre at room temperature. The surface tension of liquid metals is much higher, for example molten aluminium and iron have values of 0·5 and 1·5 newtons/metre respectively.

A drop of mercury resting on a horizontal surface will keep an almost spherical shape, whereas water would spread out to a thin layer because of the much higher surface tension of the metal, although the mercury has a much greater density.

3.16. Vapour pressure

A molecule moving towards the surface will have its velocity reduced as it passes through the region of the unbalanced force. The field of force will be sufficient to reduce to zero the translational energy of a molecule which has an initial energy equal to or less than the mean value for that temperature. Some molecules will, however, have a velocity sufficiently high to escape. These escaped molecules constitute the vapour of the liquid and exert a pressure known as the *vapour pressure* of the liquid. Owing to collisions some of these molecules will acquire velocities towards the surface, and when they strike it will be absorbed into the bulk of the liquid. If evaporation takes place inside a closed container, the number of vapour molecules will at first increase. As the density of vapour molecules increases, so also will the rate at which they return to the liquid. An equilibrium state will be reached when the rates at which molecules leave and re-enter the liquid are equal. The vapour is then saturated, and its vapour pressure is called the *saturation vapour pressure*.

When the saturation vapour pressure is equal to or greater than the total external pressure boiling can occur.

3.17. Viscosity

When a fluid is in a state of motion with different layers moving at different speeds, there is shear force between the layers which would bring all the fluid to the same average speed if external forces were not applied. This shear force is described as *viscosity*. In gases it is a transport phenomenon and has a relationship with mean free path. In that case molecules with the average velocity appropriate to their layers will be moving into adjacent layers carrying with them momentum, so that there will be a steady transfer of momentum tending to equalize the velocities of the two layers.

In liquids, the mean free paths are extremely short, so that the molecules will not in general pass from one layer to another. The intermolecular forces are, however, significant, so that each layer tends to drag the adjacent layer with it, thus reducing the relative motion.

3.18. Thermal conductivity

The conductivity of heat is also a transfer of molecular kinetic energy but, whereas with viscosity there was a definite transfer of momentum, the average momentum in this case will be zero.

QUESTIONS

1. 0·01015 gm of an organic liquid, when vaporized, displaced a quantity of air whose volume was 27·96 cm³ measured at 15° C and 750 mm of mercury pressure. Assuming Avogadro's hypothesis to hold for the vapour, calculate the molecular weight of the liquid.

2. Derive an expression for the root-mean-square velocity of the molecules of a gas contained in a volume v at pressure p, if the molecular weight of the gas is M.

Hence calculate the root-mean-square velocity of nitrogen molecules at 10 atmospheres pressure and 150° C. [P]

3. Define the *mean free path* of a molecule of a gas.

Derive an expression for the mean free path. Using this expression, calculate for argon at 15° C the pressure at which the mean free path is 0·01 m, assuming that the diameter of the argon atom is $2·88 \times 10^{-10}$ m. [P]

4. Explain the assumptions made by Van der Waals in deriving his equation from the simple gas law $pv = RT$, where p, v, R, and T have their usual meanings.

State the Van der Waals equation. To what extent can it represent the experimental pressure, volume, and temperature relationship of a gas such as carbon dioxide? [P]

5. The critical point of a gas occurs at 10° C and a pressure of 51 atmospheres, the density then being $2·2 \times 10^5$ gm/m³. Assuming Van der Waals' equation to be correct in the region of the critical point, calculate the molecular weight of the gas. (1 atmosphere $\equiv$ 0·76 m of mercury pressure.)

39

CHAPTER 4

Aggregations of Atoms—Solids

4.1. Introduction

Continued abstraction of heat and lowering of the temperature of a liquid results in a continued decrease in the kinetic energy of the molecules until, at a certain temperature known as the freezing temperature, the molecules " fall " into relatively fixed positions with respect to each other. These positions might perhaps be better described as *centres of oscillation*, for, although the random molecular motion characteristic of the liquid and vapour states has disappeared, all molecular motion has not ceased. It is merely reduced to oscillation about a fixed point.

The change of state from liquid to solid is accompanied by a change of volume. The solid is usually of smaller volume than the liquid, but some substances, of which water is the best-known example, are exceptions to this.

4.2. The crystalline state

When a substance becomes solid, it does so in a crystalline form, that is, the atoms or molecules take up positions in a pattern that repeats periodically in three directions. One network of the pattern will continue so far and then meet another network which has a different orientation, the two networks being different crystals or grains of the substance. Where a crystal extends to a free boundary, regular faces may form naturally, giving the usual elementary idea of a crystal. Where crystals meet, the boundaries will not be regular plane surfaces but curved or irregular.

The " solids " which are non-crystalline are termed *amorphous solids*, but the modern view is that they are liquids of very high viscosity. An example is glass, which is a super-cooled liquid in which the molecules are not arranged in a regular pattern, but have become fixed in a more random arrangement. Such an amorphous solid has cooled from the liquid state by steady cooling with continuous increase of viscosity without an abrupt freezing-point.

4.3. Space lattices

Consider first a two-dimensional lattice, of which a wallpaper pattern is an example. Its essential characteristic is that it is produced by the regular repetition of a unit of pattern, so that in the completed pattern the elementary units lie in equally-spaced rows, such that corresponding points of the units lie at the points of intersection of two sets of equally-spaced parallel lines as in fig. 4.1.

In three dimensions, there would be similar arrays parallel to this at equally-spaced intervals, such that lines can be drawn through each of the points 00, 01, 02, etc., which pass through the corresponding points in the parallel arrays. The whole set of points is formed by the inter-section of three sets of parallel and equally-spaced planes. Such a collec-tion of points is called a *space lattice*.

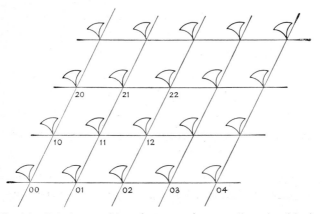

Fig. 4.1.—Regular repetition of a pattern in a two-dimensional lattice

These points are of fundamental importance in the description of crystals, for they may be the positions occupied by atoms in crystals, as is usual in metals, or they may be the points around which several atoms are clustered. Thus fig. 4.2 shows some possible crystal structures, all of which have the same space lattice. The important characteristic of a space lattice is that every point of it has identical surroundings. There are fourteen possible types of space lattice, the number being limited by the possible degrees of symmetry. However, the atoms can be built around the lattice points in an infinite number of ways.

To specify any arrangement of atoms in a crystal structure, it is customary to give their coordinates with respect to a set of coordinate axes chosen with an origin at one of the lattice points. Each space lattice has some convenient set of axes that is conventionally used with it. In some cases where there is sufficient symmetry, the axes may be mutually perpendicular and the units of length along the three axes equal. In other cases this will not apply.

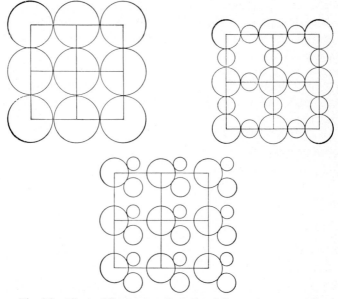

Fig. 4.2.—Three different two-dimensional " crystal structures "
with the same space lattice

In the space lattice given by the intersections of the lines shown in
fig. 4.3, the three axes are *OX*, *OY*, and *OZ*, and the units of length along

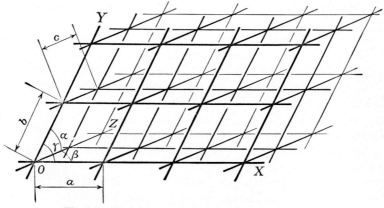

Fig. 4.3.—Lengths and angles specifying a space lattice.

them are the distances between the space lattice points, i.e. *a*, *b*, and *c*.
The angles between the axes are α, β, and γ, α being the angle between
the *OY* and *OZ*-axes, etc.

42

The space lattice is completely determined by *a*, *b*, *c* and *α*, *β*, *γ*.

The network of planes through the points of a space lattice divides the region into prisms called *unit cells*. If every point of a space lattice is at a cell corner, the cell is a *primitive cell*. In some systems it is more convenient to choose as the unit cell a prism which has a higher degree of symmetry or other feature which makes it preferable to the primitive cell for discussion purposes.* Each unit cell in a space lattice is identical in size, shape, and orientation with every other in the same crystal. It is the building block from which the crystal is constructed by repetition in three dimensions.

By means of X-ray diffraction methods it is possible to determine the shape and size of the unit cell and also the distribution of atoms within it.

4.4. Indices of planes

The various planes and directions in a crystal are specified in terms of the *Miller index notation*.

A plane is defined by the length of its intercepts on the three crystal axes (the three edges of a unit cell), measured from the origin of co-

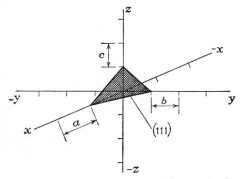

Fig. 4.4.—Intercepts of plane with crystal axis.

ordinates. The intercepts are expressed in terms of the dimensions of the unit cell, which are the unit distances along the three axes. The reciprocals of these intercepts reduced to the smallest three integers having the same ratio are known as *Miller indices*.

As the origin may be taken at any lattice point, the lengths of the intercepts for a given plane are not specified, but their ratio is constant. Any other parallel plane would have the same indices, so that a particular set of Miller indices defines a set of parallel planes.

The shaded plane in fig. 4.4 has intercepts 1, 1, 1 and therefore indices

---

* Some authors use the terms *structure cell* and unit cell to denote the unit cell and primitive cell respectively as defined here.

(111). A plane with intercepts 2, ∞, 1 (i.e. parallel to the OY-axis) has reciprocal intercepts $\frac{1}{2}$, 0, 1 and Miller indices (102). If a plane cuts an axis on the negative side of the origin, the corresponding index will be negative and written with a line above the number. Some examples of indices of planes are shown in fig. 4.5.

Parentheses ( ) around a set of indices signifies a single set of parallel planes.

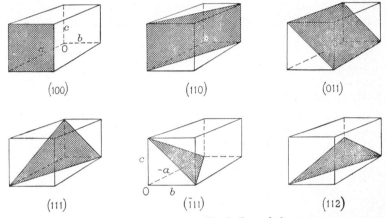

Fig. 4.5.—Examples of Miller indices of planes.

Curly brackets or braces { } signify planes of a *form*, that is sets of planes which are exactly equivalent to each other. Thus for a cubic crystal which has a high degree of symmetry {110} includes six sets of planes: (110), (101), (011), (1̄10), (101̄) and (011̄). It should be noted that reversal of the signs of all the indices merely denotes another parallel plane. Thus (1̄1̄0) is parallel to (110) and (101̄) to (1̄01).

4.5. Indices of direction

Consider a point which is to be moved from the origin in a given direction by successive motions parallel to each of the three axes. Suppose that the point is moved a distance u times the unit distance a along the X-axis, v times b along the Y-axis and w times c along the Z-axis. If u, v, and w are the smallest set of integers that will perform the movement, then they are the indices of the direction and are written in square brackets thus: $[uvw]$. The X-axis will be [100], the negative Y-axis [01̄0], etc. Several directions are shown in fig. 4.6.

A full set of equivalent directions (i.e. directions of a form) are indicated by carets ⟨ ⟩. Thus in the cubic system,

$$\langle 111 \rangle = [111] + [11\bar{1}] + [1\bar{1}1] + [\bar{1}11]$$

44

It should be observed that reciprocals are *not* used in computing directions. In a cubic system *only*, the [*hkl*]-direction is perpendicular to the (*hkl*)-plane.

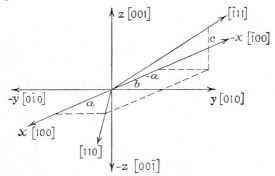

Fig. 4.6.—Examples of Miller indices of direction.

4.6. Crystal systems

There are seven crystal systems which are classified according to the various degrees of symmetry possible. Table 4.1 lists these systems and the relationships that exist between the cell dimensions and between the angles in each case.

TABLE 4.1—THE SEVEN CRYSTAL SYSTEMS

Triclinic	$a \neq b \neq c$	$\alpha \neq \beta \neq \gamma \neq 90°$
Monoclinic	$a \neq b \neq c$	$\alpha = \gamma = 90° \neq \beta$
Orthorhombic	$a \neq b \neq c$	$\alpha = \beta = \gamma = 90°$
Tetragonal	$a = b \neq c$	$\alpha = \beta = \gamma = 90°$
Cubic	$a = b = c$	$\alpha = \beta = \gamma = 90°$
Hexagonal	$a = b \neq c$	$\alpha = \beta = 90°, \ \gamma = 120°$
Rhombohedral	$a = b = c$	$\alpha = \beta = \gamma \neq 90°$

The more important space lattices are the face-centred and body-centred cubic lattices of the cubic system and the hexagonal close-packed lattice of the hexagonal system, these being the forms in which most metals crystallize. The features of each of these are describ d in the following sections.

4.7. Face-centred cubic system

The unit cell of the face-centred cubic system is shown in fig. 4.7. There is an atom at each corner of the cube and also one at the centre of each face. The corner atoms are lattice points. It will also be seen that the atoms at the centres of faces have surroundings identical with those of the corner atoms, and so are also lattice points. The primitive cell and its relationship to the unit cell are shown in fig. 4.8. Each atom at a corner of the

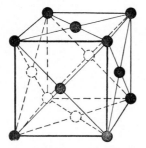

Fig. 4.7.—Face-centred cubic unit cell. The circles represent the nuclei of atoms.

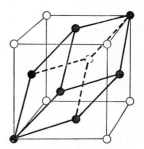

Fig. 4.8.—Relationship of face-centred cubic primitive cell to unit cell.

unit cell is shared by eight unit cells, and each face atom is shared by two unit cells. Hence the number of atoms per unit cell is $8 \times \frac{1}{8} + 6 \times \frac{1}{2} = 4$.

Fig. 4.9 shows a model of a cluster of spheres packed in a face-centred cubic manner.

Each atom has twelve equidistant atoms near it, which is the closest possible packing. Six of these in one plane form a hexagon around the

Fig. 4.9.—Face-centred cubic structure formed by spheres in contact

centre atom, and three are in parallel planes on each side, these being (111) planes. All the {111} planes in this system are planes of closest packing. The spheres touch along the ⟨110⟩ directions, which are therefore the directions of closest packing.

4.8. Body-centred cubic system

The unit cell of the body-centred cubic system has an atom at each corner and also one at the centre, as shown in fig. 4.10. The number of atoms per unit cell is $8 \times \frac{1}{8} + 1 = 2$. Each atom has eight equidistant near neighbours, so that this system is *not* one of closest packing. As may be seen from fig. 4.11, the spheres touch along the [111] direction, so that all $\langle 111 \rangle$ directions are close-packed. There is no close-packed plane.

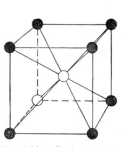

Fig. 4.10.—Body-centred cubic unit cell

Fig. 4.11.—Body-centred cubic structure formed by spheres in contact

4.9. Close-packed hexagonal system

The close-packed hexagonal system is another structure in which close-packed layers are packed on top of one another, giving the structure

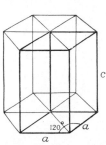

Fig. 4.12.—Hexagonal close-packed structure formed by spheres in contact.

Fig. 4.13.—Relationship of unit cell to hexagon in hexagonal close-packed structure.

shown in fig. 4.12. The unit cell is shown in relation to the hexagonal pattern in fig. 4.13. Those atom sites which are lattice points are shown in fig. 4.14, and fig. 4.15 shows the atom sites of the intermediate layer as well. These are not lattice points because the pattern of atoms surrounding any one of them is not the same as the pattern surrounding an atom site, there being a difference in the orientation. Each lattice

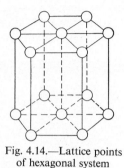

Fig. 4.14.—Lattice points of hexagonal system

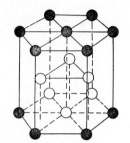

Fig. 4.15.—Atom sites of close-packed hexagonal system

point has associated with it two atoms whose coordinates relative to the crystal axes are 0, 0, 0 and $\frac{2}{3}, \frac{1}{3}, \frac{1}{2}$. A corner atom is common to eight unit cells, so that there are $8 \times \frac{1}{8} + 1 = 2$ atoms per unit cell. The volume of the unit cell is $a_1 \cdot a_2 \sin 120° \cdot c = \frac{1}{2}\sqrt{3}\, a^2 c$.

4.10. Stacking of close-packed layers

The face-centred cubic and the hexagonal close-packed systems are both equally dense and made by the stacking of close-packed layers, the difference being in the stacking pattern.

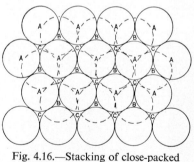

Fig. 4.16.—Stacking of close-packed layers

The atoms of the second layer can be placed on either of two positions on the first layer. In fig. 4.16, the positions of the centres of atoms of the first layer are denoted by A, and the possible positions for the centres of atoms of the second layer by B and C. If the second layer is placed, as shown by the dashed circles, with its centres at B, then the third layer can be placed with its centres at A or C. Any sequence of packing that does not have two adjacent layers with centres in identical positions will therefore give a close-packed structure. A crystal structure is formed only when a regular sequence is followed. If alternate layers are above one another giving the sequence $ABABAB \ldots$

(or *BCBCBC* . . . or *CACACA* . . .), then the structure is close-packed hexagonal, whereas if the sequence repeats at every third layer, i.e. *ABCABCABC* . . . , the structure is face-centred cubic.

The ideal axial ratio, *c/a*, of the close-packed hexagonal crystal should be 1·633 if the crystal were made of close-packed and equal spheres. In practice, it is found that metals which form crystals of this type have an axial ratio somewhat different from this value.

The values of lattice constants of the elements are given in Table 2.1.

4.11. Types of crystal

Crystals may be classified into types depending upon the method of bonding between the units of the structure.

1. *Covalent*

The atoms are linked throughout by covalent bonds. The best example of this class is the diamond, which is a crystal of carbon. As may be seen from the model in fig. 4.17, each carbon atom is linked to four others, which are symmetrically spaced around it so that their

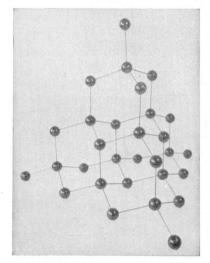

Fig. 4.17.—Structure of typical covalent solid—diamond

centres lie at the corners of a regular tetrahedron, at the centre of which the first atom is situated. When an atom forms more than one covalent bond, the directions of these bonds have definite angular relations with each other. This geometrical limitation restricts the number of possible crystal formations, so that this class is very small. Such crystals are hard

49

and have sharply defined melting-points. Since a covalent bond is between two particular atoms, the attractive forces extend only to these two atoms. Hence mechanical deformation will produce irreversible rupture of covalent bonds, so that these crystals are completely brittle.

2. Molecular covalent

Covalent bonds generally give rise to molecules. In a molecular crystal, the atoms within the molecules are strongly bonded, but the intermolecular forces, known as Van der Waals forces, are much smaller. The strength, hardness, and melting-point, which depend upon these forces are all small. As the attractive force between molecules is due to their proximity only and not due to any covalent bonding, the crystals may be deformed permanently without rupture; that is to say, they possess *ductility* and this may give them a soapy feeling, particularly in the cases where the molecules tend to be flat in shape and take up parallel positions in the crystal.

3. Ionic

The electrostatic fields involved in ionic bonding are most readily satisfied in a regular three-dimensional structure. Each positive ion will

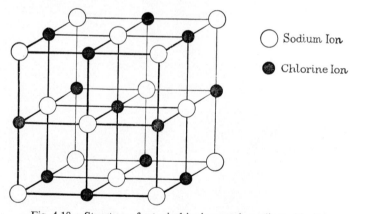

Sodium Ion

Chlorine Ion

Fig. 4.18.—Structure of a typical ionic crystal—sodium chloride

be surrounded by several negative ions, each of which in turn will be surrounded by several positive ions. One of the simplest patterns is exhibited by common salt (fig. 4.18).

Owing to the great strength of this type of bond, ionic crystals are strong, hard, and have high melting-points. Since the attractive forces can extend over long distances and are non-directed, ductility is possible.

One layer of atoms can slide over the next until it occupies a similar position, when the bonding will be as strong as before.

$$+-+-+-+-+- \quad \rightarrow \quad +-+-+-+-+-$$
$$-+-+-+-+-+ \qquad\qquad -+-+-+-+-+$$

4. *Metallic*

As described on p. 23 the atoms become positive ions held by the attractive force of the electron cloud. Though somewhat softer than classes (1) and (3), metallic crystals are at least comparable in strength and infusibility. They have high ductility because one atom is not tied to any other particular atom.

QUESTIONS

1. By considering a crystalline array explain the difference between a primitive cell and a unit cell.
   Sketch the unit cells of copper, sodium, and zinc. Indicate the close-packed directions and the positions of any close-packed layers of atoms in these structures, and explain their significance in the plastic deformation of crystals.   [P]

2. Show by considering a two-dimensional array the difference between a space lattice point and an atomic site.
   Sketch the unit cells of aluminium and titanium (at 20° C), marking lattice points by +, atomic sites by ◯ and a combination of the two by ⊕.
   Indicate the (100), (0$\bar{1}$0), and (112) planes and the [211] direction in a-iron.   [P]

3. Calculate the nearest distance between the centres of two atoms and the density of nickel from the relevant information in Table 2.1.

4. Calculate the distances between successive (100), (110) and (111) planes in gold.

5. Describe the influence of the type of inter-atomic bonding upon the mechanical properties of crystals.

CHAPTER 5

Crystal Growth and Size

5.1. Micrographic examination

To examine the microstructure of a metal visually, it must be suitably sectioned and prepared in a manner that will show up the grain structure. After the surface to be examined has been exposed, either by removing any unwanted surface layer or by sectioning, and flattening with an emery wheel or file, it is polished with successively finer grades of abrasive material. Emery paper may be used for this purpose, or alternatively, diamond dust on a cloth-covered rotating disc. The final lapping is by rouge or magnesia or alumina powder on a cloth-covered disc, after

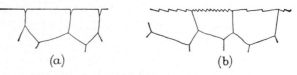

(a)   (b)

Fig. 5.1.—Action of etchant upon metal surface

(*a*)   grain boundary attack

(*b*) grain surface etch, producing facets of differing orientation
in neighbouring grains

which the surface should be free from scratches that would be visible under a microscope. It is then attacked by a suitable etchant, which may have one of two effects depending upon the metal and the etchant used: either, atoms will be removed at the grain boundaries, or, the surface of each grain will be attacked to expose facets of certain crystallographic planes as in fig. 5.1.

The metal is then examined under a metallurgical microscope. As the specimens are opaque, a vertical illuminator which will illuminate the specimens via the microscope eyepiece must be used. The optical system of a typical metallurgical microscope is shown in fig. 5.2. Suitable magnifications for metallurgical purposes are from × 50 to × 2000. The appearance of single-phase material after each of the two types of etchant acting are shown in figs. 5.3 and 5.4.

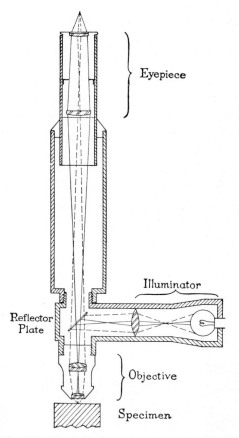

Fig. 5.2.—Metallurgical microscope with vertical illuminator

5.2. Formation of liquid drop from vapour

The growth of metal crystals from molten liquid is by a process of nucleation and grain growth, which is very similar to the formation of liquid drops from a vapour. In a vapour, due to the random motion of the atoms by variation of their thermal energy, they will come together in groups of varying numbers for an instant and then disperse. Above a certain size the group may be stable and continue to grow. The condition for stability depends upon the energy change as the group is formed. This consists of two parts: firstly the energy of the interface which in the case of a liquid drop is the surface tension, and secondly the energy change due to the difference in the free energy of the atoms in the two states of aggregation.

53

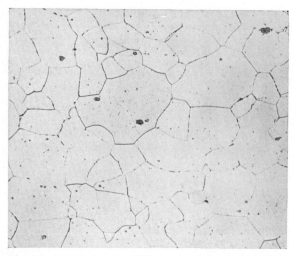

Fig. 5.3.—Armco iron (× 200) showing grains due to grain boundary attack

Fig. 5.4.—Aluminium (× 5). Grains reflect light to differing extents depending upon the orientation of the facets exposed in etching

If ΔF is the change of free energy* per unit volume of liquid in passing from the vapour to the liquid phase, then ΔF is zero at that temperature at which the saturation vapour pressure equals the pressure of the vapour and becomes negative as the temperature falls below that value. If the vapour pressure is greater than the saturation vapour pressure, then the vapour is supersaturated and ΔF is negative, favouring condensation.

Suppose a spherical group of atoms or molecules of radius r has formed due to the random motion. The energy used to create the interface is the product of the surface area $4\pi r^2$ and the surface tension τ. Then the total energy change is

$$\Delta f = 4\pi r^2 \tau + \tfrac{4}{3}\pi r^3 \Delta F$$

This can be negative only if ΔF is negative and if

$$-\tfrac{4}{3}\pi r^3 \Delta F > 4\pi r^2 \tau$$

i.e.
$$r > -\frac{3\tau}{\Delta F}$$

Drops of this size and larger are stable and will continue to grow, while smaller drops will generally disperse.

At low temperatures $-\Delta F$ is larger and so the critical size of drop is smaller. Hence more of the drops formed by random motion will be stable, that is, stable nuclei form at a faster rate. Also the rate of growth of stable drops will be greater.

5.3. Crystal growth from molten metal

Similarly in the solidification of a metal from the melt, there is a minimum size of nucleus for stability. Once stable nuclei are formed, they grow by accretion of atoms on certain crystallographic planes, hence producing definite crystal faces, or frequently tend to grow in the form of dendritic shapes as in fig. 5.5. As growth continues, different crystals will meet along boundaries that do not follow a crystallographic pattern.

Fig. 5.5.—A dendrite

* See Appendix II.

At the melting-point, both the rate of nucleation N and the rate of grain growth G are zero. Below the melting-point, as the temperature falls, G and N at first increase at different rates, the relative importance of which varies from material to material. If G has predominance, then few crystals will nucleate and will grow big, whereas if N predominates many crystals will nucleate before much growth occurs and the grain size will be small. At lower temperatures still, when the atom mobilities decrease, N may fall off faster than G.

In glass, N is negligible until temperatures much below the melting-point are reached. Hence glass does not crystallize (except very slowly over a period of centuries), but forms an amorphous solid. Metals cannot be retained in an amorphous state.

5.4. Crystal shapes

As the crystal boundaries are regions where the atom pattern is distorted, they have a high energy, and hence there will be a tendency for the boundaries to assume the smallest possible surface area. Just as a single soap bubble assumes a spherical shape, this being the shape of minimum surface area for a given volume, so a collection of soap bubbles assumes shapes that make the total surface area a minimum.

Along an edge where three boundaries meet, the surface tension of each being the same, the boundaries will have angles of 120° between them. In a similar way, the boundaries between metal grains will tend to give angles of 120°, although this may not be apparent if the section examined is not perpendicular to the line of intersection of the grain boundary surfaces.

5.5. Crystal pattern in castings

In casting, the metal near the mould surface is cooled quickly and many small crystals tend to form. Then grain growth continues towards the centre of the mould, the rate of solidification being governed mainly by the rate at which the latent heat of fusion can be extracted. As the grain growth rate varies with crystallographic direction, some of the crystals in the surface layer are more favourably oriented for growth perpendicular to the surface of the casting than others. Hence only some of the grains continue to grow and columnar crystals are formed as in fig. 5.6. If a mould material is used which does not chill the metal so rapidly, or if the mould is heated before the metal is poured, the grain size in the surface layers is large.

5.6. Grain growth in strain-free solid metal

When the strain-free metal is heated to a sufficiently high temperature for migration of atoms to occur, the grain boundaries can migrate, firstly to produce the minimum surface area discussed in Section 5.4, and then to produce a uniform increase in grain size up to a specific size for each temperature. This is known as *normal grain growth*. It is a process of energy decrease by decreasing the grain surface area and occurs extremely slowly.

Fig. 5.6.—Section from centre of cast ingot of copper
showing columnar crystals. ($\times$ 3)

5.7. Grain growth in strained solid metal

If the metal has been deformed plastically, then there are highly distorted regions left which possess high energy. The number and amount of stored energy of these regions is dependent upon the amount of deformation. On heating, these regions readily form nuclei of new grains; a process known as *recrystallization*. On heating to higher temperatures, grain growth will occur around the new nuclei. Hence, the final crystal size will depend upon the amount of straining and the temperature reached. There is a critical amount of straining that gives the largest crystal size. Further straining would give more nuclei and hence smaller grains. The variation of grain size with amount of deformation and annealing temperature for copper is shown in fig. 5.7.

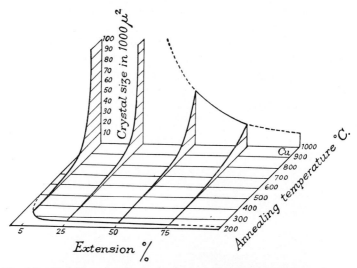

Fig. 5.7.—Variation of grain size in copper with amount of deformation and annealing temperature. [Elam]

5.8. Specification of grain size

The most satisfactory way of indicating grain size would be the number of grains per unit volume. This, however, would be very difficult to determine. The method used is to count the number of grains that appear in unit area of a prepared section of the metal. The grain size may then be quoted as the number of grains that appear per square inch or per square centimetre of cross-section, or may be expressed in a logarithmic manner as the A.S.T.M. (American Society for Testing Materials) grain size.

If the number of grains per square inch of micrograph at × 100 magnification, i.e. the number per 10^{-4} in^2 of the actual section, be n, then the A.S.T.M. grain size N is given by

$$2^{N-1} = n$$

Since small variations in grain size are insignificant in their effect upon mechanical properties, N is quoted to the nearest whole number. For example, a grain size of 615 grains per 10^{-4} in^2 would give $N = 10$ ($\log_2 615 = 9.27$).

When the metal is sectioned, some grains are sectioned centrally and some are sectioned near their corners, so that even if the grains are of uniform volume the section will show a scatter in grain size.

5.9. Growth of single crystals

For investigations of the fundamental properties of metal crystals it is necessary to prepare single crystals for experimental work. The following methods are used for this purpose:

(i). A " seed " in the form of a small piece of single crystal is dipped into the surface of molten metal and withdrawn extremely slowly, so that grain growth can occur without nucleation of any new grains.

(ii). A specimen in the form of a wire is heated by a travelling furnace, so that each portion in succession melts and then cools slowly. In general, a single nucleus will form, and the wire finally becomes a single crystal. A modification of this method is to place a seed crystal at one end which does not get melted. By this means the orientation of the crystallographic planes in the final crystal can be predetermined.

(iii). A specimen of the metal is given a critical amount of strain, discussed in Section 5.7, and is then annealed. If the critical strain is exactly right, the number of nuclei formed per unit volume will be very small and large crystals are obtained.

CHAPTER 6

Aggregations of Two Sorts of Atoms—Binary Alloys

6.1. Introduction

A mixture of atoms of two or more elements, of which the principal one at least is metallic and which exhibits metallic properties, is known as an *alloy*. The mechanical and physical properties of the mixture may be appreciably different from those of any one of the constituent pure elements. Because of the great variation of properties obtainable by alloying, alloys are of the greatest importance in engineering; pure metals have a much more restricted use.

A study of the atomic arrangements possible in alloy systems must precede any discussion of the resulting mechanical and physical properties.

6.2. Mixtures of two liquids

When two liquids, including liquid metals, are mixed, the resulting mixture may fall into one of three classes:

(i). One liquid dissolves completely in the other in all proportions so that one homogeneous solution is formed. A common example is that of water and ethyl alcohol.

(ii). Each liquid is partially soluble in the other, so that if a little of one liquid is added to a lot of the other it all dissolves, forming a single homogeneous solution, but if more is added so that the limit of solubility is reached, then two solutions form and, on standing, separate into two layers, the denser at the bottom. Each layer will have one of the constituents as the solvent with a limited quantity of the other dissolved in it. An example is phenol and water, to which further consideration is given on p. 69.

(iii). Each liquid is completely insoluble in the other, so that a mixture will always separate into two layers, each being the pure substance. It is the limit of case (ii) with the solubilities tending to zero. It is difficult to say whether an example of this case actually exists. A mixture of liquid lead and aluminium is a case where the solubilities are extremely small.

The majority of liquid metal mixtures fall into the first category. It is not possible to make homogeneous metal castings from those metal mixtures which do not form a single homogeneous solution in the liquid state. In such cases, alloys can be made only by the method of powder metallurgy.

6.3. Mixtures in the solid state

In the solid state, a mixture of two elements may again crystallize separately or may be soluble in one another giving solid solutions. Certain compositions of mixture behave as crystalline compounds of fixed composition, possessing a unique crystal structure and having sharp melting-points. These are known as *intermetallic* or *intermediate compounds*.

6.4. Solid solutions

In a solid solution, the solute atoms are distributed throughout the crystal grains, the crystal structure being the same as that of the pure metal, which is the solvent.

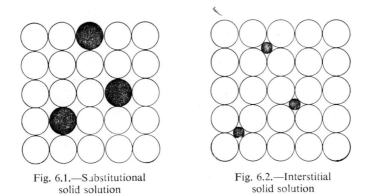

Fig. 6.1.—Substitutional
solid solution

Fig. 6.2.—Interstitial
solid solution

A solid solution may be formed in two ways:

(i). A *substitutional* solid solution, in which solute atoms replace some solvent atoms so that they lie at normal atom sites of the crystal structure (fig. 6.1).

(ii). An *interstitial* solid solution, in which the solute atoms are located in the interstices of the solvent lattice (fig. 6.2).

In the former case, the solute atoms may replace solvent atoms at random, or may take up a more *ordered* structure (fig. 6.3a). Such an ordered structure can exist at a particular composition only. For near-by compositions the structure would be as ordered as possible, as in fig. 6.3*b*. Where ordered structures (also known as *superlattices*) exist, they

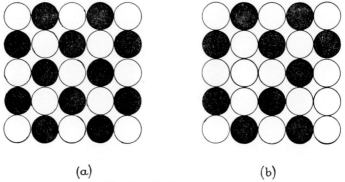

(a)   (b)

Fig. 6.3.—Ordered structure
(*a*) complete ordering with 1:1 ratio of atoms
(*b*) incomplete ordering when atom ratio is not quite 1:1

usually do so at lower temperatures, becoming *disordered* at higher temperatures. For an example, see the β-brass in fig. A.11.

6.5. Effect of atomic size

The type of solid solution formed and the limits of solubility are governed partly by the relative sizes of the solute and solvent atoms.

The distances between atoms in metals and between ions in ionic crystals approximately obey an additive law, each atom or ion being packed in a structure as if it were a sphere of definite size. The radius of the sphere is not constant for any given ion or atom, but depends on the number of equally-spaced near neighbours—the *coordination* number. In a close-packed lattice (p. 46) the number is 12, in a body-centred cubic lattice it is 8, in a diamond it is 4, etc. In passing from 12-fold to 8-fold coordination, there is a contraction of 3% in the radius and a greater contraction when passing to lower coordination numbers. For purposes of comparison, atomic radii are best expressed as the value appropriate to one particular coordination number. The atomic radii for 12-fold coordination of the majority of the elements are given in Table 6.1. In some cases where the element has a crystal structure with a low degree of or no coordination, the values quoted are one-half of the smallest inter-atomic distance.

Interstitial solid solutions can form only when the diameter of the solute atom is about 0·6 or less of the diameter of the solvent atom. Apart from the inert gases, the alkali and alkaline-earth and some of the rare-earth metals, nearly all atoms have diameters which lie in the range 2·1 Å to 3·6 Å, and the metals which form the basis of commercially important alloys lie in the range 2·5 Å to 3·2 Å. The only atoms small enough to form interstitial solid solutions are the first five in Table 6.1.

TABLE 6.1—THE RADII OF THE ATOMS IN ORDER OF MAGNITUDE

The values quoted are those appropriate to 12-fold coordination, except those given in parentheses which are half the smallest inter-atomic distance in the pure material (values taken from *Metals Reference Book*, second edition edited by Smithells, Butterworth).

	Å		Å		Å
H	0·46	Ir	1·35	Mg	1·60
O	0·60	V	1·36	Ne	1·60
N	0·71	I	(1·36)	Sc	1·60
C	0·77	Zn	1·37	Zr	1·60
B	0·97	Pd	1·37	Sb	1·61
S	(1·04)	Re	1·38	Tl	1·71
Cl	(1·07)	Pt	1·38	Pb	1·75
P	(1·09)	Mo	1·40	He	1·79
Mn	(1·12)	W	1·41	Y	1·81
Be	1·13	Al	1·43	Bi	1·82
Se	(1·16)	Te	(1·43)	Na	1·92
Si	(1·17)	Ag	1·44	A	1·92
Br	(1·19)	Au	1·44	Ca	1·97
Co	1·25	Ti	1·47	Kr	1·97
Ni	1·25	Nb	1·47	Sr	2·15
As	(1·25)	Ta	1·47	Xe	2·18
Cr	1·28	Cd	1·52	Ba	2·24
Fe	1·28	Hg	1·55	K	2·38
Cu	1·28	Li	1·57	Rb	2·51
Ru	1·34	In	1·57	Cs	2·70
Rh	1·34	Sn	1·58	Rare earths	
Os	1·35	Hf	1·59	1·73-2·04	

A more detailed treatment of the formation of interstitial solid solutions of carbon in the different allotropic forms of iron is given on pp. 93–96.

6.6. Factors controlling substitutional solid solubility

Substitutional solid solutions are favoured when the atoms are more nearly of the same size. When the difference between the diameters is more than 14%, solid solubility is likely to be restricted. Complete solid solubility can, of course, exist only when both pure metals have the same crystal structure.

Two factors which also influence the extent of solid solubility are the relative electronegative valence and the relative valency. When one of the elements is more electropositive and the other is more electronegative, i.e. appear in lower and higher groups respectively of the periodic table, the formation of intermediate compounds is probable, and this restricts the possible range of solid solutions.

Secondly, adding a metal with more valency electrons to one with fewer valency electrons increases the ratio of the total number of valency electrons to the total number of atoms. Such increase is limited to some more or less fixed value for any particular crystal structure. The reciprocal effect of decreasing the electron concentration by adding a metal of lower valency to a metal of higher valency is even more restricted.

Some examples chosen to illustrate the effects of these factors are shown in Table 6.2. The first three examples are all metals of Group I with a valency of 1 and have the same crystal structure. Hence size is the factor that will control the extent of solid solubility. In the three cases Ag-Au, Au-Cu, and Ag-Cu the differences in size are 0·2%, 12·8%, and 13% respectively of the size of the smaller atom. The first case should obviously show complete solid solubility while the others will be border-line cases. The Ag-Cu system shows limited solubility, while the Au-Cu system does not, but the equilibrium diagram (fig. A.8) shows it to be near the limit with a tendency to form a eutectic (see p. 73).

In the Ag-Cd and Cu-Cd systems, the crystal structure and valency of cadmium differ from those of silver and copper, factors that would restrict the solid solubilities. The size differences are 5% and 16% respectively, so that the solubilities are much smaller in the second case.

The Cu-As system is an example of an alloy system between two elements that have different crystal structures and are well separated in the periodic table, arsenic being almost a non-metal. The size difference is only 2%, but solubilities are small and an intermediate compound is formed.

6.7. Intermediate compounds

These compounds have a crystal structure different from either of the pure elements. They are variously referred to as intermetallic, intermediate, and chemical compounds. The term intermetallic is applicable only when both elements are metallic. Many of the intermediate compounds of engineering importance contain a non-metallic element, especially carbon and nitrogen in carbides and nitrides. Three types of intermediate compounds are discussed.

TABLE 6.2—EXAMPLES OF SUBSTITUTIONAL SOLID SOLUTIONS

Metals	Atom diameter Å	Crystal structure	Group of Periodic Table	Valency	Relative solubility	Compounds formed
{Ag	2·889	F.C.C.	I	1	Continuous	—
{Au	2·884	F.C.C.	I	1		
{Au	2·884	F.C.C.	I	1	Continuous (but liquidus shows a minimum)	—
{Cu	2·556	F.C.C.	I	1		
{Ag	2·889	F.C.C.	I	1	Restricted 8·8% Cu, 8% Ag	—
{Cu	2·556	F.C.C.	I	1		
{Ag	2·889	F.C.C.	I	1	Restricted 6% Ag, 44% Cd	Electron compounds
{Cd	3·04	H.C.P.	II	2		
{Cu	2·556	F.C.C.	I	1	Slight 0·12% Cu, 1·7% Cd	Electron compounds
{Cd	3·04	H.C.P.	II	2		
{Cu	2·556	F.C.C.	I	1	Restricted 8% As, no data on Cu solubility	Valency compound Cu_3As
{As	2·50	Rhombohedral	V	3		

65

(i). *Valency compounds*

Valency compounds are compounds of electropositive metals with electronegative elements of Groups IVb, Vb and VIb of the periodic table (Table 2.2). The bonding may be either ionic or covalent, and the normal valency rules are obeyed. They are usually hard and brittle, and poor conductors. They have sharp melting-points which may be above the melting-point for either pure element.

(ii). *Electron compounds*

Metals not greatly different in electrochemical properties and having a fairly favourable size factor but having different numbers of valency electrons may show intermediate phases which are essentially metallic in properties and are not of exactly fixed composition.

Hume-Rothery has pointed out that the crystal structure is often related to the ratio of the total number of valency electrons to the total number of atoms. Thus monovalent copper will dissolve bivalent zinc in the face-centred cubic structure until the electron/atom ratio is about 1·4 (corresponding to 40% zinc by numbers of atoms). The body-centred structure is more stable when the electron/atom ratio is about 1·5, and further structures appear at higher ratios. When trivalent aluminium is alloyed with copper, the limit of solubility in the face-centred cubic copper lattice is about 20% by numbers of atoms, again corresponding to a valency electron/atom ratio of 1·4, and a body-centred cubic phase exists in the vicinity of an electron/atom ratio of 1·5.

In the electron compounds, the bonding is metallic and the range of composition corresponds to a solid solution. The more complex structures tend to be brittle.

(iii). *Interstitial compounds*

Interstitial compounds form between the elements which can go into interstitial solid solution and metals in which they have little solid solubility. If the size factor is favourable, the metal takes up a simple crystal structure with the non-metallic atoms in interstitial positions. In some cases, such as cementite, which is discussed in the following section, the size conditions are borderline, and the structure is complex.

Interstitial compounds have high melting-points and are very hard and brittle. Carbides are of great importance in cutting tools, and nitrides are formed in one process of surface-hardening steel.

6.8. Formulae of intermediate compounds

In the iron-carbon system, an intermediate compound, *cementite*, is found at a composition of 6·67% carbon by weight. The ratio of numbers of atoms can be found by dividing the relative weights of elements by the atomic weights. Thus:

$$\frac{\text{atoms of carbon}}{\text{atoms of iron}} = \frac{6 \cdot 67/12}{93 \cdot 33/55 \cdot 85} = \frac{0 \cdot 556}{1 \cdot 671} = \frac{1}{3}$$

Hence the empirical formula is Fe_3C.

This should not be taken to mean that cementite is composed of molecules, each of which consists of one carbon and three iron atoms.

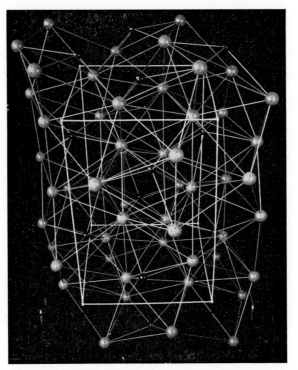

Fig. 6.4.—Model of cementite structure. White rods outline unit cell

The crystal merely contains three times as many iron as carbon atoms. The structure, of which fig. 6.4 shows a model, is orthorhombic, the unit cell sides being

$$a = 4 \cdot 52 \text{ Å}$$
$$b = 5 \cdot 08 \text{ Å}$$
$$c = 6 \cdot 37 \text{ Å}$$

and each unit cell contains twelve iron and four carbon atoms.

6.9. Phase

A phase is defined as a portion of matter, homogeneous in the sense that the smallest parts into which it can be divided mechanically are indistinguishable from one another. If two portions of matter co-existing in equilibrium are different in composition, crystal structure, or state, they are different phases of the matter considered.

A mixture of phenol and water in approximately equal portions at room temperature will separate into two layers, the upper being water with phenol dissolved, and the lower being phenol with water dissolved in it. The two layers are of different composition and hence are two phases of the phenol-water system.

Allotropic forms of the same metal, such as the α and γ forms of iron, and different types of crystal structures occurring at different compositions of an alloy system are different phases.

QUESTIONS

1. Distinguish between an interstitial and substitutional solid solution. What part does the ratio of the atomic radii play in determining the type and range of solid solution? Are any other factors involved?

2. Copper and nickel form a continuous solid solution at all compositions, whereas copper and silver form two solid solutions of limited solubility. How can this be explained in terms of atomic radii?

3. Discuss the factors that control the extent of solid solubility in alloy systems.
For each of the following alloy systems state, with reasons, whether one might expect complete, partial, or negligible solid solubility: (a) copper-silver, (b) silver-gold, (c) silver-cadmium, (d) copper-cadmium.   [MST]

4. Tin and lanthanum form intermediate compounds containing 28%, 44%, and 70% of lanthanum. Determine the empirical formulae of the three compounds.

5. From the information given in Section 6.8, calculate the specific gravity of cementite.

CHAPTER 7

Equilibrium Diagrams

7.1. Introduction

A description of the internal structure of each of the alloys possible between two or more metals, giving the compositions and temperatures over which the various phases exist, is most conveniently presented as an equilibrium or constitution diagram.

The base line or abscissa of the diagram for an alloy system between two elements A and B shows the composition of all possible alloys from 100% of one component A and 0% of the other component B at the left-hand end, to 0% of A and 100% of B at the right-hand end, as in fig. 7.1.

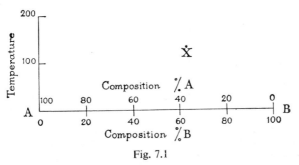

Fig. 7.1

The ends of the abscissa are labelled with the names or symbols of the components. Thus A appears at the left-hand end and B at the right-hand end. It is not necessary, though often convenient, to show the graduations of the scale. The composition is usually expressed by weight, but may be shown in terms of numbers of atoms. The ordinate scale represents the temperature range. Thus in fig. 7.1, the point X indicates an alloy containing 37% of A and 63% of B at a temperature of 130° C.

Lines can be drawn on this diagram to show the boundaries of the composition-temperature ranges over which the various phases exist.

7.2. Equilibrium diagram for two liquids

A simple example for consideration is the phenol-water mixture previously mentioned. At 10° C the relative solubilities are 7·5 kg of phenol in 100 kg of aqueous solution and 25 kg of water in 100 kg of phenol solution. Thus if 7 kg of phenol is mixed with 93 kg of water, it can all dissolve forming an unsaturated solution—a single phase. If more than 7·5% of phenol is used, then two phases will form, being two saturated solutions, the relative amounts of the two solutions being such as to give the correct overall composition. On increasing the temperature, the solubilities increase. The variations of solubility are shown in fig. 7.2.

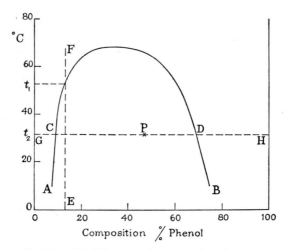

Fig. 7.2.—Solubility curve for water-phenol mixture

The lines AC and BD show the boundaries of the single-phase regions. At 68·3° C it is seen that the two regions have come together so that at this and higher temperatures, one phase only will exist for any composition.

A mixture containing 13% of phenol, represented by EF, would have two phases at 10° C, but on heating to a temperature t_1 the solubility of the aqueous layer would have increased sufficiently for there to be only one solution, and so it would be single-phase above that temperature.

7.3. Rules for interpreting binary equilibrium diagrams

At a temperature t_2, for a composition given by point P there would be two phases whose compositions would be the saturated solutions that can co-exist at that temperature, i.e. C and D. The relative amounts of the two phases can be determined as follows:

Let a, b, and p be the fractions of phenol in the mixtures of composition C, D and P respectively, i.e.

$$a = \frac{GC}{GH}, \quad b = \frac{GD}{GH}, \quad p = \frac{GP}{GH}$$

Let the mixture contain a fraction x of the phase represented by C and a fraction $(1-x)$ of D.

Then the proportion of phenol in the total is

$$p = ax + b(1-x)$$

whence

$$x = \frac{b-p}{b-a} = \frac{PD}{CD} \quad \text{and} \quad 1-x = \frac{CP}{CD}$$

These considerations lead to the two rules by which we can determine the compositions and proportions of phases present for any point in a two-phase region.

Rule 1.—Draw a horizontal line at the chosen temperature. The intersections of this line with the two boundaries of the two-phase field give the compositions of each of the phases existing at that temperature.

Rule 2 (The lever rule).—Let the point representing the composition and temperature be the fulcrum of a horizontal lever. The lengths of the lever arms from the fulcrum to the boundaries of the two-phase field multiplied by the weights of the phases present must balance.

While these two rules give the composition and structure of the phases, it is also possible to determine from the equilibrium diagram the way in which the phases are distributed. This will become clear in the following sections which deal with the various types of equilibrium diagrams. Discussion is restricted to those cases in which there is complete solubility in the liquid state.

7.4. Equilibrium diagram for the case of complete solid insolubility

When two substances are soluble in the liquid state but insoluble in the solid state, it is found that the freezing-point of one substance is lowered by the addition of some of the other substance to the liquid. Raoult's law states that *the amount by which the freezing-point is lowered is proportional to the concentration of the second substance and to its molecular weight.*

Thus the freezing-point curve would be of the form shown in fig. 7.3, beginning at the freezing-point of the pure substance A and dropping steadily as more B is added. Such a line which indicates the temperature at which freezing begins for any particular alloy is called a *liquidus* line.

Above the line only the liquid phase exists. When freezing commences on cooling, crystals of pure A form, so that the composition of the remaining liquid will change, becoming richer in B. This new liquid will have a lower freezing-point than the original liquid, and no more crystallization will occur until the temperature has fallen sufficiently. Hence crystallization of A occurs steadily over a range of temperature. Under the liquidus is a two-phase region, which is shaded in fig. 7.3.

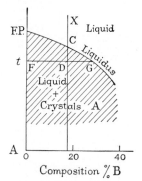

Fig. 7.3.—Depression of freezing-point of an element A by addition of an element B which is soluble in liquid A and insoluble in solid A.

For an alloy of composition X cooled from the liquid phase, crystallization of A begins at a temperature given by C. At a lower temperature t, this alloy is in a two-phase region. Applying the two rules, it follows that (i) the compositions of the two phases are given by F and G, (ii) the relative amounts are:

$$100 \frac{DG}{FG}\% \text{ solid (pure A)}$$

$$100 \frac{FD}{FG}\% \text{ liquid (composition G)}$$

The liquidus curve for the freezing of pure B from liquids at the B-rich end of the system would be a similar curve starting from the freezing-point of pure B and falling as a higher proportion of A is present.

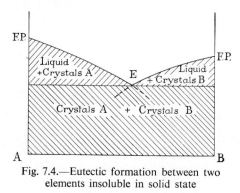

Fig. 7.4.—Eutectic formation between two elements insoluble in solid state

When the two liquidus curves are put on to one diagram as in fig. 7.4, they will intersect at E. A liquid of any composition will on cooling deposit either pure A or pure B, its composition thereby changing until point E is reached. At this composition and temperature, it is saturated with both A and B and can precipitate crystals of both elements. The result is that precipitation of both A and B proceeds as rapidly as removal of latent heat will permit until solidification is completed. During this process, the composition and temperature of the remaining liquid do not change.

The process can be regarded in more detail as follows. If a crystal of pure A nucleates in the liquid of composition E and continues to grow, the concentration of B will increase in the immediately adjacent liquid so that the liquid is supersaturated in B and nucleation of B crystals will occur. These will grow causing local supersaturation in A, leading to nucleation of more A, and so on.

Point E is known as the *eutectic point* and the change occurring there is the *eutectic reaction.* It may be written as

$$\text{liquid E} \underset{\text{heating}}{\overset{\text{cooling}}{\rightleftharpoons}} \text{crystals A + crystals B}$$

For any composition, solidification is completed at the temperature of E. A horizontal line on the equilibrium diagram at this temperature

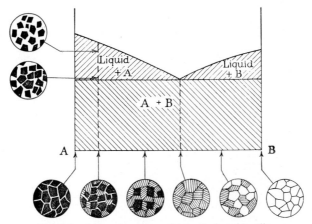

Fig. 7.5.—Microstructures of eutectic-forming alloy

will divide the liquid+solid two-phase regions from the solid+solid two-phase region. This line below which everything is solid is called the *solidus.*

The arrangement of the solid phases, known as the microstructure, can be foretold. On cooling a liquid, firstly pure A or pure B will separate until the temperature reaches the eutectic temperature. This will be the primary or pro-eutectic crystals. Then the remainder undergoes the eutectic reaction forming a finely divided mixture of the two pure elements. Diagrammatic sketches of the microstructure found at various temperatures for a particular composition and for various compositions at a low temperature are shown in fig. 7.5. Here crystals of A are shown black and crystals of B white with typical grain boundary shapes. The liquid is shown white, while the eutectic is shown shaded, representing the mixture of A and B.

7.5. Cooling curves

When a specimen is cooled over a temperature range for which its specific heat is constant and there is no phase change, the time-temperature curve is like (a) in fig. 7.6. Since the cooling will approximately follow Newton's law of cooling, which states that the rate of loss of heat is proportional to the temperature difference between a body and its surroundings, the curve will be roughly of logarithmic form.

A pure metal being cooled from the liquid state will have a similar curve down to the freezing-point. Then during solidification, the latent

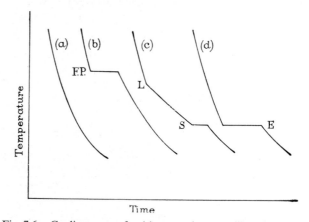

Fig. 7.6.—Cooling curves for (a) pure substance, (b) pure substance with change of state, (c) eutectic forming alloy with pro-eutectic component, (d) alloy of eutectic composition.

heat will be lost at constant temperature, after which the temperature will again fall in a logarithmic curve. A plateau will thus appear in the cooling curve at the freezing-point temperature (curve b in fig. 7.6).

For an alloy intermediate in composition between a pure metal and the eutectic composition, the cooling curve of the liquid phase will continue down to the temperature of the liquidus. Between the liquidus and solidus temperatures there is continuous solidification, and hence a steady loss of latent heat as well as specific heat while the temperature is falling. More heat has to be lost per degree fall of temperature than in the liquid state, and hence the rate of fall of temperature is less. There will be an abrupt change of slope at the liquidus temperature (curve c in fig. 7.6). At the eutectic temperature, the remaining liquid, now of eutectic composition, solidifies and the cooling curve shows a plateau at the solidus temperature. For a liquid, initially of eutectic composition, there will be

74

a plateau at the eutectic temperature and no abrupt changes of slope elsewhere (curve *d* in fig. 7.6).

Hence by obtaining cooling curves for samples of such an alloy system, the points on the liquidus and solidus curves may be derived enabling the equilibrium diagram to be constructed.

7.6. Equilibrium diagram for complete solid solubility

Where the two elements of a binary alloy system show complete solid solubility in the solid state as well as in the liquid state, then only one phase exists for any point on the equilibrium diagram in the entirely solid region. It is found, however, in most cases that the crystals deposited from the liquid do not have the same composition as the liquid. A typical equilibrium diagram of this system is shown in fig. 7.7*a*. Raoult's law does not apply in this case and the freezing-point of a pure metal

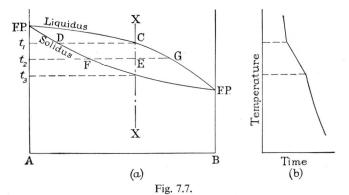

Fig. 7.7.

(*a*) Equilibrium diagram for two elements showing complete solid solubility

(*b*) Cooling curve for composition X

may be either raised or lowered by addition of the other metal. For an alloy whose composition is represented by the line XX in fig. 7.7*a*, the liquidus temperature is given by t_1, at which point crystals separate whose composition is given by D. The liquid is thus impoverished in A, and the temperature falls so that the remaining liquid follows the liquidus line CG.

At a temperature given by t_2, the application of Rule 1 (p. 71) shows that the liquid phase is of composition given by G and the solid phase of composition given by F. The crystals first formed were richer in A, but for equilibrium should now at temperature t_2 have a composition given by F. As long as cooling is slow enough, then solid-state diffusion will occur, atoms of B diffusing into the crystals already formed to bring their composition to F.

At temperature t_3, crystallization will be complete if cooling has been sufficiently slow for all crystals to homogenize. The cooling curve (fig. 7.7b) will show an abrupt decrease of slope at the liquidus and then an abrupt increase at the solidus.

When cooling is rapid, as may occur in practice when alloys are cast into cold moulds, this homogenization will not have had time to occur. The crystals then vary in composition, being richer in A at their centres, and the proportion of liquid remaining at any temperature will not be exactly that given by the equilibrium diagram. When a micro-structure is prepared it will be possible to see that there is such coring if the difference in composition in different parts of the crystal is sufficient to give a difference in appearance when etched with a suitable etchant. The cored structure may be homogenized by an annealing process, i.e. heating at a sufficiently high temperature for sufficient time to allow diffusion to occur.

7.7. Equilibrium diagram for partial solid solubility

In cases where the solid solubility is limited, no new principles, other than those considered in the two previous cases, are involved. The form of the diagram is shown in fig. 7.8. The outer boundaries of the (liquid +

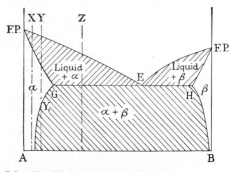

Fig. 7.8.—Equilibrium diagram for two elements showing partial solid solubility

crystal) two-phase fields are not vertical lines, as in the case of complete solid insolubility, but curve away from these verticals so that the upper portion of each two-phase field has a similar appearance to the upper end of the two-phase region in the case of complete solid solubility. The crystals deposited are not pure metals but solid solutions, which, to preserve equilibrium, must change composition by solid-state diffusion as the temperature falls.

The liquidi intersect at the eutectic point E, and the eutectic will be a mixture of crystals of composition G and of composition H.

It is usual to denote phases in alloy systems—both solid solutions and intermediate compounds—by Greek letters, usually in sequence from left to right. Here the solid solution of B in A has been termed the α-phase and that of A in B the β-phase.

Below the eutectic line GEH the solubilities decrease with falling temperature and the single-phase regions become narrower.

The compositions and proportions of phases for any alloy at any temperature can be found by direct application of the rules (p. 71). The arrangement of the phases can also be determined by a study of the equilibrium diagram.

Consider alloys of compositions denoted by the vertical lines X, Y and Z in fig. 7.8. The structure of alloy X would be cored in cases of rapid cooling as for cases of complete solid solubility, but homogeneous after slow cooling.

Alloy Y when slowly cooled would show a homogeneous structure down to point Y_1. Below that temperature, it would become super-saturated with B-atoms and would precipitate them. The equilibrium B-rich structure is however the β-phase and so the precipitated B-atoms would take sufficient A-atoms to give β-crystals. Thus β-crystals would separate at the grain boundaries and within the grains of α-crystals. Precipitation within the parent grains will take place along certain crystallographic planes and show up as a distinct pattern in the micro-structure. Such a pattern is known as a Widmanstätten structure. The name is due to the first discovery of the pattern in iron meteorites by Alois von Widmanstätten in 1808.

As grain growth occurs around the nuclei of the second phase, solute atoms have to migrate towards these nuclei so that the rate of precipitation of a second phase is limited by the rate of diffusion of the solute atoms.

Alloy Z will give, just below the eutectic temperature, primary or pro-eutectic α-crystals with a eutectic mixture of α and β of compositions G and H. Below this temperature, both α- and β-phases become super-saturated and precipitate β- and α-crystals respectively.

The way in which the precipitation is carried out, i.e. by different rates of cooling, can cause differences in size and distribution of the second phase which can result in changes of properties which may be of engineer-ing importance. This is dealt with later in Chapter 11.

Limiting cases of this diagram are those where G and H move towards E and just meet, so that only one solid phase is formed, but the liquidus shows a minimum (fig. 7.9); and where E moves to one boundary so that the eutectic liquid is a pure metal (fig. 7.10). Examples of these systems are the copper-gold (fig. A.8) and copper-bismuth systems respectively.

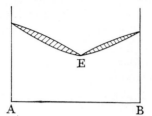

Fig. 7.9.—Equilibrium diagram for complete solid solubility with a minimum in the liquidus.

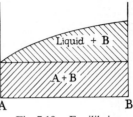

Fig. 7.10.—Equilibrium diagram showing eutectic at pure A.

7.8. Intermediate compounds

The nature of intermediate compounds has been discussed in Section 6.7. Valency compounds and interstitial compounds have fixed composition and sharp melting-points, so the occurrence of one denoted by the general formula A_xB_y in a binary alloy system can be represented as in fig. 7.11.

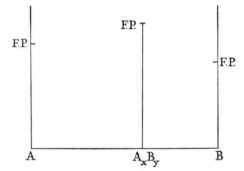

Fig. 7.11.—Freezing-points of pure element and intermediate compound

The equilibrium diagram is now divided into two parts, one showing the phases that occur between A and A_xB_y, and the other showing phases that occur between A_xB_y and B. Each of these parts may be one of the forms already described, i.e. there may be complete or partial solubility, or complete insolubility between either pure metal and the intermediate compound.

An example is shown by the lead-magnesium system in fig. A.13. The intermetallic compound occurs at 18% by weight of magnesium and can be shown to have the empirical formula Mg_2Pb. The pure lead is designated α, the intermetallic compound β, and the solid solution of lead in magnesium γ. The compound does not in this case have any range of solubility for either lead or magnesium.

In the copper-aluminium system (fig. A.3) there is an intermetallic compound at 54% by weight of copper, giving the formula $CuAl_2$. This compound, known as the θ-phase, has a limited range of solubility for both aluminium and copper, so that the θ single-phase region on the equilibrium diagram is of finite width.

7.9. Peritectic reaction

This may be considered as an inverse of the eutectic reaction. During freezing of certain alloys, an interaction takes place between solid crystals already formed and the residual liquid to form another solid structure. This reaction occurs at a constant temperature and is known as a *peritectic* reaction. The solid phase formed may be either an intermediate compound or a solid solution as in figs. 7.12 and 7.13 respectively.

In fig. 7.12, the intermediate compound A_xB_y when heated to the peritectic temperature decomposes at a constant temperature to give liquid of composition represented by L and solid consisting of pure B. The peritectic reaction may be written

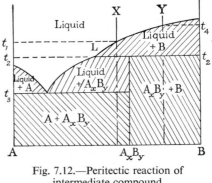

Fig. 7.12.—Peritectic reaction of intermediate compound

$$\text{liquid L} + \text{solid B} \underset{\text{heating}}{\overset{\text{cooling}}{\rightleftharpoons}} \text{solid } A_xB_y$$

For an alloy of composition X cooled from the liquid state, crystals of B start to separate at t_1 and continue to do so down to t_2 which is the peritectic temperature. The peritectic reaction then occurs, all the B-crystals disappearing and an excess of liquid remaining. On further cooling, more A_xB_y is formed from the liquid, which gets richer in A until the eutectic reaction occurs at t_3.

For an alloy of composition Y, precipitation of B occurs from the liquidus temperature t_4 to the peritectic temperature t_2. There is now a higher proportion of B than was the case in alloy X and when the peritectic reaction occurs, all the liquid reacts with part of the solid B to give

A_xB_y. Below the peritectic temperature we therefore have crystals of A_xB_y and B only, and their proportions do not change on further cooling.

Fig. 7.13 shows a form of diagram that may occur when a solid solution is formed by a peritectic reaction. On cooling alloy W, β-crystals would separate between t_1 and t_2, the composition of the remaining

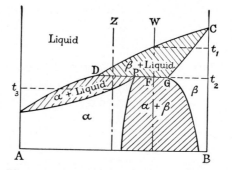

Fig. 7.13.—Peritectic reaction of solid solution

liquid following the liquidus CD, and at t_2 all the remaining liquid would react with some of these β-crystals to give crystals of the α solid solution. Just above the peritectic temperature, the proportions of phases would be

$$100 \frac{FG}{DG}\% \text{ of liquid (composition D)}$$

$$100 \frac{DF}{DG}\% \text{ of } \beta \text{ (composition G)}$$

while just below this temperature the proportions would be

$$100 \frac{FG}{PG}\% \text{ of } \alpha \text{ (composition P)}$$

$$100 \frac{PF}{PG}\% \text{ of } \beta \text{ (composition G)}$$

Alloy Z commences to freeze in a similar manner, but at the peritectic temperature all the β-crystals react with some of the liquid to form α-crystals. On further cooling, the remaining liquid is absorbed into the α-phase, solidification being complete at the solidus temperature t_3.

Examples of the peritectic reactions are to be found in the β, γ, δ, ε, and η-phases of the copper-zinc system (fig. A.11) and in the γ-phase of the iron-carbon system (fig. 8.9).

7.10. Comparison of eutectic and peritectic reactions

It will be observed that a eutectic reaction involves one phase changing to two on cooling, whereas a peritectic reaction consists of two phases

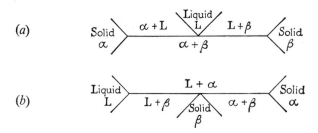

Fig. 7.14.—Diagrammatic representation of (a) eutectic and (b) peritectic reactions

changing to one on cooling. The form of the equilibrium diagram around a eutectic and a peritectic temperature can be represented diagrammatically as in fig. 7.14.

7.11. Changes occurring below the solidus

The condition of an alloy when it has just solidified is not necessarily that which it will have at lower temperatures. The phase changes that occur are very similar to the phase changes occurring during the formation of the solid from the liquid state. However, diffusion in solids is extremely sluggish at temperatures that are low compared with the melting temperature range, and so equilibrium conditions are not readily obtained. The lower portions of equilibrium diagrams are therefore often uncertain. The changes that can occur are:

(i) Allotropy.
(ii) Precipitation of a second phase due to a decrease in solubility (see p. 77).
(iii) Eutectoid reaction.
(iv) Peritectoid reaction.
(v) Order-disorder changes (see p. 62).

7.12. Allotropy

Pure substances may exist in more than one crystalline form, each form being stable over more or less well-defined limits of temperature and pressure. This is known as *allotropy* or *polymorphism*, and is shown by many metals. Iron, one of the commonest examples, is considered in the next chapter. Two of the elements which show this form of behaviour and which are of importance in modern nuclear energy work are uranium and plutonium. Uranium has three and plutonium has six allotropic forms. Each of these forms, being of different crystal structure, may have a different density of packing, so that there will be a change of volume at each change of temperature. The coefficient of thermal expansion of each allotropic modification may also differ, so that the changes of length

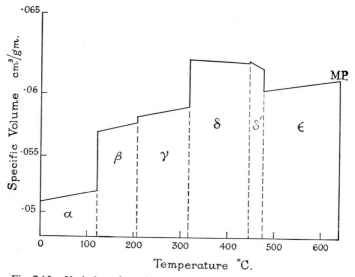

Fig. 7.15.—Variation of specific volume of plutonium with temperature

with temperature can be far from regular. The variation of volume with temperature for plutonium is shown in fig. 7.15.

When the different allotropic forms give solid solutions in a binary system, then the transition temperature will vary with composition, the manner of variation depending upon the relative solubilities of the second element in the various allotropic phases. Some examples of the way in which this can vary are shown in fig. 7.16.

7.13. Eutectoid reaction

Just as a liquid solution can simultaneously precipitate two solid phases in a eutectic reaction, so a solid solution can exhibit exactly similar behaviour in what is termed a *eutectoid reaction*. The commonest example is that of pearlite formation in the iron-carbon system (p. 98).

7.14. Peritectoid reaction

This reaction is exactly similar to a peritectic reaction except that all three phases involved are solid phases. These changes are not common in alloy systems of engineering importance.

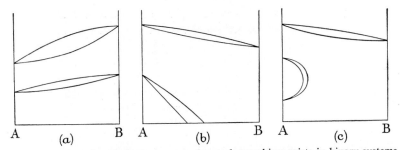

Fig. 7.16.—Examples of phase changes when polymorphism exists in binary systems

(*a*) high-temperature and low-temperature forms of A and B isomorphous (i.e. of same crystal form); (*b*) A undergoes polymorphic change, high-temperature modification being isomorphous with B; (*c*) A has two polymorphic changes, high and low-temperature modifications are iso-morphous with B.

†7.15. Ternary equilibrium diagrams

For plotting the equilibrium diagrams of ternary alloys, that is, alloys made of three components, three independent variables have to be considered. Two are necessary to specify the composition, and the third is temperature. A three-dimensional space model is therefore necessary to show the phases present for any composition and temperature.

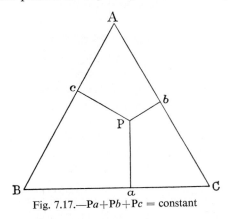

Fig. 7.17.—$Pa+Pb+Pc$ = constant

The most convenient form of diagram is that with an equilateral triangle as base and a temperature axis perpendicular to this base. The three perpendiculars to the sides of an equilateral triangle from any point P within the triangle have a constant sum whatever the position of P. If this sum be taken as 100%, then the three perpendicular distances can be used to represent the proportions of the three components. Thus in fig. 7.17, the distances Pa, Pb, and Pc can represent the proportions of elements A, B, and C respectively. The equilateral triangle can be divided up as shown in fig. 7.18, and the composition corresponding to any point can be read directly.

The side AB will represent binary alloys of elements A and B. The first line parallel to this side will represent all alloys containing 10% C.

By analogy with binary equilibrium diagrams, it is possible to develop the space models for various types of ternary alloys.

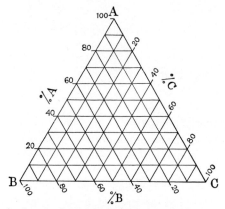

Fig. 7.18.—Scales for plotting composition on ternary equilibrium diagrams

7.16. Ternary system with complete solid solubility

For a ternary system of components completely miscible in the solid and in the liquid states, the sides of the model, i.e. the binary equilibrium diagram, would be of the form shown in fig. 7.7. The liquidus and solidus surfaces would be bounded by the liquidi and solidi of the binary diagrams and enclose a two-phase region in the form of a convex lens (fig. 7.19). While a simple diagram can be represented as a two-dimensional view, it does not lend itself to quantitative measurement, and for such purposes two-dimensional sections are used. These are usually isothermal sections or vertical sections.

The isothermal section will be an equilateral triangle on which phase boundaries are shown. Thus an isothermal section of fig. 7.19 which cuts the liquidus and solidus would look like fig. 7.20. Note that at X there exist a liquid and a solid phase, but further evidence is needed to give the actual composition of each phase. This information can be found only by experiment and is shown on the isothermal section by *tie-lines* which join compositions that co-exist in equilibrium. In fig. 7.20 tie-line PQ which passes through X shows that for the alloy of composition represented by X and for any other alloy whose composition lies on PQ, the two phases are liquid of composition P and solid of composition Q.

A series of isothermal sections for different temperatures can give a complete representation of an equilibrium diagram. One phase-boundary

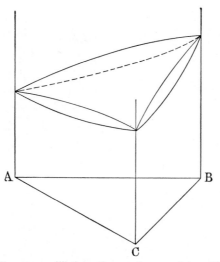

Fig. 7.19.—Ternary equilibrium diagram for complete solid solubility

surface can be defined by several isothermals on one diagram in the form of a contour map. Fig. 7.21 shows this for the liquidus of the alloy system of fig. 7.19.

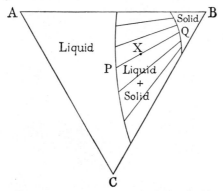

Fig. 7.20.—Isothermal section of fig. 7.19

Vertical sections are useful for showing how a binary system is affected by the presence of a third metal. It is usual to take such sections parallel to one side of the base triangle, that is at a constant proportion of one of the elements, as in fig. 7.22. The liquidus and solidus lines have the same significance as in binary diagrams, but the compositions of the phases

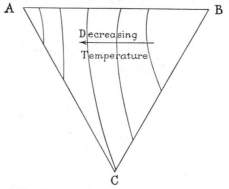

Fig. 7.21.—Isothermals of liquidus surface of fig. 7.19 at equal temperature intervals

existing at a point in the two-phase region cannot be read off the section unless the tie-line happens to lie in the plane of the section.

When a section is taken along a tie-line, then the lever rule of binary equilibrium diagrams can be applied.

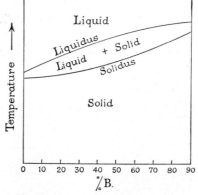

Fig. 7.22.—Vertical section of fig. 7.19 for 10% C

7.17. Ternary eutectic system

In the case of a ternary system where there is complete immiscibility in the solid state, the sides of the model will be binary eutectic diagrams of the type of fig. 7.4. Between these, the liquidi will be smooth curved surfaces which intersect to form three valleys KE, LE, and ME, with all three surfaces meeting at E (fig. 7.23). The view of the model from above is shown in fig. 7.24. A liquid with composition represented by X will, on cooling, first intersect the A-liquidus and pure A will solidify. The

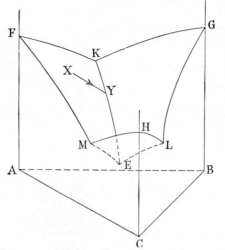

Fig. 7.23.—Ternary equilibrium diagram for complete solid insolubility

composition of the remaining liquid must move in a direction directly away from A along AX produced. Along this line the ratio of B to C will remain constant.

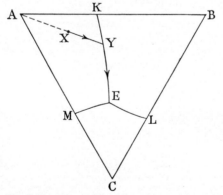

Fig. 7.24.—View of liquidi surfaces of fig. 7.23

Ultimately the liquid composition reaches KE at Y. The proportion of the whole that is solid A is XY/AY. At Y the B-liquidus is reached and the *binary eutectic reaction*

$$\text{liquid} \rightleftharpoons A + B$$

occurs. As the binary eutectic continues to form, the composition of the liquid remains on the intersection of the two surfaces, eventually reaching

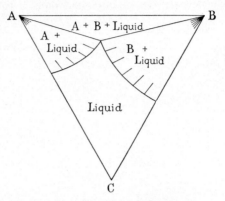

Fig. 7.25.—Isothermal section of fig. 7.23 below temperature of AB binary eutectic and above melting-point of C

E. At E the amounts of A, B, and liquid present will be such that their centre of gravity lies at X. On further extraction of heat, the *ternary eutectic reaction*

$$\text{liquid} \rightleftharpoons A + B + C$$

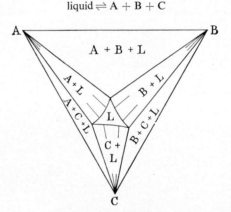

Fig. 7.26.—Isothermal section of fig. 7.23 below temperatures of binary eutectics and above temperature of ternary eutectic

occurs. The composition of the liquid remains at E until solidification is complete.

Two isothermal sections of the intermediate stages of cooling are shown in figs. 7.25 and 7.26. From these the following points may be observed:

(i) Boundaries between single and two-phase regions are curved.

(ii) Boundaries between two and three-phase regions are straight lines, and in fact are the limiting tie-lines of the two-phase regions.

(iii) Three-phase regions are triangles.

7.18. Rules for phase compositions and quantities in a ternary equilibrium diagram

In a two-phase region the rules for binary diagrams (p. 71) apply along tie-lines.

In a three-phase region the compositions of the three phases are given by the corners of the triangle, and the quantities of each are such that if placed at the respective corners they would balance about the point representing the alloy composition, i.e. an extension of the lever rule.

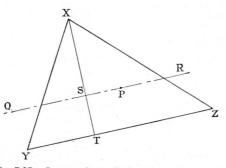

Fig. 7.27.—Lever rule applied to three-phase region

Point P in fig. 7.27 lies in the three-phase region XYZ. If x, y, and z respectively represent the weights of the phases present, then they must be in equilibrium about any horizontal axis through P. Taking axis QR parallel to YZ and a perpendicular from X cutting QR and YX in S and T respectively, then by moments about QR,

$$x \cdot \text{XS} = (y+z) \cdot \text{ST}$$

The proportion of phase X is given directly from

$$\frac{x}{x+y+z} = \frac{\text{ST}}{\text{XT}}$$

The proportions of Y and Z are found in a similar manner.

More complicated ternary diagrams are beyond the scope of this work, although no new principles are involved.

QUESTIONS

1. From the copper-nickel equilibrium diagram (fig. A.9) determine the compositions and proportions of the phases present at 1200° C in an alloy containing 30% nickel.

2. From the lead-magnesium equilibrium diagram (fig. A.13) determine the chemical formula of the intermediate compound. Describe the changes which occur in a mixture containing 30% lead and 70% magnesium as it is slowly cooled from 650° C to 200° C. Give the quantities and compositions of the phases present at 500° C and 300° C.
[MST]

3. From the equilibrium diagram of the sodium-potassium system (fig. A.12) calculate the formula of the intermetallic compound. On a copy of the diagram indicate the constitution of the material in each region.

Describe in detail the changes that occur as a 50–50 alloy is slowly cooled from 50° C to −50° C. What is the distribution of phases at 0° C?

4. Construct on graph paper, using the data given below, the equilibrium diagram of the zirconium-molybdenum system to the following scales: 1 in = 20% by weight and 1 in = 400° C.

Zirconium (Zr) exists as a-phase up to 862° C, when it changes to β-phase which melts at 1860° C.

Molybdenum (Mo) exists as γ-phase up to its melting-point at 2620° C.

An intermediate compound $ZrMo_2$ is formed at 1880° C by the peritectic reaction

liquid (58% Mo) + Mo rich solid solution → $ZrMo_2$

Limits of solubility are 22% Mo in βZr, negligible solubility of Mo in $a Zr$, and 10% Zr in Mo. The solubility of Zr in Mo falls to zero at 0° C.

A eutectic between the β solid solution and $ZrMo_2$ exists at 31% Mo and 1520° C.

A eutectoid decomposition of β occurs at 7·5% Mo and 780° C.

Typical curves for phase boundaries between the points given may be assumed.
[P]

5. In an alloy system between elements A and B, A melts at 700° C and B melts at 500° C. The γ-phase melts at 800° C, at which temperature its composition is 60% B. The following isothermal reactions occur:

Peritectic: γ (70% B) + liquid (90% B) $\rightleftharpoons \delta$ (85% B) at 550° C.
Eutectic: liquid (25% B) $\rightleftharpoons a$ (16% B) + γ (40% B) at 450° C.
Eutectoid: γ (50% B) $\rightleftharpoons a$ (12% B) + δ (90% B) at 300° C.
Peritectoid: a (9% B) + δ (93% B) $\rightleftharpoons \beta$ (35% B) at 200° C.

The solid solubilities of B in A and A in B at 0° C are negligible. The β-phase exists at 0° C from 32% B to 40% B.

Draw, to scale, the equilibrium diagram, assuming the usual shapes for phase boundaries, and indicate the phase or phases present in each region. [MST]

6. Two hypothetical metals, A and B, whose melting-points are 700° C and 500° C respectively, are miscible in all proportions in the liquid state and are partially soluble in one another in the solid state, the maximum solubilities being 5% B and 25% A by weight. The solubilities are 2% and 5% respectively at 0° C.

The two metals form a compound A_2B which melts at 750° C and in which neither metal is soluble. The atomic weights of A and B are 30 and 50 respectively. Eutectics are formed at 22% and 60% by weight of B and at temperatures of 450° C and 320° C respectively.

Construct and label the equilibrium diagram, assuming that all the lines on it are straight.

Find, for an alloy containing 45% by weight of A, (a) the temperatures at which melting begins on heating and at which melting is complete, and (b) the composition and distribution of the phases at 100° C. [MST]

7. When are the rules used in the interpretation of binary equilibrium diagrams applicable to vertical sections of ternary equilibrium diagrams?

8. Three elements are soluble in all proportions in the liquid phase but only partially soluble in the solid phase. Sketch typical isothermal sections of the ternary equilibrium diagram, labelling them to show the phases present in each region, at temperatures lying in the following ranges:

(a) Below the freezing-points of two of the elements, but above the binary eutectic temperature for those two elements and above the freezing-point of the third element.

(b) Below all the binary eutectic temperatures, but above the ternary eutectic temperature.

(c) Below the ternary eutectic temperature. [MST]

9. From the isothermal section at 650° C of the chromium-iron-nickel equilibrium diagram (fig. A.14) estimate the compositions of and percentages of the various phases present at

(a) 30% Cr, 30% Fe, 40% Ni;
(b) 70% Cr, 10% Fe, 20% Ni;
(c) 50% Cr, 30% Fe, 20% Ni.

In the two-phase region, assume that the tie-line is parallel to the nearest side of the equilateral triangle. [MST]

CHAPTER 8

The Iron-carbon System

8.1. Allotropic forms of pure iron

On cooling molten pure iron, it solidifies at 1539° C into a body-centred cubic structure. On further cooling, this structure changes at 1400° C to a face-centred cubic structure and again at 910° C back to body-centred cubic. These structures have been designated α, γ, and δ from room temperature upwards. The α-iron loses its ferromagnetic properties when heated above 770° C—a temperature known as the Curie

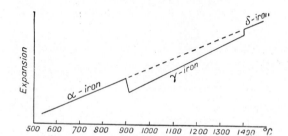

Fig. 8.1.—Change of length with temperature of pure iron.   [Gregory]

point. The non-magnetic α-iron was formerly known as β-iron until X-ray crystallographic methods showed that there was no change of crystal structure at 770° C.

The γ-iron is a structure of closest packing, whereas the α- and δ-iron are not. Hence there will be an abrupt change of dimensions at the temperatures of the α-γ and γ-δ transitions. A graph of change of length with temperature is shown in fig. 8.1. This phenomenon is known as *dilatation*. Dilatation can be expressed quantitatively either as the *volume dilatation*, i.e. the change of volume per unit volume, or as the *linear dilatation*, i.e. the change of length per unit length. The allotropic changes also involve a change of heat content—analogous to the latent heat of fusion, so that if a specimen is cooled with a steady rate of heat loss, the temperature-time graph shows arrests at the change points as in fig. 8.2.

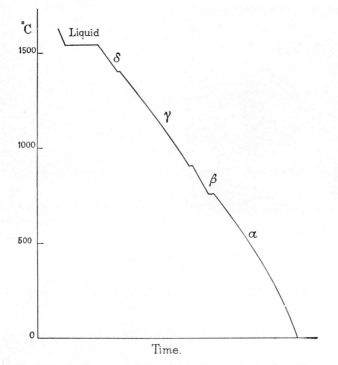

Fig. 8.2.—Cooling curve of pure iron with steady rate of heat loss

8.2. Solubility of carbon in iron

The carbon atom is smaller than the iron atom (the diameters are 1·54 Å and 2·56 Å respectively) and dissolves interstitially in all three phases. The solubility in γ-iron is at a maximum of 1·7% at 1130° C, the solid solution being known as *austenite*. The solubilities in the body-centred cubic phases are considerably smaller, the maxima being 0·1% at 1492° C in δ-iron and 0·03% at 723° C in α-iron. The solid solution of carbon in α-iron is known as *ferrite*, while that in δ-iron has not been given a special name.

The reason for the difference in solubility may be seen when the crystal structure is examined. Each space in a face-centred cubic structure is bounded by six spherical surfaces symmetrically arranged giving a " cubical " space (fig. 8.3). Expressed as coordinates in terms of the unit cell, the centres of these spaces are at $(0, 0, \frac{1}{2})$ and $(\frac{1}{2}, \frac{1}{2}, \frac{1}{2})$. The three dimensions that govern the size of a sphere that could be inserted into the space are equal. If D is the diameter of the iron atom, the diameter of

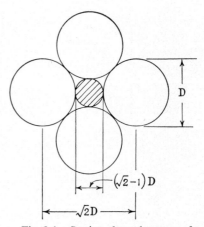

Fig. 8.3.—Model of " space " between spheres packed in face-centred cubic structure

Fig. 8.4.—Section through centre of " space " in face-centred cubic structure, showing largest sphere that can be inserted

the largest sphere that could be put into the space is $0.414D$, i.e. 1.06 Å. This may be seen from the section in fig. 8.4. The diameter of the carbon

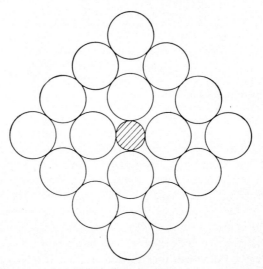

Fig. 8.5.—Hypothetical distortion around a carbon atom in interstitial solid solution in γ-iron

atom is 1.54 Å, so that it can get into the space only by causing local distortion, which may be pictured as in fig. 8.5. There will be an overall distortion of the lattice, causing an increase in the measured lattice parameter, but also quite a lot of distortion in the immediate vicinity of the carbon atom. The limit of solubility, which is about 1·7% by weight, shows that the ratio of carbon atoms to iron atoms is

$$\frac{1\cdot7/12}{98\cdot3/56} \approx \frac{1}{12}$$

that is, the maximum number of carbon atoms that can go into interstitial solution in the γ-iron is about one to every twelve available spaces, since there will be one space per iron atom. Now each space has twelve equidistant nearest neighbouring spaces. The distortion due to one carbon atom can therefore be assumed to be such that, on average, eleven of the twelve nearest spaces cannot also take a carbon atom.

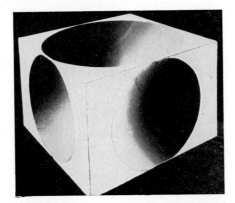

Fig. 8.6.—Model of " space " between spheres packed in body-centred cubic structure

The body-centred cubic lattice is not so densely packed as the face-centred cubic lattice, and hence the spaces are larger. They are not, however, of the cubical shape of the face-centred cubic lattice, but have one smaller and two larger dimensions. A picture of the " space " is shown in fig. 8.6. The position into which the largest sphere could be fitted in this space has the coordinates $(\frac{1}{2}, \frac{1}{4}, 0)$. In this position it would lie with its centre in one face of the unit cell and touching four atoms (fig. 8.7). The diameter of the sphere that would just fit is $[\sqrt{(5/3)}-1]D$ or 0·74 Å for the α-iron lattice. Obviously, this space would not take a carbon atom as easily as the spaces in γ-iron, and if an atom did go into such a space, the distortion would be so great that another carbon atom could not get in for some considerable distance. The site of the carbon

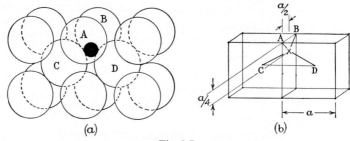

Fig. 8.7.

(a) Interstitial atom (black) that just fits into body-centred cubic structure, touching atoms A, B, C, and D

(b) Centres of atoms.

$AC = AD$, etc. $= \sqrt{3}a/2 =$ diameter D of larger atom.
$AX = BX = CX = DX = \sqrt{[(\frac{1}{2}a)^2+(\frac{1}{4}a)^2]} = \sqrt{5}a/4 = \sqrt{5}D/2\sqrt{3}$
Radius of interstitial atom $= AX - \frac{1}{2}D = \frac{1}{2}D[\sqrt{(5/3)}-1]$

atoms in ferrite is not this position, but that shown in fig. 8.8, and is also one that will not take many atoms, actually about one carbon atom per 700 spaces at maximum solubility.

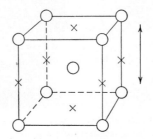

Fig. 8.8.—Actual positions occupied by carbon atoms in ferrite lattice shown by crosses. Arrow shows direction of resulting distortion of lattice parallel to one axis only.

8.3. Cementite and ledeburite

Iron and carbon form an intermediate compound which contains $6 \cdot 67\%$ carbon. This compound, known as *cementite*, and having the formula Fe_3C has been considered in Section 6.8.

The equilibrium diagram (fig. 8.9) shows that between iron and cementite there is a eutectic-forming series of alloys with the eutectic reaction occurring at $4 \cdot 3\%$ carbon and $1130°$ C. The eutectic is between cementite and austenite and is given the name *ledeburite*. When iron ores are smelted with coke (i.e. carbon) in a blast furnace, the iron oxide is reduced to iron, the oxygen forming carbon monoxide. When the temperature is

96

above 1130° C, an iron alloy containing 4·3% dissolved carbon would melt, so that any alloy of this composition would first run to the base of the furnace. The crude iron-carbon alloy formed in a blast furnace will thus be of about eutectic composition. It is known as *pig iron.*

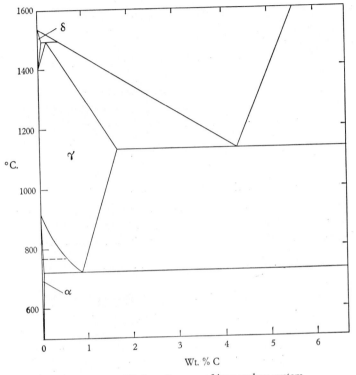

Fig. 8.9.—Equilibrium diagram of iron-carbon system

The greatest solubility of carbon in austenite is 1·7% at the eutectic temperature. Above and below this temperature, the solubility decreases. Thus for compositions above about 0·2% carbon the limit of solubility is reached, on heating, when the solidus line is reached and the two-phase (austenite + liquid) region entered. Also all compositions above about 0·9% on cooling will precipitate cementite when the limit of solubility is reached.

8.4. Modifications of allotropic change temperatures

Austenite has a much higher solubility for carbon than either ferrite or δ-iron, the result of which is that the presence of carbon raises the temperature of the $\gamma \to \delta$ change and lowers that of the $\gamma \to \alpha$ change. The temperature range of austenite thus increases initially with an increase of carbon content.

On cooling, say, a 0·3% carbon alloy from the austenite phase, the change to ferrite does not begin until the temperature falls to 850° C. At this temperature, ferrite crystals nucleate at positions on the austenite grain boundary.

The lower boundary of the austenite region is formed by two lines, one from 910° C at pure iron—the ferrite separation line—and the other from 1130° C at 1·7% carbon—the cementite separation line. These intersect, showing that a eutectoid reaction will occur. The equilibrium temperature for this reaction is given as 723° C, and the composition of the eutectoid is given in various works as anything from 0·80% to 0·89%. In the absence of conclusive evidence as to the correct value, the value of 0·89% has been used throughout this book.

8.5. Eutectoid and peritectic decomposition of austenite

The eutectoid forms by simultaneous precipitation of ferrite and cementite and is known as *pearlite*. The structure is often laminated, consisting of alternate thin plates of cementite and ferrite. These evenly-

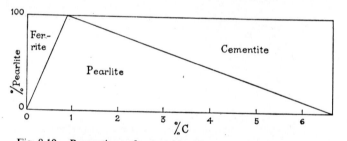

Fig. 8.10.—Proportions of eutectoid and pro-eutectoid structures in microstructures of iron-carbon alloys at room temperature

spaced lines sometimes produce an irridescent appearance after polishing and etching—an appearance resembling mother-of-pearl—hence the name. The composition of pearlite is $(0·89/6·67) \times 100 = 13·3\%$ cementite and 86·7% ferrite.

The structure of any alloy at room temperature will be part ferrite and part pearlite if the carbon content is below 0·89%, and part pearlite and part cementite if above. The proportions of these constituents for any composition can be determined from fig. 8.10.

The upper part of the austenite region terminates in a peritectic reaction at 0·18% carbon and 1492° C.

8.6. Nomenclature of iron-carbon alloys

Any alloys with less than 0·03% carbon (i.e. entirely ferrite at 723° C) are known as *pure irons*.

Those alloys with carbon contents between 0·03% and 1·7% (i.e. entirely austenite at 1130° C) are known as *steels* and are further divided into *hypo-eutectoid* and *hyper-eutectoid* steels, being those with carbon contents respectively less and more than the eutectoid composition. Alloys containing more than 1·7% and less than 6·67% carbon are known as *cast irons*.

8.7. Microstructures of steels

Pure irons containing ferrite only, show sharp grain boundaries as in fig. 5.3. With increase of carbon content, pearlite appears in increasing quantity. Under the microscope the pearlite appears dark or striped and may be distinguished clearly from the ferrite as in fig. 8.11a. In hyper-eutectoid steels, the primary or pro-eutectoid* cementite is concentrated on the former austenite grain boundaries and appears white between the dark pearlite areas as in fig. 8.11d.

The cementite layers of the pearlite, which appear dark at intermediate magnifications, are actually etched at their boundaries only, and under high magnification the boundaries may be resolved, showing white cementite between.

8.8. Phase-transformation diagrams

The phases and their proportions at any temperature for any particular alloy can be read directly from the equilibrium diagram. Also the manner in which the phases are distributed can be deduced. The results are most easily presented on a *phase-transformation diagram*.

Consider the slow cooling from a temperature of 1500° C of an alloy containing 0·5% carbon. At a temperature of about 1500° C austenite commences to separate from the liquid and continues to do so as the temperature falls until at 1430° C all the liquid has transformed. The austenite remains unchanged until at about 775° C, when ferrite nucleates and continues to separate until 723° C when the composition is 0·47/0·86 austenite containing 0·89% carbon and 0·39/0·86 ferrite containing

---

* *Pro-eutectic* and *pro-eutectoid* refer to phases formed before the eutectic and eutectoid structure respectively.

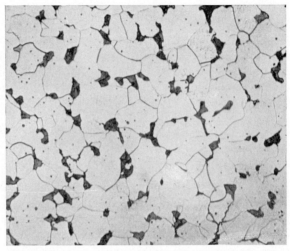

Fig. 8.11a.—Microstructures of steels: 0·15% C (× 400)

Fig. 8.11b.—Microstructures of steels:
0·53% C (× 400)

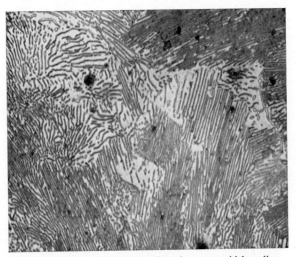

Fig. 8.11*c*.—Microstructures of steels: eutectoid lamellar pearlite ($\times$ 500)

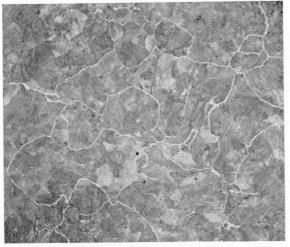

Fig. 8.11*d*.—Microstructures of steels: **1·2**% C ($\times$ 200)

0·03% carbon. At 723° C this austenite changes to the eutectoid pearlite. The final composition is

$$\frac{0·39}{0·86} = 45·3\% \text{ pro-eutectoid ferrite}$$

$$·867 \times \frac{0·47}{0·86} = 47·4\% \text{ eutectoid ferrite}$$

$$·133 \times \frac{0·47}{0·86} = 7·3\% \text{ eutectoid cementite}$$

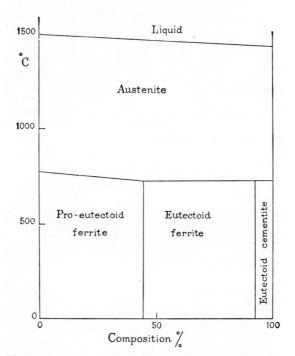

Fig. 8.12.—Phase-transformation diagram for a 0·5% C steel

The phase-transformation diagram showing the changes is given in fig. 8.12. It will be seen that this form of diagram shows for each temperature the proportion of each structural constituent and the phase from which it was formed.

Changes involving the δ-phase or ledeburite would be more complicated, as may be seen from the examples in figs. 8.13 and 8.14.

The changes associated with the δ-phase are of little practical importance, because no commercial processing of alloys is carried out in that range. The austenite-ferrite change is of great importance, because it is on this change that all the heat treatment of steels depends.

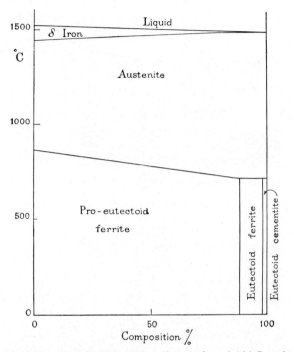

Fig. 8.13.—Phase-transformation diagram for a 0·1 % C steel

8.9. Nomenclature of change points

To facilitate reference to the various changes and the temperatures at which they occur, they are referred to by the letter A (*arrêt*—referring to the arrest in a time-temperature curve) with various subscript numerals to identify the changes as follows:

	Change on heating	*Change on cooling*
A_1	Pearlite to austenite	Austenite to pearlite
A_2	Loss of ferromagnetism	Gain of ferromagnetism
A_3	Last ferrite absorbed in austenite	First ferrite nucleates from austenite
A_{cm}	Last cementite absorbed in austenite	First cementite nucleates from austenite
A_4	First δ-iron forms from austenite	Last δ-iron dissolves in austenite

The lines of the equilibrium diagram with their appropriate labels are

103

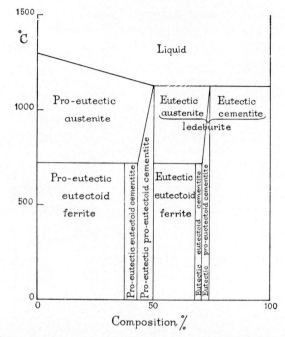

Fig. 8.14.—Phase-transformation diagram for a 3·0% C iron-carbon alloy

shown in fig. 8.15. For carbon contents above *a*, ferromagnetism is lost when the last ferrite disappears, so that A_2 and A_3 coincide along *ab*. Also for hypereutectoid steels all the ferrite present at low temperatures is in the pearlite, so that the A_1, A_2, and A_3 temperatures are the same.

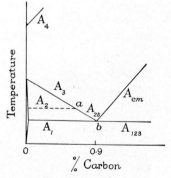

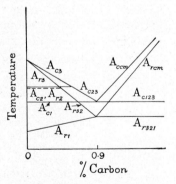

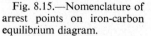

Fig. 8.15.—Nomenclature of arrest points on iron-carbon equilibrium diagram.

Fig. 8.16.—Nomenclature of change points in steel for heating and cooling.

104

This equilibrium diagram shows the temperatures and compositions for changes carried out under equilibrium conditions, i.e. at infinitely slow rates of heating and cooling. In practical cases, these rates are finite and, because the changes depend upon the diffusion of carbon, the rate of which is limited, there is a thermal lag. Each change temperature is higher during heating than during cooling with the exception of the A_2-temperature. The loss of magnetism at this temperature is not due to change of structure and does not involve migration of atoms.

A further subscript is used to distinguish between heating and cooling change temperatures; *c* (from the French *chauffage*) indicates the transformation temperature on heating and *r* (from *refroidissement*) on cooling. The difference between A_{c1} and A_{r1} in plain carbon steels is of the order of 25–50° C and is much greater in alloy steels. The constitution diagram for actual changes is then as shown in fig. 8.16.

8.10. Determination of change points

The temperatures of the changes for a particular alloy may be found from heating and cooling curves. At the A_1-temperature there will be considerable absorption or evolution of heat giving a plateau on the curve. Between A_1 and A_3 heat of change has to be supplied as well as specific heat. Above A_3 only specific heat has to be supplied, so that there will be a change of slope at A_3. Change of slope also occurs at the A_2-temperature. Heating and cooling curves for some steels are given in fig. 8.17.

Alternatively the change temperatures can be found by observing the change of length with temperature. An instrument for doing this is a dilatometer, one form of which is shown in fig. 8.18. The specimen is heated by an electric furnace, its temperature being measured by a thermocouple. The extension of the specimen is transmitted to a dial gauge via silica rods and Invar* bars. Both of these have low coefficients of thermal expansion, and the silica, being an insulator, does not conduct much heat from the ends of the specimen, so that a fairly uniform temperature is maintained throughout its length. The main frame of the instrument is also made of Invar bars, so that if these do change their temperature the effect on the readings will be small. By choice of suitable currents in the electric furnace, controlled rates of heating and cooling can be achieved. During heating and cooling, simultaneous readings of temperature and length change are made. Some typical results are shown in fig. 8.19.

---

* Invar is a trade name for an iron-nickel alloy containing about 36% nickel. Its coefficient of thermal expansion is approximately 6% of that of a carbon steel at room temperature.

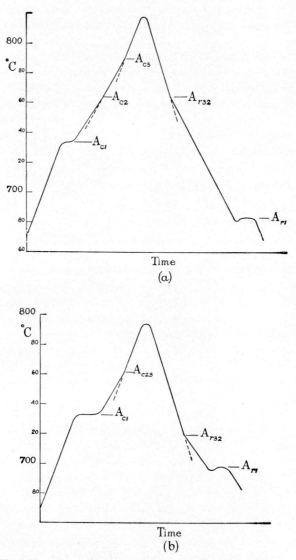

Fig. 8.17.—Time-temperature curves for heating and cooling of steels containing (*a*) 0·34% C, (*b*) 0·53% C.

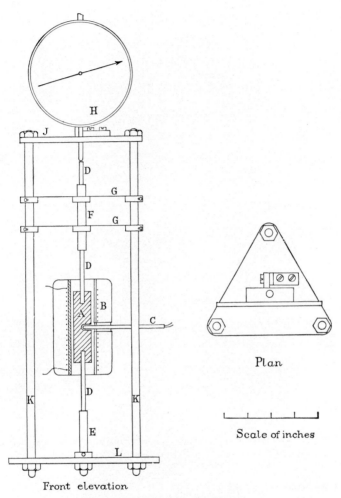

Front elevation

Plan

Scale of inches

Fig. 8.18.—Typical form of dilatometer

A—specimen (sectioned) inside furnace B (sectioned). C—thermocouple.
D—silica rods to reduce conduction heat losses, fitted into lower Invar bar
E in base L and upper Invar bar F restrained by spring steel guides G. Dial
gauge H secured by bracket on top plate J. K—Invar bar main frame.

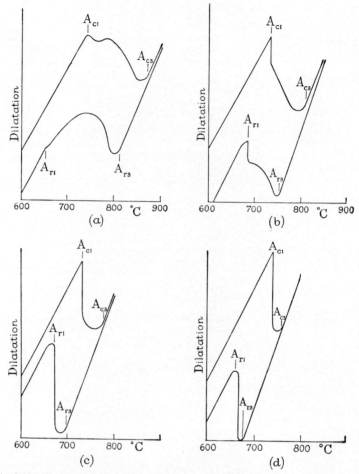

Fig. 8.19.—Temperature-length curves for heating and cooling of steels containing
(*a*) 0·12% C, (*b*) 0·36% C, (*c*) 0·52% C, (*d*) 0·69% C

8.11. Cast irons

As stated on p. 99 the term *cast iron* is applied to all iron-carbon alloys containing more than 1·7% carbon. Thus it will be seen from the equilibrium diagram that they are never single-phase on first solidification, but always contain some cementite. The changes on cooling are complex as shown in the phase-transformation diagram in fig. 8.14. The final structure is a mixture of ferrite and cementite.

The formation of cementite is, however, a metastable condition and under certain conditions the cementite breaks down to ferrite and free carbon in the form of graphite. In hypereutectic alloys, some graphite forms from the liquid. A cast iron containing all the carbon as cementite is known as a *white cast iron*, while a graphitized one is known as *grey cast iron*. Graphitization is favoured by a slow rate of cooling and by the presence of silicon.

White cast iron (fig. 8.20), being largely cementite, is extremely hard, but brittle. It gives excellent wear-resisting properties to the surfaces of castings. In grey cast iron (figs. 8.21 and 8.22) the graphite is distributed as flakes, which break up the continuity of the metal matrix—a carbon steel of itself possessing considerable strength and ductility. In ferritic

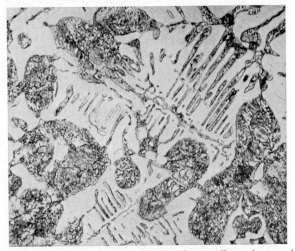

Fig. 8.20.—White cast iron (× 200) showing pearlite and cementite

grey cast iron all the carbon is graphite. In pearlitic grey cast iron, some is in pearlite. The graphite flakes have no strength and act as internal cracks making the material weak and brittle and extremely liable to fracture under shock loads.

Malleable cast iron is made by annealing white iron castings for periods of several days under controlled conditions, when the graphite will separate as nodules of approximately spherical shape (fig. 8.23). The weakening effect of the graphite is reduced so that malleable cast iron has a higher strength, and greater ductility and shock resistance. The objection is the cost of the prolonged annealing treatment.

It was found about 1948 that by additions of cerium or magnesium under controlled conditions to the molten metal before pouring into the moulds, the graphite forms spherical particles on casting (fig. 8.24). This

Fig. 8.21.—Pearlitic grey cast iron (× 200)
Graphite flakes in pearlite matrix

Fig. 8.22.—Ferritic grey cast iron (× 200)
Graphite flakes in ferrite matrix

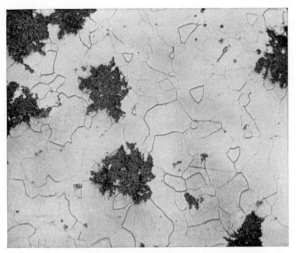

Fig. 8.23.—Blackheart malleable cast iron (× 200)
Graphite nodules in ferrite matrix

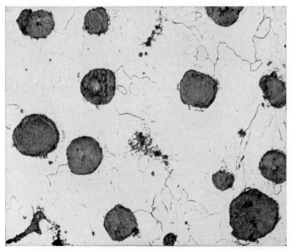

Fig. 8.24.—Spheroidal graphite cast iron (× 200)
Graphite spheroids in ferrite matrix

spheroidal graphite cast iron is found to have a strength superior to malleable cast iron and, with suitable annealing, which precipitates further graphite from the pearlite matrix, the ductility is as good.

QUESTIONS

1. Calculate the linear dilatation as a polycrystalline specimen of α-iron changes to γ-iron, assuming that the atoms are rigid spheres.

2. Calculate the linear dilatation as a polycrystalline specimen of titanium changes from close-packed hexagonal to body-centred cubic at 880° C. Assume that the closest distance between atom centres is the same in each structure.

3. Explain, referring to suitable examples, the meanings of the terms *phase, change of state, allotropic change, crystal lattice, unit cell.*

From the lattice parameter of α-iron, find the radius of the iron atom, assuming that the atoms behave as hard spheres in contact. Compute the lattice parameter of γ-iron, assuming that the atoms behave as hard spheres of this same radius.   [MST]

4. Draw a phase-transformation diagram to show how the proportions and distribution of the phases present vary with temperature, as a 0·35% carbon steel is cooled under equilibrium conditions from the liquid state to 0° C.

Sketch the resultant microstructure.

Sketch a graph of the variation of length with temperature for a specimen of this steel during heating from 0° C to 1000° C and subsequent cooling to 0° C.   [MST]

5. An Fe-Fe₃C alloy containing 3% carbon has been slowly cooled from the liquid state. At 500° C what is the ratio of the cementite in the pearlite derived from the eutectic austenite to the proeutectoid cementite derived from the proeutectic austenite?   [MST]

6. Describe briefly two experimental methods for the determination of change points in a mild steel as it is heated from room temperature to 900° C and then cooled to room temperature again.

Sketch and explain the form of experimental results which should be obtained. [P]

CHAPTER 9

Thermal Energy

9.1. Kinetic energy of a gas molecule

The kinetic energy of translation of the molecules of a perfect gas was discussed in Chapter 3 and shown to be equal to $\frac{1}{2}mn\overline{C^2}$. Also it was shown that

$$pV = RT = \frac{2}{3} \times \frac{1}{2}mn\overline{C^2}$$

for one mole, so that the kinetic energy was $\frac{3}{2}RT$ per mole or $\frac{3}{2}kT$ per molecule on the average.

Now a gas molecule has three degrees of freedom for translational motion (e.g. the components of its velocity in three mutually perpendicular directions define its velocity). Maxwell has shown that if a system which has several degrees of freedom obeys the ordinary laws of mechanics, then the total energy of a system is equally divided among the different degrees of freedom. This is termed the principle of the *equipartition of energy*. Hence the kinetic energy of translation of a molecule in one degree of freedom is on the average $\frac{1}{2}kT$.

The next problem is the total number of degrees of freedom of a molecule. (So far we have considered only translational degrees of freedom and ignored any possible rotational or vibrational freedoms.)

(i). *A monatomic gas*

In a monatomic gas each molecule can have three translational degrees of freedom, but no rotational freedom. It can be said simply that an atom is spherically symmetrical and therefore any rotation could not be detected.*

(ii). *A diatomic gas*

Suppose each molecule consists of two atoms at a fixed distance apart as shown diagrammatically in fig. 9.1. The molecule can rotate about two perpendicular axes which are themselves at right angles to the line

---

* The correct explanation is that the angular momentum obeys the Bohr quantization rule (p. 11). The moment of inertia of a single atom or of a diatomic molecule about the axis passing through both atoms is so small that the angular velocity for the lowest value of angular momentum is very high, and the kinetic energy would be much greater than $\frac{1}{2}kT$ at ordinary temperatures. It is therefore unlikely that this rotation could be excited.

joining the atoms, but there will be no rotation about the axis that passes through both atoms. This last assumption is similar to the one made in the case of the monatomic molecule. Each molecule therefore has three translational and two rotational degrees of freedom, making five in all. By the principle of equipartition of energy, each degree of freedom will have an average energy of $\frac{1}{2}kT$, so that the total energy is

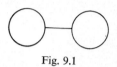

Fig. 9.1

$$\tfrac{5}{2}kT$$

More complicated molecules may also have a third rotational degree of freedom and possibly other degrees if relative movement or vibration between atoms can occur.

9.2. Specific heat of a gas

Now the specific heat of a gas at constant volume is the quantity of heat required to raise the temperature of unit quantity of the gas by one degree, while the volume remains unchanged. This heat goes only to increase the total kinetic energy of the molecules. Therefore for one mole of a monatomic gas it should be $\frac{3}{2}R$ and for one mole of a diatomic gas it should be $\frac{5}{2}R$. A few examples to illustrate this are given in Table 9.1.

TABLE 9.1—EXPERIMENTAL AND THEORETICAL VALUES OF
SPECIFIC HEAT FOR SOME GASES
(in cal/gm mole °C or B.t.u./lb mole °F)

Gas	Experimental value of C_v	Theoretical value of C_v
Argon	2·98	$\left.\vphantom{\begin{matrix}a\\b\end{matrix}}\right\}\ \frac{3}{2}R = 2\cdot980$
Helium	2·98	
Air	4·95	$\left.\vphantom{\begin{matrix}a\\b\\c\end{matrix}}\right\}\ \frac{5}{2}R = 4\cdot967$
Carbon monoxide	4·94	
Nitrogen	4·93	

9.3. Specific heat of a solid

Whereas the molecules of a gas were free to move, the atoms in a solid are much less mobile. Each can vibrate about its mean position, and sometimes diffusion will occur whereby atoms may migrate through the bulk of the metal. Further reference to diffusion will appear later.

Now the vibration of each atom can be considered as being compounded from three vibrations, each parallel to one of three perpendicular axes. The energy of an atom in one of its modes of vibration can be expressed at any instant as the sum of its kinetic and its potential energy. The kinetic energy is due to its having a velocity, and it has potential energy because it is moving in a potential field of force. These two energy terms are independent. Hence six independent terms are necessary to specify completely the motion of the atom, i.e. it has six degrees of freedom.

By the principle of equipartition of energy, the energy associated with each degree of freedom will be $\frac{1}{2}kT$ per atom or $\frac{1}{2}RT$ per gram atom. The total energy is therefore $6 \times \frac{1}{2}RT = 3RT$, and

$$C_v = 3R$$

This was expressed in Dulong and Petit's law in 1819 which was based on experimental results for solid elements at ordinary temperatures. This law states that the product of the specific heat at constant volume and the atomic weight, that is, the *atomic heat*, is the same for all substances, and is equal to 5·96 calories per gram atom per degree.

9.4. Experimental results for simple substances

Dulong and Petit's law does not represent the behaviour of metals at all temperatures. The actual behaviour can be summarized as follows:

(i). Near absolute zero, the atomic heat is proportional to the cube of the absolute temperature. (This is the Debye T^3 law.)

(ii). At ordinary and higher temperatures, the atomic heat at constant volume converges to $3R$.

(iii). The curves for atomic heat against absolute temperature for all substances are exactly similar in shape and can be made to coincide by altering the scale of the temperature axis, i.e.

$$C_v = F\left(\frac{T}{\Theta}\right)$$

where the function F is the same for all substances and Θ is a constant which has a particular value for each substance. The shape of the curve is shown in fig. 9.2.

A theoretical analysis by Debye based on quantum mechanical principles led to the formula*

$$C_v = 3R\left[12\frac{T^3}{\Theta^3}\int_0^{\Theta/T}\frac{x^3\,dx}{e^x-1} - \frac{3\Theta/T}{e^{\Theta/T}-1}\right]$$

---

* For a derivation of this formula and others relating to specific heats, see J. de Lauray, " The Theory of Specific Heats and Lattice Vibrations," *Solid State Physics*, Vol. 2, 1956, p. 219. Academic Press Inc., London and New York.

which gives curves in very close agreement with the observed shape. At very low temperatures this reduces to

$$C_v = \frac{12\pi^4 R}{5}\left(\frac{T}{\Theta}\right)^3$$

the Debye T^3 law.

Θ is known as the Debye temperature. Its exact meaning is beyond the scope of this work. It happens to be the temperature at which C_v is within $3\cdot4\%$ of the value of $3R$.

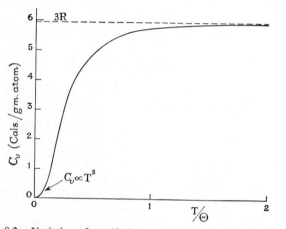

Fig. 9.2.—Variation of specific heat of a solid with temperature. By expressing temperature in the form T/Θ, where Θ is a characteristic temperature for each solid material, one curve applies to all materials.

As the temperature of the solid is increased, the energy is increased, that is, the amplitudes of the vibrations are increased and the centres of oscillation need to move farther apart. This is the explanation of thermal expansion. The amplitude of vibration is of the order of 10% of the interatomic distance at ordinary temperatures. Melting occurs when the amplitude reaches about 12%.

9.5. Stable and metastable states

A stable state of equilibrium of a system may be defined as one in which the free energy is a minimum; that is, to disturb the system slightly from this state some work must be done. Now it is possible for many physical or chemical systems to exist more or less indefinitely in states which are not those of minimum free energy. Hence they cannot be regarded as being stable states.

As an example, consider a system consisting of oxygen and hydrogen at room temperature. The stable state is that in which they are combined in the molecular form. But if the gases are mixed at this temperature, they do not combine chemically. Once a spark has passed, however, they will combine, and in doing so give out much heat energy, showing that the system has now attained a state of lower free energy and hence a more stable one.

Such a system is said to be in a *metastable* state. True equilibrium can be reached by raising the temperature. Also the speed of chemical reactions can be raised by increasing the temperature.

Thus a higher temperature favours a more rapid rate of approach to equilibrium. A metastable state is possible when the temperature is too low to enable changes to occur at an appreciable rate.

9.6. A simple example of a metastable state

A box resting on a flat surface in the position shown in fig. 9.3a is stable because the centre of gravity G is in the lowest position possible. In the position shown in fig. 9.3b, it is not in stable equilibrium because G is not in the lowest position. But on tilting it slightly, the potential energy rises, showing that the immediately neighbouring positions are

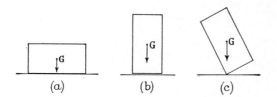

(a) (b) (c)

Fig. 9.3.—(a) Stable, (b) metastable, and (c) unstable positions of box

less stable. Hence, unless disturbed, the box will remain indefinitely in this position which is one of metastability. For the box to pass from the metastable to the stable position, it must pass through the position shown in fig. 9.3c, which is that of the maximum potential energy it can have while still in contact with the surface. It could balance here but would topple one way or the other if given the slightest disturbance. This position is therefore one of *unstable* equilibrium.

A graph of potential energy against angle of tilt from the metastable position for a box in which one dimension is twice the other is shown in fig. 9.4.

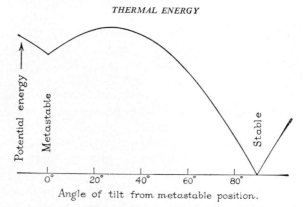

Angle of tilt from metastable position.

Fig. 9.4.—Variation of potential energy of box in fig. 9.3 with angle of tilt

9.7. Activation energy

The same principle operates in many physical and chemical changes, where an atom can move from a metastable position to another of greater stability by passing through intermediate positions of higher energy. This is represented diagrammatically in fig. 9.5.

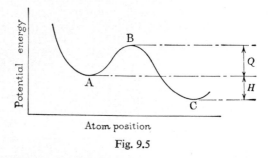

Atom position

Fig. 9.5

An atom at position A can reach a more stable position C only by passing through the unstable position B. It will be able to do this only if it can receive the necessary additional energy to take it to the level B. The additional energy Q, i.e. the difference in the energy levels of positions A and B is the *activation energy*.

The final position C has a lower energy level so that in passing from B to C a total energy of $Q+H$ is released. Thus there is a net energy release of H. This is termed the *heat of reaction* and may appear in any of the forms that energy can take—heat, light, sound, etc. Since atoms may have energy due to thermal excitation and there is a scatter of energy values, some atoms will at times have enough energy to overcome the barrier.

The speed at which such a change can occur in a large population of such atoms will depend on the magnitude of Q and also on the number of atoms that possess energy equal to or greater than Q at any instant.

When Q is small, other things being equal, the reaction can proceed faster than when Q is large.

The number of atoms possessing energy Q at any instant depends upon the distribution of energy in a system. Owing to collisions and the forces between the atoms, there is a constant interchange of energy and fluctuations of energy of any particular atom. In a system with a large population of atoms, there is a steady-state distribution of energy with a certain fraction of atoms in each energy range.

9.8. Maxwell-Boltzmann law

The proportion of atoms in each energy range can be calculated from the Maxwell-Boltzmann Law. The number of atoms which have an energy greater than q is proportional to

$$e^{-q/kT}$$

where k is Boltzmann's constant and T is the absolute temperature.

If the energy is expressed as Q per gram atom or gram mole (i.e. $Q = N_0q$), then the expression becomes

$$e^{-Q/RT}$$

where R is the universal gas constant. The form of the distribution curve is shown in fig. 9.6.

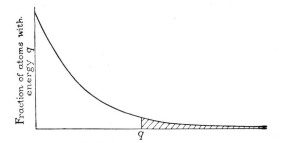

Fig. 9.6.—Maxwell-Boltzmann distribution law. Shaded area is proportional to number of atoms with energy greater than q

9.9. Arrhenius' rate law

For a reaction for which the activation energy is Q per gram atom or gram mole, the number of atoms with sufficient energy to overcome the potential barrier will be proportional to $e^{-Q/RT}$. The rate of reaction is proportional to this number so that

$$\text{rate of reaction} = v = Ae^{-Q/RT} = Ae^{-q/kT}$$

where A is a constant.

Writing this in the form

$$\log v = \log A - \frac{Q}{RT}$$

it will be seen that $\log v$ varies linearly with $1/T$. If, for a particular reaction, experimental values of $\log v$ when plotted against $1/T$ exhibit a straight line, then the reaction is a thermally-activated one and the slope of the line will be $-Q/R$, from which the activation energy Q may be calculated.

Some practical cases of thermally-activated processes will be discussed in the following sections.

9.10 Diffusion

The atoms in a crystal, in addition to vibrating about their mean positions, can also change positions, a process known as diffusion.* In a homogeneous pure material this cannot be detected. If, however, some artificially-induced radioactive isotopes (see p. 266) are introduced into a piece of the material, the diffusion can be observed. Atoms of a second kind can also diffuse into a pure metal, a process which can be detected and measured.

The rate at which diffusion can occur has been formulated into Fick's laws, the first of which is:

If C is the concentration of the diffusing atoms at any point, and $\partial C/\partial x$ is the concentration gradient in the x-direction, then the rate at which atoms cross unit area perpendicular to the x-direction is

$$\frac{dm}{dt} = D\frac{\partial C}{\partial x}$$

where dm is the mass crossing unit area in time dt. Here D is the diffusion coefficient and has units of (length^2/time).

In general C is not constant at any one point, and the variation of C with time is required. This can be expressed by Fick's second law:

$$\frac{\partial C}{\partial t} = \frac{\partial}{\partial x}\left(D\frac{\partial C}{\partial x}\right)$$

* For a review, see C. E. Birchenall, "The Mechanism of Diffusion in the Solid State," *Met. Rev.*, Vol. 3, 1958, p. 235.

or if D is assumed to be constant

$$\frac{\partial C}{\partial t} = D\frac{\partial^2 C}{\partial x^2}$$

An atom can change its position only by crossing a potential barrier. Hence diffusion is a thermally-activated process, and the diffusion co-efficient is found to obey Arrhenius' rate law.

Example.—The diffusion coefficient of carbon from a gas into the surface of a certain steel is given by

$$D = 0.49\, e^{-36,600/RT}\ \text{cm}^2/\text{sec}$$

If carburizing is carried out at 927° C (1200° K) then

$$D = 0.49\, e^{-36,600/2 \times 1200}$$
$$= 1.17 \times 10^{-7}\ \text{cm}^2/\text{sec}$$

At a temperature 50° higher,

$$D = 0.49\, e^{-36,600/2 \times 1250}$$
$$= 2.15 \times 10^{-7}\ \text{cm}^2/\text{sec}$$

The rate has been approximately doubled by raising the temperature by 50°.

9.11. Chemical reactions

Many chemical reactions have activation energies of approximately 10,000 cal/gm mole. The ratio of the rates of reaction at 27° C and 37° C is then

$$\frac{e^{-10,000/2 \times 310}}{e^{-10,000/2 \times 300}} = \frac{e^{-16.13}}{e^{-16.67}} = e^{0.54} \approx 1.7$$

i.e. the rate of reaction is approximately doubled when the temperature is raised by 10° C. This explains why a little gentle heat from a Bunsen burner will promote a reaction in a test tube.

9.12. Thermionic emission

It has already been stated that the valency electrons in a metal are free to move—not being attached to any particular atom. They are, however, confined within the boundary of a metal except when energy is supplied in some form. It therefore appears that some form of potential barrier exists at the surface, and that the electrons must be given enough energy to pass this barrier before they can escape.

The release of electrons when a substance is heated may be studied in a diode—a form of electronic valve containing an emitter, which can be heated, and an electrode which is given a positive potential relative to the emitter to collect the electrons. With a suitable geometry of construction of the diode and a sufficient voltage, all electrons leaving the emitter will reach the positive electrode—or anode—and the thermionic current i may be measured.

Some experimental results for the emission from clean tungsten are given in Table 9.2. It is found in this as in other cases that i increases as

TABLE 9.2—VARIATION WITH TEMPERATURE OF EMISSION
FROM CLEAN TUNGSTEN
(values from S. Dushman, H. N. Rowe, J. W. Ewald and
C. A. Kidner, *Phys Rev.*, Vol. 25, 1925, p. 338).

$T°$ K	i (amp/cm²)
1470	$7 \cdot 63 \times 10^{-8}$
1543	$4 \cdot 84 \times 10^{-7}$
1640	$4 \cdot 29 \times 10^{-6}$
1761	$4 \cdot 62 \times 10^{-5}$
1897	$4 \cdot 31 \times 10^{-4}$
2065	$4 \cdot 72 \times 10^{-3}$
2239	$4 \cdot 66 \times 10^{-2}$

the absolute temperature T of the emitter is raised, and that a plot of $\log i$ against $1/T$ gives a straight line within the limits of experimental accuracy as in fig. 9.7. This suggests a relationship of the form

$$i = f e^{-\omega/kT}$$

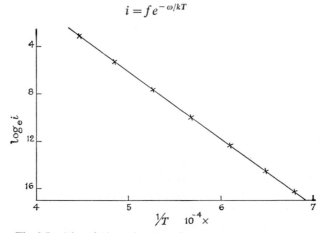

Fig. 9.7.—Plot of $1/T$ against $\log_e i$ for values given in Table 9.2

where ω is the activation energy necessary for an electron to leave the metal. Both f and ω will have values characteristic of the emitter material.

It is found by theoretical treatment* of the problem that

$$i = AT^2 e^{-\chi/kT}$$

This differs from the previous value in containing the term T^2. The emission varies so greatly with temperature that it is not possible to distinguish by experiment between these two equations. The quantity χ is called the *work function* and is slightly less than ω.

The work function also turns up in the case of photoelectric emission. When a metal is irradiated with electromagnetic radiation of a sufficiently short wavelength, electrons are spontaneously emitted from the metal and may be detected with suitable electronic equipment. The energy of the photons at the critical wavelength for emission is found to equal the work function found from thermionic-emission experiments. This phenomenon is utilized in photoelectric cells.

QUESTIONS

1. Given that the kinetic energy of translation of a molecule of a gas at an absolute temperature T is $\frac{3}{2}kT$, where k is Boltzmann's constant, derive expressions for the specific heats of monatomic and diatomic gases.

Discuss the variation in specific heat of simple solids as they are cooled from room temperature towards absolute zero. [P]

2. State Arrhenius' rate law and explain what is meant by activation energy.

The rate v of linear growth of new crystals in a sample of cold-worked aluminium at different temperatures T is given in the following table:

T (°C)	200	250	300	350	400
v (cm/sec)	$5 \cdot 62 \times 10^{-11}$	$1 \cdot 38 \times 10^{-8}$	$1 \cdot 35 \times 10^{-6}$	$6 \cdot 76 \times 10^{-5}$	$1 \cdot 82 \times 10^{-3}$

Show that this is a thermally-activated process, and calculate the activation energy per gram atom.

3. Many physical and chemical thermal rate processes have activation energies of about $\frac{1}{2}$eV† per atom. Show that the rate is approximately doubled by raising the temperature by 10° C near room temperature.

4. Calculate the specific heat of (*a*) copper, and (*b*) iron at temperatures above their Debye temperature.

5. State Arrhenius' rate law for a thermally-activated process. Give examples of processes of technological interest which obey this law.

Some experiments on the diffusion of hydrogen in nickel have given the following results:

Temperature (° C)	162·5	237	355	496
Diffusion coefficient (cm² sec⁻¹)	9×10^{-8}	$4 \cdot 6 \times 10^{-7}$	$3 \cdot 1 \times 10^{-6}$	$1 \cdot 34 \times 10^{-5}$

Show that these data are consistent with Arrhenius' law and determine the activation energy. [MST]

* Reimann, *Thermionic Emission* (Chapman & Hall, 1934).   † eV = electron volt. See p. 265.

CHAPTER 10

The Deformation of Metal Single Crystals

10.1. Introduction

An examination of the behaviour of single crystals during deformation is necessary to an understanding of the deformation of polycrystalline aggregates. Single crystals of metals in suitable form for carrying out mechanical tests may be prepared by several methods, some of which are outlined in Section 5.9.

If such a crystal is pulled, there is first a very small elastic deformation proportional to the load, and then at a certain load plastic deformation commences and continues with a certain amount of increase of load until the specimen fractures.

10.2. Geometry of deformation by slip

When the crystal deforms plastically, it remains a crystal with the same structure. In the more common manner of deformation, namely *slip*, whole layers of atoms have moved over one another, so that atoms in a layer that has moved take up positions where other atoms were before. Each kind of crystal is found to have definite planes on which slip occurs and definite directions of sliding in each plane. They are known as *slip* or *glide planes* and *slip* or *glide directions* respectively, and together they constitute the *glide elements*. A list of the glide elements for some of the commoner metals is given in Table 10.1.

For the face-centred cubic and the hexagonal close-packed structures there is only one type of slip plane. In the hexagonal close-packed crystals this is the (001) plane which is the base of the hexagon. It is a unique plane, there being no other planes of the same form. It is the plane of closest packing, so that the distance between adjacent parallel layers of atoms is greater than for any other plane, and hence it is more easy for atoms to slide over one another than it would be for any other set of planes. The slip direction is the [100] direction, which is along any of the diagonals of the hexagon, i.e. the close-packed directions. (The [100], [010], and [110] directions are all equivalent in this lattice.) The relationships of the glide elements for this type of lattice are shown in fig. 10.1.

Slip is observed to occur along the direction in which the resolved shear stress is greatest.

Slip does not occur on every plane by an equal amount, but only on certain planes which may be hundreds of atom layers apart, and by large amounts on those planes. If the specimen were originally circular, with the glide planes lying at an angle to the axis, then the boundaries of the glide planes would be ellipses and after sliding over one another would

TABLE 10.1—GLIDE AND TWIN ELEMENTS OF COMMON
METAL CRYSTALS AT ROOM TEMPERATURE

Structure	Metal	Glide plane	Glide direction	Critical stress Ton/in^2	Twinning plane	Twinning direction
Face-centred cubic	Al Cu Ag Au Ni	(111)	[10$\bar{1}$]	·07 ·06 ·04 ·06 ·37	(111)	[11$\bar{2}$]
Body-centred cubic	a-Fe	(101) (112) (123)	[11$\bar{1}$]		(112)	[111]
	W Mo K Na	(112) (112) (123) (112)	[11$\bar{1}$]			
Hexagonal close-packed	Mg Zn Cd Be	(001)	[110]	·04 ·01 ·006 —	(102)	

Various values of critical stresses have been determined by different workers on materials of different purity. The lowest value has been quoted in each case.
[Data taken from C. S. Barrett, *Structure of Metals*, 2nd Ed. (McGraw-Hill, 1952).]

give the effect shown in fig. 10.2. The glide steps are so large and so far separated in terms of atomic distances that they are visible to the naked eye. An actual photograph of a deformed crystal showing the slip band markings on the surface is shown in fig. 10.3. Work with the electron microscope has shown that there is a fine structure within the slip bands as shown in fig. 10.4.

For the face-centred cubic structure, the slip plane is the close-packed plane (111) and the slip direction is [10$\bar{1}$]. A model exposed on the slip plane is shown in fig. 10.5. There are four such planes of the form {111} and three possible slip directions for each, giving twelve possible slip systems. As in the previous case, the slip system that operates is the

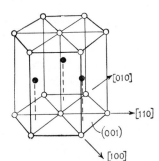

Fig. 10.1.—Glide elements for hexagonal close-packed lattice.

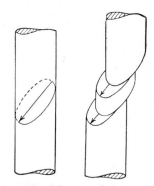

Fig. 10.2.—Diagram of single crystal of circular cross-section before and after slip on two parallel planes.

Fig. 10.3.—Photograph of slip bands on extended copper-aluminium single crystal. [Elam]

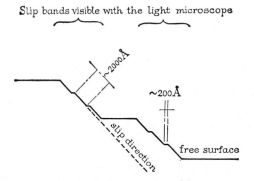

Fig. 10.4.—Schematic representation of fine structure of slip bands. [Brown]

one on which the resolved shear stress is greatest, and there is a high probability of two slip systems operating at the same time.

For the body-centred cubic metals listed in Table 10.1 there are three families of slip planes listed for α-iron and one or another of these for

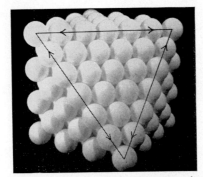

Fig. 10.5.—Model of face-centred structure showing
(111) plane and three slip directions

each of the other metals. Models sectioned on the possible slip planes are shown in fig. 10.6. In the body-centred cubic crystals, there are no close-packed planes. There is, however, a close-packed direction which is [111], the cube diagonal, and this is always the slip direction.

10.3. Deformation by twinning

Another manner in which crystals can transform is by *twinning*. The displaced portion is separated from the undisplaced portion by a crystallographic plane characteristic of the particular crystal lattice and is symmetrically disposed to the undisplaced portion about this plane of separation. This may be most easily visualized as one portion being a mirror image of the other. The effect is shown in fig. 10.7. The twinning planes and directions of some commoner metals are listed in Table 10.1.

Twinning commonly occurs during the deformation of body-centred cubic and hexagonal close-packed metals but rarely, if ever, occurs in face-centred cubic metals due to deformation. In this last class, it occurs frequently due to crystal growth, especially during the recrystallization of cold-worked metals. A twin in this class of crystal is, in effect, a stacking fault, the close-packed layers (see p. 48) being arranged ABCABACBA, etc.

Twinning due to deformation of a single crystal is usually accompanied by a sharp noise, indicating an abrupt process. The stress necessary for twinning in cadmium has been observed to be of the order of 0·1–0·25

(a)

(b)

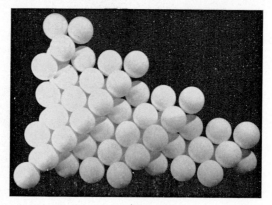

(c)

(d)　　　　　　　　　　　　(e)

Fig. 10.6.—Models of body-centred structure showing slip planes

(a) view on (110) plane, (b) view of (112) plane, (c) view of (123) plane, (d) view of (112) plane along slip direction, (e) view of (123) plane along slip direction.

Ton/in^2, which is a much higher order than the stress necessary to cause slip in an undeformed cadmium crystal (see Table 10.1).

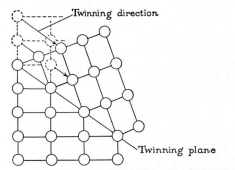

Fig. 10.7.—Atomic movements on twinning. Section on (110) plane of body-centred cubic lattice perpendicular to (112) twin plane

10.4. Resolved shear stress

The shear stress on the slip plane in the slip direction depends upon the load applied to the crystal and upon the orientation of the glide elements to the direction of the load.

Consider a load P applied axially to a crystal as shown in fig. 10.8. Let

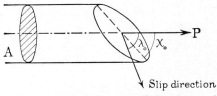

Fig. 10.8.—Angle relationships of slip plane and slip direction to crystal axis

A be the area of cross-section of the specimen,
χ_0 be the angle between the axis of the specimen and the slip plane,
λ_0 be the angle between the axis of the specimen and the slip direction.

The area of the slip plane is $\dfrac{A}{\sin \chi_0}$.

The resolved component of force in the slip direction is

$$P \cos \lambda_0$$

Hence the resolved shear stress in the slip direction is

$$\tau_0 = \frac{P}{A} \cos \lambda_0 \sin \chi_0$$

10.5. Load-extension curves

A series of stress-elongation curves for cadmium are shown in fig. 10.9. Each curve relates to a crystal of different initial orientation of the slip plane to the crystal axis, the values of χ_0 being given in each case. The origins of successive curves have been displaced in the direction of the elongation axis to reduce confusion. It will be observed that the initial nominal stress (i.e. P/A) is greatly different for the different orientations. If, however, the resolved shear stress in the slip direction is calcu-

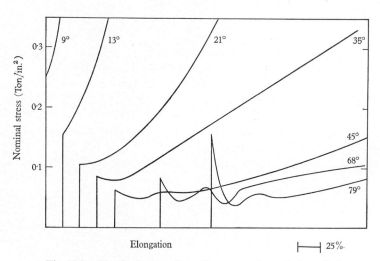

Fig. 10.9.—Nominal stress-elongation curves for cadmium single crystals. Figures on curves indicate angle between slip plane and direction of tensile stress [after Boas].

lated, it is found to be constant and independent of the initial orientation. This is the *Law of Critical Shear Stress* which is obeyed by all metal crystals.

Some values of the critical shear stress are given in Table 10.1 (p. 125). It will be observed that they are mostly of the order of 0.01–0.1 Ton/in^2. Tests with material of higher purity give lower values of critical shear stress.

When χ_0 is small, the area of the slip plane is large, and when χ_0 approaches $90°$ the resolved component of the force is a smaller fraction of the applied force, so that the nominal stress in either case is greater than when χ_0 has values in the region of $45°$.

10.6. Relationship of elongation to strain

The amount of shear (or shear strain) is defined as the relative displacement of two planes which are parallel to the slip plane and which are at unit distance apart measured in a direction perpendicular to the plane.

Let the slip plane be the xy-plane of a coordinate system, and let the y-axis be the slip direction as in fig. 10.10. Let OP_0 and OP_1 be the positions of the axis before and after deformation, the coordinates of P_0 and P_1 being (x_0, y_0, z_0) and (x_1, y_1, z_1) respectively. Also let l_0 be

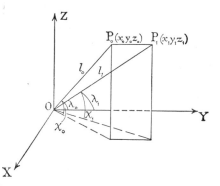

Fig. 10.10.—Coordinate system for analysis of deformation
of crystal from OP_0 to OP_1

the initial length OP_0 of the crystal and the angles χ_0 and λ_0 have the meanings assigned in Section 10.4. Also let the same symbols with the subscript 1 denote the values after deformation.

It is assumed that the scale is such that the dimensions are much larger than the size of the slip bands, so that the deformation can be regarded as homogeneous.

Since the deformation is a pure shear, P_0 moves to P_1 where P_0P_1 is parallel to OY and the amount of this movement P_0P_1 is sz_0, where s is the magnitude of the shear strain.

Then
$$x_1 = x_0$$
$$y_1 = y_0 + sz_0$$
$$z_1 = z_0$$

Also, since
$$l_0^2 = x_0^2 + y_0^2 + z_0^2$$
$$l_1^2 = x_1^2 + y_1^2 + z_1^2$$

then

$$\frac{l_1^2}{l_0^2} = \frac{x_1^2+y_1^2+z_1^2}{x_0^2+y_0^2+z_0^2}$$

$$= \frac{x_0^2+y_0^2+z_0^2+2sz_0y_0+s^2z_0^2}{x_0^2+y_0^2+z_0^2}$$

$$= 1 + \frac{2sz_0y_0+s^2z_0^2}{l_0^2}$$

But

$$y_0 = l_0 \cos \lambda_0 \quad \text{and} \quad z_0 = l_0 \sin \chi_0$$

so that

$$\left(\frac{l_1}{l_0}\right)^2 = 1+2s \sin \chi_0 \cos \lambda_0+s^2 \sin^2 \chi_0$$

Hence if the initial orientation of the crystal is known, the amount of shear s for any measured extension of the crystal axis can be calculated.

Also because $z_1 = l_1 \sin \chi_1$ and $z_0 = l_0 \sin \chi_0$, and because $z_1 = z_0$, then if e is the fractional elongation of the axis,

$$(1+e) = \frac{l_1}{l_0} = \frac{\sin \chi_0}{\sin \chi_1}$$

Also $l_0 \sin \lambda_0 = l_1 \sin \lambda_1$, so that

$$(1+e) = \frac{l_1}{l_0} = \frac{\sin \lambda_0}{\sin \lambda_1}$$

Thus as the crystal elongates, χ and λ become smaller. The orientation of the crystal changes during extension so that the slip plane and the slip direction approach the specimen axis. Also the total volume will remain constant so that $A_0l_0 = A_1l_1$, where A_0 and A_1 are the respective cross-sectional areas.

10.7. Shear hardening curves

From the relations given in the equations derived in Sections 10.4 and 10.6 it is possible to calculate for each point on a load-extension curve for a single crystal the resolved shear stress and the shear strain, provided that the initial orientation of the crystal axis is known. The *shear hardening* curve so obtained is characteristic of the metal. It is found to depend upon the purity of the metal and the temperature, but is independent of the crystal orientation. Fig. 10.11 shows the shear hardening curves for several metals at room temperature.

In every case there is *shear hardening*, that is to say, the shear stress necessary to cause further shear increases as the amount of deformation increases. There is a marked difference between the curves for the hexagonal close-packed metals, cadmium, zinc and magnesium, and those for the face-centred cubic metals, aluminium, copper and nickel, harden· ing being much more rapid for the latter.

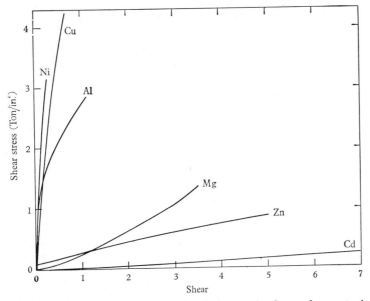

Fig. 10.11.—Shear hardening curves for single crystals of some face-centred cubic and hexagonal close-packed metals. [after Boas]

10.8. The nature of slip

The simplest assumption that can be made about the manner in which slipping occurs is that the whole of one slip plane slides simultaneously over the next, behaving as a rigid entity. This would mean that all the atoms move simultaneously, which would be possible only if the shearing force causing the movement had a completely uniform distribution over the slip plane, i.e. the shear stress is constant at all points. Thermal vibrations would, however, make this an impossible condition to achieve, even if the force could be applied to give an otherwise uniform shear stress. Therefore some areas must try to slip before others. There is no reason why this should not happen, since there is some flexibility in the coupling between the atoms in any plane. Slip can therefore start at one place and spread outwards.

At any stage of the slipping, a boundary could be drawn between the slipped region and the unslipped regions, and there would be a region of misfit along this boundary. This misfit is called a *dislocation* and the boundary is a *dislocation line*. It must always be a closed loop inside a crystal or have its ends at free surfaces of the crystal.

10.9. Theoretical shear strength

If all the atoms in one plane were to slip simultaneously, it should be possible to calculate the shear stress necessary.

Consider the shearing of two layers of atoms past each other in a

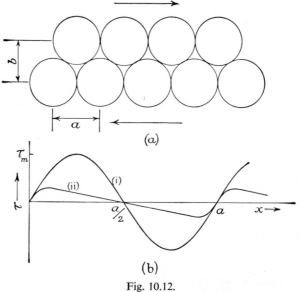

Fig. 10.12.
(*a*) Two rows of atoms being sheared by shear stress τ.
(*b*) Variation of τ with amount of shear.

homogeneously strained crystal. Let the spacing between atom centres in the direction of slip be a and the spacing of the rows be b as in fig. 10.12a. Let the shear displacement of the upper row over the lower be x when the shear stress is τ.

The shear stress is obviously zero when the upper row is in any equilibrium position, i.e. $x = 0$, a, $2a$, etc. Also it will be zero when the upper layer is displaced by $\frac{1}{2}a$, $\frac{3}{2}a$, etc. because these are unstable positions at which each atom of the upper layer is sitting on top of an atom in the lower layer, and a slight movement either way in the absence of a shear force would cause the upper layer to move to one of the stable positions. For sufficiently small displacements from any of the stable equilibrium positions, Hooke's law would be obeyed, the shear stress being the product of the modulus of rigidity G of the material and the shear strain:

$$\tau = G\frac{x}{b}$$

The curve of τ against x will change sign for every increase of x by $\frac{1}{2}a$, and its precise shape depends upon the nature of the interatomic forces. Frenkel made the assumption that the curve might be represented by a sinusoidal function of period a, that is

$$\tau = \tau_m \sin\frac{2\pi x}{a}$$

as curve (i) in fig. 10.12b.

The value of the constant τ_m is determined by the condition that the slope for small displacements must agree with the relation above. For the sinusoidal relationship near the origin,

$$\tau = \tau_m \frac{2\pi x}{a}$$

and from the Hooke's law relation,

$$\tau = G\frac{x}{b}$$

Hence

$$\tau = \frac{G}{2\pi}\cdot\frac{a}{b}\cdot\sin\frac{2\pi x}{a}$$

The maximum value τ_m of τ which is the shear stress that would have to be applied before slip would occur, i.e. the critical shear stress, is

$$\tau_m = \frac{G}{2\pi}\cdot\frac{a}{b}$$

Now since $a \approx b$, then $\tau_m \approx G/2\pi$, which is of the order of 1000 Tons/in² for most materials.

As stated in Section 10.5, the observed values of the critical shear stresses for most metal crystals is of the order of $0\cdot01$–$0\cdot1$ Ton/in². Hence there is a discrepancy of 10^4–10^5 between the theoretical result derived above and the observed values.

The assumptions made in the calculation must therefore be examined. Calculations involving the nature of the inter-atomic forces show that

135

the shape of the curve should be more nearly as curve (*ii*) in fig. 10.12*b*. The maximum shear stress for this curve is found to be of the order of $G/30$ and to occur for a displacement of about $0 \cdot 1\ a$. The major part of the discrepancy still exists.

Hence the conclusion is reached that sources of mechanical weakness, known as dislocations, exist in real crystals and are such that slip can start from them at very low applied stresses, and that dislocations traverse the crystal, slipping occurring only on the dislocation line.

10.10. The geometry of dislocations

When a dislocation passes across a crystal, the atoms behind it have sheared relative to the adjacent layer by the unit of slip, which is of a definite amount and in a definite direction. The vector which defines this displacement is called the *Burgers vector*. In a hexagonal close-packed crystal, for example, the Burgers vector has a magnitude equal to the unit cell side *a* and a direction parallel to one of the hexagon diagonals.

When a dislocation has passed any region, it leaves a perfect crystal structure behind it.

Dislocations may be classed according to the direction of the line of misfit relative to the Burgers vector. If the line is perpendicular to and moves in the direction of the Burgers vector, the dislocation is an *edge dislocation*. This form was suggested independently by Taylor, Orowan, and Polanyi in 1934.

If the dislocation line is parallel to the Burgers vector and moves in a direction perpendicular to it, the dislocation is a *screw dislocation*. This is so called because movement on one plane of atoms around the dislocation line results in a corkscrew motion.

Diagrams of edge and screw dislocations are shown in figs. 10.13 and 10.14. In each case, the dislocation line EF lies in the plane of slip ABCD and divides the slipped portion ABEF from the unslipped portion EFDC. The arrows show the direction of the relative slip movement in each case.

In general a dislocation line can be curved, being partly edge and partly screw dislocations. Also if different slip planes exist with a common slip direction, the dislocation line can lie partly in each plane, so that it is not necessarily confined to two dimensions.

The width of a dislocation line in copper has been calculated to be of the order of six atoms.

There is strain energy stored up in the dislocation due to the elastic distortion, but by comparison it requires very little energy to cause it to move. Hence if a dislocation is present in a slip plane it will move under

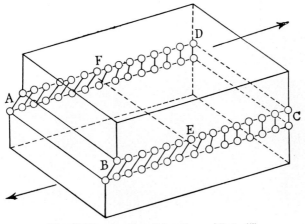

Fig. 10.13.—An edge dislocation. [Cottrell]

small forces. The magnitude of the strain energy is about $2 \cdot 5 \times 10^{10}$ eV*
per metre length, or about 8 eV per atom spacing.

The nature of edge dislocations and the way in which they move have
been illustrated by a bubble model developed by Bragg.† Bubbles of
uniform size blown on the surface of a soap solution group themselves
into hexagonal patterns. "Crystal" boundaries are formed where
groups of bubbles meet as shown in fig. 10.15. By suitably displacing

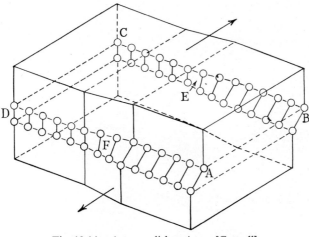

Fig. 10.14.—A screw dislocation. [Cottrell]

* eV = electron volt. See p. 265.
† Sir Lawrence Bragg and J. F. Nye, *Proc. Roy. Soc.* A, Vol. 190, 1947, p. 474. Sir Lawrence Bragg and
W. M. Lomer, *ibid.*, Vol. 196, 1949, p. 171. W. M. Lomer, *ibid.*, Vol. 196, 1949, p. 182.

the bubbles it is possible to get dislocations as in fig. 10.16 and to study their behaviour. Like dislocations repel one another, while unlike dislocations attract one another, and if they are on the same plane, they will cancel one another.

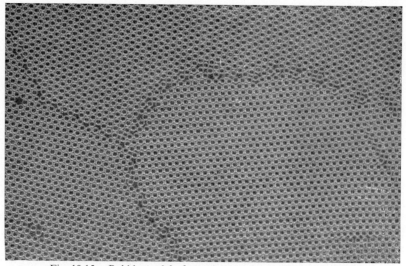

Fig. 10.15.—Bubble model of a grain boundary. [Bragg and Nye]

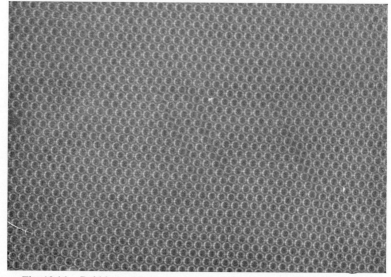

Fig. 10.16.—Bubble model showing parallel dislocations. [Bragg and Nye]

10.11. The origin of dislocations

It has been calculated that the average stress necessary to create an edge dislocation in a perfect crystal is of the same order of magnitude as Frenkel's theoretical stress for the simultaneous slip of a layer of atoms. Hence we are led to the belief that dislocations must exist in crystals when they are formed.

Frank* has drawn attention to the fact that it is practically impossible for a crystal to grow from vapour or a dilute solution unless dislocations are present. An atom arriving at the crystal surface from the liquid or vapour side will not attach itself permanently to the crystal unless a step or ledge is present. Hence a single atom on a plane face as in fig. 10.17*a* will not remain attached, but if an atom reaches a point such as A in fig. 10.17*b*, the attractive forces are sufficient to hold it there.

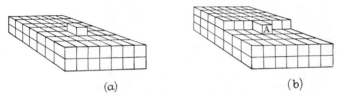

(a)　　　　　　　　　　　　　(b)

Fig. 10.17.—Atoms, represented by cubes, during crystal growth
(*a*) single atom will not attach itself to surface,
(*b*) step provides sufficient forces to hold atom A.

Continual growth of a crystal will be possible if the structure is such that the crystal always has steps on its faces however much it grows. This kind of structure exists around a screw dislocation, the crystal building up as a spiral plane. Spiral growth has been observed on many crystals, some examples being shown in fig. 10.18.

Hence unless a dislocation forms during nucleation, a crystal is unlikely to grow.

Also during crystal growth, atom sites may be left vacant. It is possible for vacancies to move together by diffusion and, having done so, the larger vacancy then formed may collapse creating a dislocation ring, of which a section would show two dislocations as in fig. 10.19.

Since in general there are several possible slip systems in a crystal, dislocations can occur in planes that are not parallel to one another. In general, growth dislocations are likely to be in different directions. Since a dislocation line can end only on an outer surface, these dislocations

* F. C. Frank, *Advances in Physics*, Taylor and Francis, London, Vol. 1, 1952, p. 91.

must run together. It is possible for three dislocations to meet at a point if the three Burgers vectors add up to zero as in fig. 10.20. Hence the dislocations can build up a three-dimensional network. Experimental

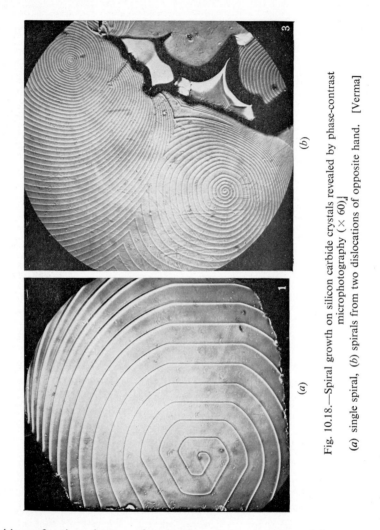

Fig. 10.18.—Spiral growth on silicon carbide crystals revealed by phase-contrast microphotography ($\times$ 60).
(*a*) single spiral, (*b*) spirals from two dislocations of opposite hand. [Verma]

evidence for the existence of such networks has been found,* an example being shown in fig. 10.21. The dislocation density in annealed metals is 10^6–10^8/cm^2.

---

* P. B. Hirsch, " Direct Experimental Evidence of Dislocations," *Met. Rev.*, Vol. 4, 1959, p. 101.

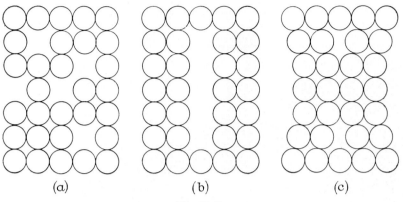

(a)   (b)   (c)

Fig. 10.19

(a) Vacancies randomly scattered in crystal (the number of vacancies
    is exaggerated).
(b) Vacancies have diffused into a single layer.
(c) Collapse of vacancy giving two dislocations.

Some of these dislocations would lie in planes that would not be favourable for slip under a particular applied stress. The dislocations in planes where slip would be favoured would thus be anchored at the ends linked to the trapped dislocations, giving what is termed a *Frank-Read source of dislocations.** Fig. 10.22a shows a disloca-tion which is anchored at its ends A and B and which has its slip plane in the plane of the diagram. When a shear stress is applied in the direction shown, the dislocation line will form a loop moving in the direc-tion shown by the arrows in fig. 10.22b and c. The loop grows until it sweeps around A and B, and eventually the two sides meet forming a complete loop and another line dislocation between A and B as in fig. 10.22d.

Fig. 10.20.—Three Burgers vectors which have zero sum.

$$b_1 + b_2 + b_3 = 0$$

Under the applied shear force, the loop will move out to the boundaries of the crystal, and the source can form a succession of loops. It would appear that such a source could give an indefinite number of dislocations.

This mechanism can explain the observed behaviour that slip is a cascade process, slip of about 1000 atom spacings occurring on one plane, and also that slip occurs on certain planes only, these being the planes on which there are possible Frank-Read sources. The shear stress necessary to activate a Frank-Read source depends upon the distance

* F. C. Frank and W. T. Read, *Phys. Rev.*, Vol. 79, 1950, p. 772

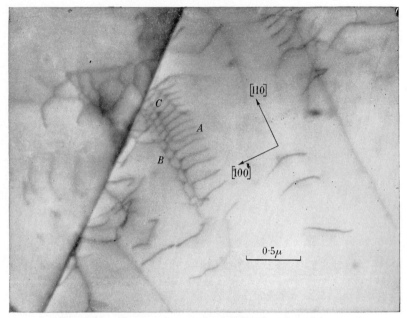

Fig. 10.21.—Hexagonal network of dislocations in stainless steel deformed by rolling, revealed by electron microphotography at × 34,000 magnification. [Whelan, Hirsch, Horne and Bollmann]

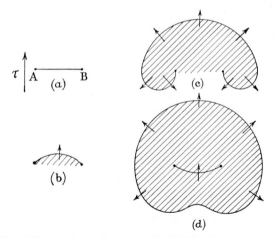

Fig. 10.22.—A Frank-Read source forming a dislocation loop under the action of the applied shear stress τ

AB, being greater for smaller values of AB, and as this distance is not necessarily constant for different sources, the stresses to cause slip on different planes will be of different magnitude.

QUESTIONS

1. Explain the term *glide elements*, illustrating the answer by reference to the deformation of close-packed hexagonal and face-centred cubic single crystals.

2. A single crystal specimen of pure zinc of 0·1 in² cross-sectional area yielded in tension at a load of 35·2 Lb. The tensile load was then increased to a maximum value of 50 Lb, and the resulting plastic extension of the specimen on a 2-in gauge length was found to be 0·68 in. If the inclinations of the active slip plane and the slip direction to the specimen axis in the unloaded specimen were 22° 21′ and 34° 42′ respectively, calculate: (*a*) the critical shear stress for zinc; (*b*) the inclinations of the slip plane and the slip direction to the specimen axis at the conclusion of the test; (*c*) the value of the shear stress on the slip plane in the slip direction when the specimen was under maximum load. [P]

3. A specimen, 0·05 in² in cross-sectional area, was made from a single crystal of pure magnesium. The inclinations of the active slip plane and the slip direction to the specimen axis were 27° 00′ and 38° 24′ respectively. If, when tested in tension, the specimen yielded at a load of 16·9 Lb, calculate the critical shear stress for magnesium. [P]

4. Describe the mode of deformation of a single crystal of a hexagonal close-packed metal.

The theoretical shear strength of a metal crystal is of the order of $G/2\pi$, where G is the shear modulus of the metal. What mechanism has been postulated to explain the difference between this theoretical value and the much smaller observed value of the shear stress? [S]

5. Derive Frenkel's approximate expression for the theoretical yield strength in shear of a single crystal in terms of the shear modulus G.

The critical shear strength of copper determined by experiment is 0·064 Ton/in². What is the ratio of theoretical to experimental shear stress? What mechanism has been postulated to explain this discrepancy?

(For copper, take $G = 6 \times 10^6$ Lb/in².) [P]

CHAPTER 11

The Strengthening of Metals

11.1. Introduction

It has been shown in the preceding chapter that the strength of a metal single crystal is of the order of 100 Lb/in². This means that metal crystals are extremely soft and of no value as materials of construction. The majority of metals and alloys in common use by the engineer have strengths which lie between 10 and 100 Tons/in². Hence between the single crystal and the commercial material there are strengthening factors which increase the mechanical strength by a factor of the order of 200–2000 times.

It is important for the engineer to appreciate the nature of these factors, so that when other requirements demand a certain class of material, the best method for strengthening that type of material can be used, consistent with the economic factors involved.

11.2. Dislocations and barriers

Strengthening is brought about by obstructing the movement of dislocations. Consider the example shown diagrammatically in fig. 11.1

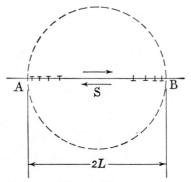

Fig. 11.1.—Piling-up of dislocations at obstacles

where dislocations created at a Frank-Read source S due to the application of an applied shear stress have moved along the slip plane until held up by obstacles at A and B. Like dislocations on the same slip plane have a repulsion for one another which opposes their getting into close proximity to each other, so that there is a pile-up spreading from each obstacle. Around each dislocation there is a region in which the crystal structure is somewhat distorted, that is, there will be local stress in the region which is known as the *stress field*. The stress fields due to these dislocations will cause a back stress at the source opposed in direction to the externally applied stress, so that the source ceases to send out further dislocations unless the applied stress is increased. A rough estimate of the number of dislocations necessary to do this can be made in the following manner.

If slip did not occur, the whole region between A and B would have an elastic shear strain equal to τ/G where τ is the applied shear stress and G is the shear modulus. Suppose that when slipping occurs it does so to such an extent that the elastic strain over the central part of the region AB drops to a negligible value. (This is a reasonable assumption if the stress necessary to cause the Frank-Read source to operate is small compared to the applied stress τ.) The area enclosed by the dotted circle in fig. 11.1 is roughly the area in which the elastic strain will drop to zero. If $2L$ is the distance between the obstacles, and hence the diameter of the area, the amount of slip necessary along the central part of AB is $2L\tau/G$. If n dislocation loops are created from the source and the Burgers vector is $\mathbf{b}$, then the displacement produced at S is $n\mathbf{b}$. Hence, by equating the two expressions for the displacement

$$nb = 2L\tau/G$$

In a slip band of length 10^{-3} in, for example, in copper for which $G = 15 \times 10^6$ Lb/in² and $\mathbf{b} = 10^{-8}$ in, and at a value of $\tau = 3 \times 10^4$ Lb/in², n will be about 400. That is to say, very large numbers of dislocations can be piled up at obstacles at stresses commonly experienced by commercial metals.

Since stress fields of dislocations are additive, the total stress field of a piled-up group of n dislocations will be about n times as great and extend n times as far as for a single dislocation. Hence there will be large highly stressed regions in the crystal around the piled-up groups at obstacles.

The methods by which obstacles are placed in the way of dislocations may conveniently be considered in six classes.

11.3. Polycrystalline materials

In a polycrystalline material, neighbouring grains have different orientations, so that slip planes in one crystal are not usually parallel to those in its neighbours, and so the intercrystal boundaries will act as obstacles and cause piling up of dislocations. Fig. 11.2 shows an actual photograph of piled-up dislocations. Eventually a stage may be reached when the resolved shear stress on the most favourable slip plane in the neighbouring crystal reaches the critical shear stress, so that slip can also occur; then there can be some movement to cause relief of the pile-up of dislocations in the first crystal.

It may be seen from fig. 11.3 that the strengthening effect is much greater in the hexagonal close-packed metal zinc than in the face-centred cubic metal aluminium. This is in contrast to the behaviour of single crystals shown in fig. 10.11. This is because the hexagonal close-packed metal has only one set of slip planes per crystal, and so the slip planes in adjacent crystals may have very different orientations. In the example shown in fig. 11.4 no slip in crystal B could accommodate slip in crystal A. The face-centred cubic metal has four possible slip planes in each crystal which are at such angles to each other that there will always be one whose orientation is very close to the active slip plane in the neighbouring crystal.

The smaller the grains, the greater will be the number of boundaries, and hence the greater the strength. It is found that the strength is proportional to the surface area of the grain boundaries, that is, proportional to $1/(\text{grain size})^2$, where grain size refers to mean grain diameter.

11.4. Solid solution alloying

When a foreign atom is introduced into a lattice, there is some distortion, which is more marked the greater the difference in the size between the foreign atom and the atoms of the parent lattice. Hence the foreign atom will act as a barrier to the passage of dislocations.

Another form of action of a solute atom in a substitutional solid solution can be understood from fig. 11.5 which shows the form of the atom arrangement around a dislocation. Those atoms above the dislocation are squeezed into holes too small for them and those below are stretched to fill the holes. The energy of the dislocation would be reduced if there were migration of the smaller atoms to the upper side and the larger atoms to the lower side of the dislocation, a migration that would tend to occur by diffusion. If such a dislocation is to move, then since diffusion is a slow process, the energy of the dislocation would have to be increased because it would move to a position where the atoms were randomly distributed, that is, the force needed to move the dislocation is increased.

The effect of substitutional solid-solution alloying is illustrated in

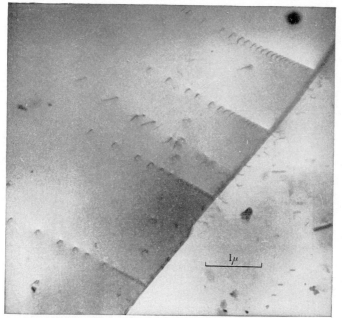

Fig. 11.2.—Pile-up of dislocations against a grain boundary in slightly deformed stainless steel (× 15,000). [Whelan, Hirsch, Horne and Bollmann].

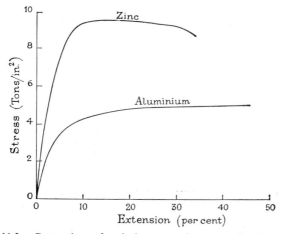

Fig. 11.3.—Comparison of typical stress-strain curves of polycrystalline hexagonal close-packed and face-centred cubic metals

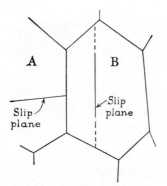

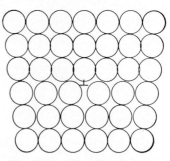

Fig. 11.4.—Slip planes in adjacent crystals such that slip in B cannot accommodate slip in A.

Fig. 11.5.—Distortion of atoms around a dislocation

fig. 11.6 which shows the variation of strength with composition for single crystals of silver-gold alloys. Although the difference in size of the atoms of these metals is less than 0·2%, the maximum strength, which occurs at about the 50% alloy, is about seven times that of the stronger pure metal.

In the case of interstitial solid solutions, the solute atoms would diffuse into the cavity immediately under the dislocation. The dislocation

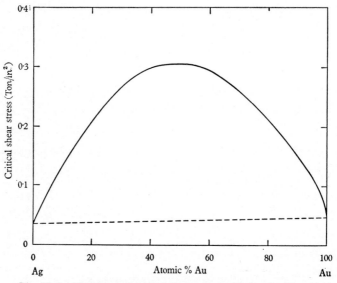

Fig. 11.6.—Variation of critical shear stress with composition in silver-gold single crystals [after Boas]

148

would then not move until a sufficient force were applied to break it away from the locking effect of the solute atom. Once the dislocation had moved, it would then continue to move under a lower force. Cottrell has suggested that this is the explanation of the sharp yield point that is observed in mild steel (fig. 12.5) and some other alloys. The carbon and nitrogen in solid solution in the ferrite would be responsible in steels. Once yielding has occurred, no yield point is seen during a second loading immediately after the first. As the dislocations have been moved away from the solute atoms, a large break-away force is no longer required. Also on resting a specimen that has been yielded, the solute atoms have time to diffuse to the new positions of the dislocations, and this causes a return of a yield-point phenomenon. This action is called *strain ageing*. In some mild steels it will occur in a matter of days at room temperature or in minutes at 100° C, because the diffusion rate of the interstitial atoms is much greater at the higher temperature.

11.5. Two phases in equilibrium

In an alloy series of two metals which are insoluble or nearly so in each other in the solid state, the strength varies approximately linearly between the strengths of the pure constituents. In the case of the lead-tin alloys, of which the equilibrium diagram is shown in fig. 11.7, there are regions of solid solubility at each end of the composition range and a eutectic is formed between. Values for the strengths of alloys of this series are also shown. It will be observed that there is a rapid increase of strength with addition of the second element in the regions of solid solubility. This is to be expected as the difference in atomic size is considerable. In the two-phase region, the strength varies in a much more gradual manner. The eutectic grains may be strong due to the large numbers of phase boundaries, and so have a strengthening effect upon the aggregate of pro-eutectic and eutectic grains.

This effect is most marked if the eutectic (or eutectoid) is formed with an intermediate compound, as these tend to have a complex structure with no planes of easy glide. In the case of the iron-carbon alloys, cementite has a hardness of 700 D.P.N.* Pure iron has a hardness of about 90 D.P.N., and an increase of carbon content, thereby increasing the proportion of cementite, increases the hardness in an almost linear manner as shown by the curve marked " pearlitic " in fig. 11.8.

The effects of solid solution and two-phase alloying in varying mechanical properties can also be seen in the copper-zinc alloys or *brasses*, for which the equilibrium diagram is shown on fig. A.11 and the mechanical

---

* See p. 170 for a discussion of the meaning of hardness.

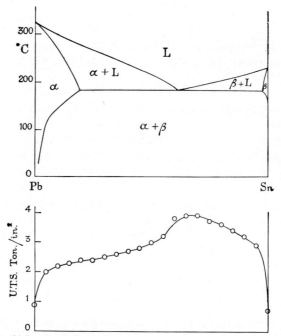

Fig. 11.7.—Lead-tin equilibrium diagram and strengths of lead-tin alloys. [U.T.S. values from *The Properties of Tin Alloys* (Tin Research Institute, 1947).]

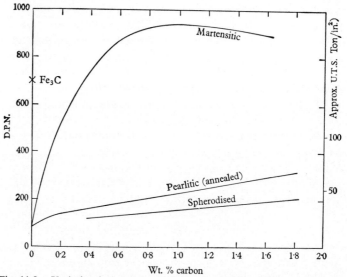

Fig. 11.8.—Variation in hardness of steel with carbon content in annealed, quenched, and quenched + fully tempered condition

properties in fig. 11.9. Up to about 37% zinc there is a single-phase solid solution known as α-brass. This has the same crystal structure as copper, i.e. face-centred cubic. As the amount of zinc is increased, the strength is increased and there is some improvement of ductility. Between about 45% and 50% a second phase exists, the body-centred cubic β-brass. This is harder than the α-brass, but it is not so ductile and so tends to break in a brittle manner at low loads instead of showing high strength. In the intermediate region (37% to 45%) the alloys are two-phase α-β brasses, which for the lower zinc contents are stronger, but as the zinc content increases the decrease of ductility makes the strength fall off.

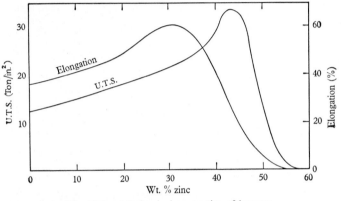

Fig. 11.9.—Mechanical properties of brasses

The types of brass in common engineering use are known as 70/30 or *cartridge brass* and 60/40 brass or *Muntz metal.* The figures denote the approximate copper/zinc ratio in each case. The 70/30 alloy, being α-brass, is easily deformed and can be cold-worked, this being the usual method employed in the final stages of manufacture; cold rolling, cold drawing of tubes, etc. The 60/40 alloy, being an α-β brass, cannot be cold-worked much without fracturing, and is used either cast to shape or hot-worked.

11.6. Work hardening

It has already been noted that with increasing deformation, the strength of single crystals becomes greater. This is known as *work hardening* and applies also to polycrystalline aggregates. The evidence suggests that the main obstacles to dislocations are other dislocations moving on intersecting slip planes. Single crystals of hexagonal close-packed metals which have only one slip plane strain-harden very little by comparison with face-centred cubic single crystals (see fig. 10.11). If, however, a face-centred cubic crystal is loaded so that only one slip system becomes operative, then it behaves initially like a hexagonal single crystal with little work hardening, a phenomenon known as *easy glide*.

Work hardening is used in practice to harden metal sheets and wires by cold rolling and cold drawing respectively. While this increases the strength considerably, the ductility is greatly reduced, so that the materials are much more brittle.

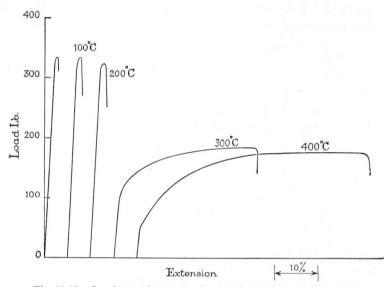

Fig. 11.10.—Load-extension curves for 0·08-in diameter copper wire as hard-drawn and after annealing at various temperatures

The effect of work hardening upon recrystallization has been mentioned in Section 5.7. Three stages are observed as the temperature of a cold-worked metal is raised: *recovery*, recrystallization, and grain growth. The first stage—recovery—is the reduction of internal stresses at low temperatures, thought to be due to the movement of dislocations, such as climbing by the aid of vacancies to positions such that the lattice strains are reduced. The activation energy for formation of new nuclei is such that the nucleation rate is appreciable at the recrystallization stage. Grain growth is also a thermally-activated process and proceeds more rapidly at higher temperatures.

The effect of annealing temperature upon the load-extension curves of cold-drawn and subsequently annealed copper wires is shown in fig. 11.10. Between 200° C and 300° C, in which range recrystallization occurs, there is a considerable drop in strength and a large increase in ductility. Raising the annealing temperature to 400° C increases the ductility, but above that temperature there is little further change.

11.7. Quench hardening

In steels, the high-temperature form of the iron is the face-centred cubic γ-phase which will dissolve up to $1\cdot7\%$ carbon to form the interstitial solid solution austenite. On slow cooling, two phases form, viz. cementite, which contains nearly all the carbon, and ferrite, which is almost pure α-iron. This change involves diffusion of the carbon atoms and so takes time. If the austenite is quenched, i.e. rapidly cooled by plunging into a cold liquid, the equilibrium changes are suppressed, and the face-centred cubic structure changes by a shear-type transformation to a body-centred tetragonal structure. This is, in effect, a body-centred cubic structure distorted to make one cube edge longer than the other two. The carbon atoms have not had time to diffuse out of the lattice that wants to be ferrite and have distorted the would-be ferrite lattice. As a consequence of this distortion, the lattice will not permit the passage of dislocations, and the material is very hard and non-ductile. The structure is called *martensite*. Various mechanisms have been proposed for the austenite-martensite transformation.*

The variation of the hardness of martensite with the amount of carbon in the steel is shown by the curve marked " martensitic " in fig. 11.8.

There is a *critical cooling rate* which has to be exceeded if 100% martensite is to be formed. At lower rates of cooling, some ferrite and pearlite are also formed.

If the structure is tempered, i.e. reheated to some temperature below the lower critical temperature, the martensite breaks down to the equilibrium phases, i.e. to cementite and ferrite. However, these are not now in the eutectoid structure of pearlite, but the cementite is in more or less spherical particles in the ferrite. Tempering at a higher temperature produces fewer and larger cementite particles. This will mean fewer obstacles to dislocations, so that a higher temperature of tempering produces a greater reduction of strength and increase of ductility.

The heat treatment of steel is treated at greater length in Chapter 14.

The martensite type of transformation can also occur in other alloys which show a eutectoid reaction, the one of next importance from the engineering standpoint being the heat-treatable aluminium bronzes, i.e. copper-aluminium alloys which contain between 9 and 11% of aluminium. (See the equilibrium diagram in fig. A.3.)

---

* For a review, see E. O. Hall, *Twinning and Diffusionless Transformations in Metals* (Butterworth, 1954).

11.8. Precipitation hardening

A second phase which is of itself non-ductile can have a greater hardening effect if it is distributed as a fine-grained precipitate. The cementite in tempered martensite is one case of this, the tempered structure frequently being stronger than the annealed or pearlitic structure, and becoming less strong as tempering is carried out at higher temperatures causing coalescence of the cementite. In certain other types of alloys which do not have a eutectoid reaction, the second phase can be dispersed by heat treatment as a different mechanism is involved.

The treatment is possible in alloys which have a region of solid solubility in which the solubility decreases with falling temperature as in fig.

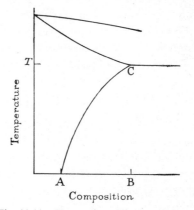

Fig. 11.11.—Form of equilibrium diagram
for precipitation hardening alloys

11.11. Any alloy with a composition between A and B will be entirely single-phased at the temperature T. On slow cooling, the second phase would start to precipitate when the line AC is crossed. This precipitation is a process of nucleation and growth, and so takes time. On rapid cooling, i.e. quenching, the second phase does not have time to precipitate at the equilibrium temperature, but a supersaturated solid solution is formed, the structure remaining the same as it was at the temperature T. The solid solution will change to the equilibrium structure of two phases as fast as diffusion permits. This may occur at room temperature or a somewhat higher temperature. The second phase precipitates in the form that eventually becomes sub-microscopic or microscopic particles of the second phase scattered throughout the crystals of the first phase. The mechanism, in the aluminium-copper alloys for example, is that regions very rich in copper atoms develop in certain crystallographic planes of the aluminium crystals. These regions, which are called *Guiner-Preston zones*, are about 2 atoms thick and from 50 to 800 Å in the other dimensions. These zones gradually transform to an intermediate phase known as θ', and then to the θ or $CuAl_2$ phase. The Guiner-Preston zones assume different shapes in different alloys. Recent work suggests that the original precipitation occurs at dislocations.

The full heat treatment to produce this kind of hardening is as follows:

1. Solution treat, i.e. heat the alloy to the temperature of maximum solubility and hold at that temperature for a sufficient length of time for all the second phase to dissolve in the solid solution.

2. Quench to produce a supersaturated solution. This is the softest condition and forming to shape of components is frequently done in this condition.

3. Allow precipitate to form at room temperature (*age hardening*) or by raising the temperature (*precipitation hardening*).

At higher temperatures, the precipitate forms more quickly, but coalescence of the precipitate into larger grains also occurs. Also at a sufficiently high temperature the second phase redissolves in the solid solution. A larger grain size of precipitate will cause fewer obstacles to

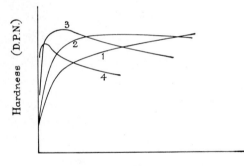

Fig. 11.12.—Hardness of a precipitation hardening alloy due to precipitation treatment. Typical curves obtained for treatment at progressively increasing temperatures 1–4.

dislocations and so give lower strength. The variation of hardness with time and temperature for a typical alloy is shown in fig. 11.12. Each alloy has its own optimum time and temperature to produce greatest hardness.

The most commonly used precipitation-hardening alloys are some of the aluminium alloys, mainly those based on the aluminium-copper system mentioned above (see fig. A.3 for the equilibrium diagram). These can either be age-hardened or precipitation-hardened at temperatures in the region of 100° to 150° C. Those alloys that will harden at room temperature will remain in the supersaturated condition for a considerable time at only slightly lower temperatures. Hence a refrigerator is a convenient means of storing softened parts in a soft condition until required.

Among many other alloys which can be precipitation-hardened is beryllium bronze, copper alloyed with beryllium. As may be seen from the equilibrium diagram in fig. A.7, those alloys containing about 2% of beryllium can be successfully treated. The solution temperature is about 850° C and the precipitation treatment is most successful at about 300° C.

QUESTIONS

1. Why are the shear hardening curves of aluminium and magnesium so different? [MST]

2. The strength of pure metals may be increased by alloying. Discuss, in terms of the structures produced in equilibrium and non-equilibrium changes, the mechanisms of strengthening in alloys. [MST]

3. Explain the meanings of and the processes involved in (a) work hardening, (b) quench hardening, (c) precipitation hardening, quoting instances in which each method is used in engineering practice. [MST]

4. Discuss the effects on a metal of cold working and subsequent heating to different temperatures. [S]

5. Describe the variations in the mechanical properties and microstructure of brass with variations in zinc content.
Give two examples each of the use of brass of 70/30 and 60/40 composition and state how the uses and the methods of manufacture adopted are related to the properties of these brasses.

CHAPTER 12

Mechanical Testing of Polycrystalline Materials

12.1. Tensile testing machines

Machines for performing tensile tests comprise means for straining (i.e. stretching) a specimen and simultaneously measuring the load required to perform the straining. The simplest are of the single-lever type shown in fig. 12.1.

One end of the specimen is attached to the straining head which is moved by a screw mechanism with a hand or electric drive, or by hydraulic pressure. The other end is attached to a lever at a point near the fulcrum, and a weight is moved along the lever to apply a load to the specimen. The load may be set or increased at any desired rate, and the straining head then moved as the specimen extends to keep the lever in a position of balance. With this type of machine it is not easy to follow rapid decreases of load during extension.

In other types of machines, the straining head is also moved by mechanical or hydraulic means, but the load is continuously indicated, either by measurement of the fluid pressure in some hydraulic machines or by a weighing device. This is a stiff spring connected to the specimen either directly in machines of small capacity or through a system of levers in larger machines, the deflection of the spring being indicated by a pointer and dial, or other means. Any decrease of load with increase of strain is immediately indicated.

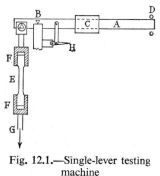

Fig. 12.1.—Single-lever testing machine

A—beam.
B—fulcrum.
C—moving weight.
D—stops to limit movement of beam.
E—specimen.
F—specimen grips.
G—straining head.
H—pointer to indicate position of beam.

12.2. Tensile specimens

Specimens for tensile tests are usually machined to a circular cross-section, but specimens from plates or sheets may be of rectangular section.

They must have a portion of uniform cross-section on which extension measurements can be made. To ensure that any fracture will occur in this uniform portion, the ends are

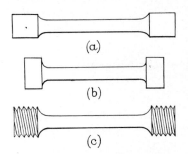

(a)

(b)

(c)

Fig. 12.2.—Types of tensile specimen
(*a*) for serrated grips
(*b*) for shoulder grips
(*c*) for threaded grips

usually machined to a larger cross-section with smooth blending curves into the central uniform part. The specimens are pulled by serrated grips at the ends, or by supporting at the shoulders of the large ends, or by threaded ends, the form of the specimen for each of these methods being shown in fig. 12.2.

The extension may be taken as the movement of the grips, but the exact length in which this extension occurs is difficult to define because of the changing cross-section at the ends. For more accurate work, extension measurements are made on a definite length of the uniform portion by an extensometer of suitable accuracy. This length is known as the *gauge length*.

12.3. Behaviour of materials in tension

When a specimen is pulled in tension, it can behave in one of three ways. In each it first stretches in an elastic manner, in the case of metals obeying Hooke's law, but for some materials such as rubber the elasticity is non-linear. In the first way it then deforms plastically and stretches, so

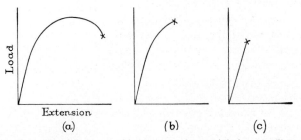

(a) (b) (c)

Fig. 12.3.—Possible types of behaviour of materials in a tensile test
(*a*) ductile (i.e. forms a neck), (*b*) and (*c*) non-ductile, fracture occurring in (*c*) without previous plastic deformation

that it does not return to its original length on unloading. Eventually a neck forms, and further deformation occurs only in the region of the neck, with a decrease in the applied load, until fracture finally occurs at the neck. In the second way, plastic deformation starts, but the specimen breaks without forming a neck. In the third way, the specimen breaks before the onset of plasticity. The form of the load-extension curve for each case is shown in fig. 12.3. The first type of behaviour is known as *ductile extension*, while the others are known as *non-ductile*, the last-named often being called *brittle*. The term brittle is, however, also used in another context as explained in Chapter 13.

12.4. Load-extension curve for a ductile material

The typical shape of the load-extension curve of a ductile metal is shown in fig. 12.4. The various points marked on the curve are as follows:

A is the limit of the initial straight line OA, i.e. it is the *limit of proportionality*. Beyond this point Hooke's law is no longer obeyed. The slope of this line gives *Young's modulus* for the material (see Section 12.6).

B is the limit to which the specimen can be strained and still return to the original length on unloading. It is the limit of elasticity or *elastic limit* and is not necessarily coincident with A.

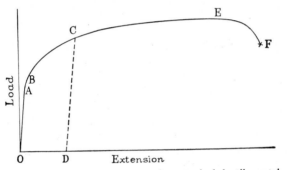

Fig. 12.4.—Load-extension curve for a typical ductile metal

C is a point in the plastic range. If the specimen is loaded to C and then unloaded, it will behave in a linear manner (line CD) and will show a permanent set OD. On reloading, the line DC is retraced and then the specimen yields plastically again on being taken beyond C. The load at C divided by the original area is known as the *yield stress* for the material in the condition D.

E is the maximum load. On a lever-type machine, where the load is controlled, the specimen would continue deforming to fracture. On a strain-controlled machine, the fall-off of load EF can be observed.

F is the point at which the separation of the test piece into two parts occurs.

The proportional limit and the elastic limit can be determined only to the limit of accuracy set by the extensometer used. In practice it is usual to quote the proof stress (except in the case of mild steel and other materials with a similar behaviour which will be considered below. The *proof stress* is defined as the stress (i.e. load/area) necessary to give a permanent deformation OD which is a definite fraction of the original length. A commonly used fraction is 0·1%, the corresponding stress being referred to as the 0·1% proof stress or the 0·1% P.S. The accuracy of commonly available extensometers is such that proof stresses for extensions of this magnitude can be determined with sufficient precision.

The maximum load divided by the original area is called the *ultimate tensile stress* (U.T.S.). It is also known as the *maximum stress* (M.S.) or the *tenacity*.

When a material is deformed plastically, it *work-hardens*, that is, the stress has to be increased to give further deformation. If a material with a stress-strain curve of the form shown in fig. 12.4 is deformed to C and unloaded, it returns to point D. On reloading, it deforms elastically to C before any further strain occurs. The point C is known as the *yield stress* for the material in condition D. Most annealed materials (other than mild steel) show practically no elastic range, and therefore cannot be said to have true yield stresses.

12.5. Yield-point phenomena

In mild steel and some other materials there is another phenomenon. At the elastic limit there is a sudden yield and fall-off of load. The material continues to deform at a lower load until work hardening sets in. The load-extension curve takes the form shown in fig. 12.5.

A is the *upper yield point*.

B is the *lower yield point*.

The stresses at these points are the *upper yield-point stress* and *lower yield-point stress* respectively.

CD is the work-hardening curve.

The apparent value of the upper yield-point stress is very sensitive to axial loading and to stress concentrations at the grips, and any departure from perfectly uniform stress across the test specimen causes a reduction of the load at which yielding commences.

When the load drops to B in fig. 12.5, regions of plastically-deformed material form around stress concentrations such as fillets and grips and, on further straining, these regions extend until the whole specimen has yielded at C. Work hardening then commences.

If the surface is sufficiently smooth, it is possible to observe the boundaries of the deformed regions travel along the specimen. These are known as *Luders lines*.

An explanation of the cause of a sharp yield point is given in Section 11.4.

For mild steel the value of the lower yield-point stress is about half of the ultimate tensile stress.

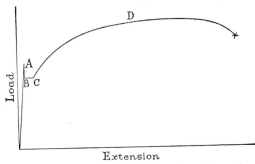

Fig. 12.5.—Typical load-extension curve for a low carbon steel

The effect of a yield-point phenomenon can be demonstrated by a simple experiment. A piece of annealed copper wire and one of annealed mild steel are in turn bent around a finger. The copper wire bends into a smooth curve because, as each region deforms, it work-hardens and requires a greater bending moment to cause further deformation than the

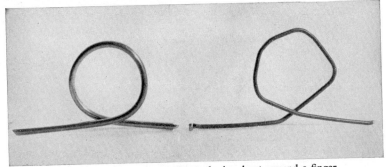

Fig. 12.6.—Copper and mild-steel wires bent around a finger

neighbouring section. A region of the steel wire starts to deform when the upper yield-point stress is reached. The stress for further yielding being less, bending will continue at that point rather than at immediately neighbouring sections, so that the wire takes a polygonal form. Two such wires are shown in fig. 12.6. Each bend in the steel wire forms with a distinct jerk.

It should be noted that the yield point or elastic limit marks the onset of plasticity, and the ultimate tensile stress is the stress at which necking commences. The U.T.S. in a ductile material is not associated with fracture. Hence all these stresses are plastic properties.

12.6. The influence of test-piece dimensions

If tensile tests are made upon different-sized specimens of the same material, the load-extension curves will be different. Fig. 12.7 shows curves for three specimens with different values of diameter d and gauge

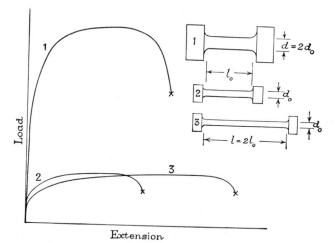

Fig. 12.7.—Load-extension curves for three specimens of the same material but of different dimensions

length l. The three curves are different. In an attempt to make the curves independent of the test-piece size, it is usual to plot a curve of stress σ against the strain ε. These quantities are defined as

$$\sigma = \frac{P}{A_0}$$

and

$$\varepsilon = \frac{l - l_0}{l_0}$$

where P = load, A_0 = original cross-sectional area, l_0 = original length and l = length at load P. The stress-strain curves derived from the three load-extension curves of fig. 12.7 will be identical up to the point of maximum load. Beyond the onset of necking they will differ as shown in fig. 12.8.

For the elastic range, Young's modulus is $E = \sigma/\varepsilon$.

The total extension to fracture is a quantity measurable after fracture and for ductile metals is of such magnitude that it can be determined with sufficient accuracy on gauge lengths of 2 to 8 in. by means of a pair of dividers and a scale. This extension to fracture divided by the original

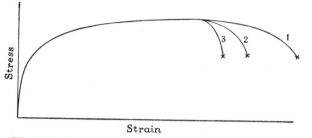

Fig. 12.8.—Stress-strain curves derived from curves in fig. 12.7

length is a commonly quoted property known as the *elongation*. It is obvious from fig. 12.7 that the elongation to fracture is dependent upon the dimensions of the specimen.

The elongation is made up of two parts: first that due to the uniform extension of the whole specimen and, second, the local extension in the region of the neck.

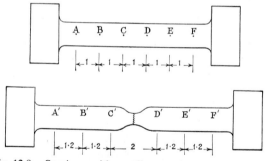

Fig. 12.9.—Specimen with equally spaced gauge marks before and after fracture

Consider a specimen on which six uniformly-spaced marks A, B, C, D, E, F have been placed as shown in fig. 12.9. Suppose after testing tc fracture the two portions are fitted together and that the marks are now at A′, B′, C′, D′, E′, F′ as shown. Also suppose the measured lengths are as shown. Regions AB, BC, DE, and EF have all extended uniformly up to the maximum load and have an elongation of 20%.

Region CD contains the neck, and has a total elongation of 1 (i.e.

163

100%) of which 0·2 was due to the uniform extension, and hence the other 0·8 must have been due to the neck.

If the gauge length is taken as 1, then the elongation would be quoted as 100%. If however BE were taken as the gauge length, the elongation would be

$$\frac{4\cdot4-3}{3} = 47\ \%$$

and if AF were the gauge length, the elongation would be

$$\frac{6\cdot8-5}{5} = 36\ \%$$

It is therefore obvious that the elongation is not independent of the gauge length.

If two specimens of different diameters, d_1 and d_2, but of identical material, are tested, the necks are of geometrically similar shape. This is *Barba's similarity law*. Therefore to compare results from different sized specimens, the gauge length taken must bear a fixed proportion to the diameter of the specimen.

In British Standard practice,* the gauge length is chosen so that

$$l_0 = 4\sqrt{A_0} = 3\cdot54\,d$$

Hence for a gauge length of 2 in, the specimen diameter should be 0·564 in.

The elongation is a measure of ductility of the specimen. Another measure of ductility is the *reduction of area* (R. of A.) which is the reduction in the area of cross-section at the neck expressed as a percentage of the original area. Thus

$$\text{reduction of area} = \frac{\frac{1}{4}\pi d_0^2 - \frac{1}{4}\pi d_n^2}{\frac{1}{4}\pi d_0^2} \times 100\ \%$$

$$= \left[1 - \left(\frac{d_n}{d_0}\right)^2\right] \times 100\ \%$$

where d_0 and d_n are the initial diameter and the diameter at the neck respectively.

12.7. True stress

When plastic deformation occurs in a tensile test there is a decrease in the area of cross-section of the specimen. The *true stress* is therefore not the value already considered, i.e. P/A_0, which we now term the *nominal*

---

* B.S. 18: 1956. *Tensile Testing of Materials*, British Standard Specifications, published by British Standards Institution.

stress, but is $\sigma_t = P/A$, where A is the actual area which becomes pro-gressively smaller as deformation proceeds. The effect that the change of definition of stress has on the stress-strain curve is shown in fig. 12.10.

During plastic deformation there is a negligible change of volume. Hence

$$Al = A_0 l_0$$

or

$$A = \frac{A_0 l_0}{l} = \frac{A_0}{1+\varepsilon}$$

The true stress is then

$$\sigma_t = \frac{P}{A} = \frac{(1+\varepsilon)P}{A_0}$$

$$= (1+\varepsilon)\sigma$$

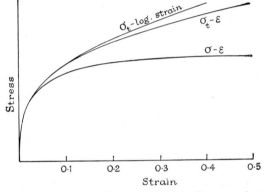

Fig. 12.10.—Effect of different definitions of stress and strain upon shape of stress-strain curve

Now the true stress will be related to strain by some relationship which can be expressed as $\sigma_t = f(\varepsilon)$. Then

$$P = \frac{A_0 \sigma_t}{(1+\varepsilon)} = \frac{A_0 f(\varepsilon)}{(1+\varepsilon)}$$

from which

$$\frac{dP}{d\varepsilon} = \frac{A_0}{(1+\varepsilon)^2}\left[(1+\varepsilon)\frac{d\sigma_t}{d\varepsilon} - \sigma_t\right]$$

The maximum load P_{max} will occur at a strain for which $dP/d\varepsilon = 0$, i.e.

$$(1+\varepsilon)\frac{d\sigma_t}{d\varepsilon} = \sigma_t$$

or

$$\frac{d\sigma_t}{d\varepsilon} = \frac{\sigma_t}{1+\varepsilon}$$

A tangent to the curve $\sigma_t = f(\varepsilon)$ from the point $\sigma_t = 0$, $\varepsilon = -1$, will touch the curve at a point Q which gives the value of true stress and strain corresponding to P_{max}. This may be seen from fig. 12.11 since

$$\tan \alpha = \frac{QB}{AB} = \frac{\sigma_t}{1+\varepsilon} = \frac{d\sigma_t}{d\varepsilon}$$

The point R at which AQ cuts the stress axis gives

$$OR = \frac{\sigma_t}{1+\varepsilon} = \sigma_{max}$$

i.e. OR is the value of the maximum nominal stress, i.e. the U.T.S. This graphical method for determining U.T.S. is known as Considèré's construction.

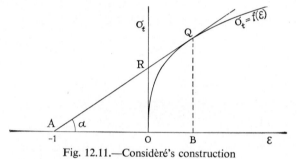

Fig. 12.11.—Considèré's construction

In many practical cases, it is found that the true stress-strain curve may be closely represented by a law of the form *

$$\sigma_t = a\varepsilon^b$$

For a material which has such a stress-strain relationship,

$$\frac{d\sigma_t}{d\varepsilon} = ba\varepsilon^{b-1}$$

Therefore the value of strain corresponding to the U.T.S. is given by

$$ba\varepsilon^{b-1} = \frac{a\varepsilon^b}{1+\varepsilon}$$

Therefore
$$\varepsilon = b(1+\varepsilon)$$

which gives
$$\varepsilon = \frac{b}{1-b}$$

* A. Nádai, *Plasticity* (McGraw-Hill, 1931), Chapter 15.

166

Then

$$\text{U.T.S.} = \sigma_{max} = \frac{\sigma_t}{1+\varepsilon}$$

$$= \frac{a\left(\dfrac{b}{1-b}\right)^b}{1+\left(\dfrac{b}{1-b}\right)}$$

$$= a(1-b)\left(\frac{b}{1-b}\right)^b$$

or

$$\text{U.T.S.} = ab^b(1-b)^{1-b}$$

12.8. Logarithmic strain

When an increment of extension δl occurs during straining, it is doing so on an actual length l and not on the original length l_0. Hence strain may be defined as $\Sigma(\delta l/l)$. In the infinitesimal form this becomes

$$\int_{l_0}^{l} \frac{dl}{l} = \log_e \frac{l}{l_0}$$

$$= \log_e(1+\varepsilon)$$

In this form the strain is referred to as the *logarithmic strain.*

The effect of using this form of strain on the shape of the stress-strain curve is shown in fig. 12.10.

12.9. Ideal plastic material

An ideal plastic material is defined as one that behaves in a linear elastic manner until the yield stress is reached, and then any further deformation continues at this constant yield stress, as shown in fig. 12.12.

A work-hardened material and also mild steel in the initial stages of deformation approximate to this behaviour, and are often treated as such in considering the plastic behaviour of composite structures.

12.10. Other related tests

The tensile test is expensive to perform in that a specimen with suitably-shaped enlarged ends and a reduced parallel central portion has to be prepared, involving extensive machining. Tests that require less preparation of specimens are compression and hardness tests. In the following sections these tests and their relationship to the tensile test will be considered.

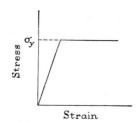

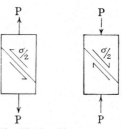

Fig. 12.12.—Stress-strain curve for an ideal plastic material.

Fig. 12.13.—Shear stress due to uniaxial tensile and compressive loading.

12.11. Compression tests

Plastic deformation is a shear process and occurs under uniaxial stressing when the shear stress reaches a definite value. Now for a uniaxial stress system the applied stresses in tension and compression would be as shown in fig. 12.13. The maximum shear stress is on a

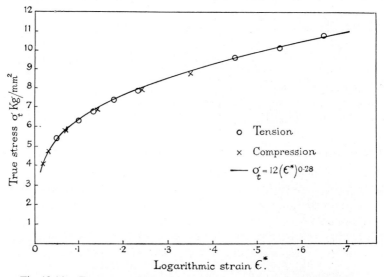

Fig. 12.14.—True stress—log. strain curve for partially annealed aluminium. Tension and compression results lie on same curve—empirically fitted by $\sigma_t = 12(\varepsilon^*)^{0.28}$ Kg/mm². [Tabor]

plane inclined at 45° to the direction of the direct stress and will have a value of $\frac{1}{2}\sigma$ where σ is the value of the direct stress. Hence we would expect the yield stress for a material in any given condition to be the same whether the specimen is tested in tension or compression. It is found by

168

experiments on pure metals that if two specimens of identical material are tested, one in tension and one in compression, the true stress-logarithmic strain curves will be practically identical as shown in fig. 12.14.

This depends on the compression test being a pure compression test, i.e. the stress is uniaxial. In practice, since the material wishes to expand laterally, it will be restricted at the compression anvils due to friction, and the specimen will assume a barrel shape as in fig. 12.15. Also, due to friction, a greater load is necessary to cause yielding. If the friction is kept to a low value by the use of suitable lubricants, barrelling is much less pronounced, and the agreement with the tensile-test results is improved.

Fig. 12.15.—Barrel shape acquired by cylindrical specimen during compression.

If the specimens have been cold-worked prior to testing, the results for tension and compression may not agree. For example, if a specimen is pre-tensioned, its yield point for further tension is raised, but that for further compression is lowered. The effect, which is shown in fig. 12.16, is known as the *Bauschinger effect*.

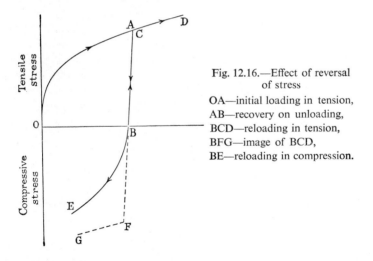

Fig. 12.16.—Effect of reversal of stress

OA—initial loading in tension,
AB—recovery on unloading,
BCD—reloading in tension,
BFG—image of BCD,
BE—reloading in compression.

12.12. Hardness tests

Hardness has been defined and measured in a variety of ways. The principal methods fall into the following three classes:

Resistance to indentation by a particular shape of indenter.
Resistance to scratching.
The rebound of a steel ball from the surface.

The first of these—static indentation hardness—is the only class that will be considered in this book, and three tests only of that class.

12.13. Brinell hardness

A spherical hard steel ball is pressed into the surface under a steady load, the load maintained for a few seconds for a steady state to be reached, and the indenter removed. The diameter of the permanent impression is measured with a suitable measuring microscope, either by a micrometer eyepiece or by projection on to a graduated screen. The *Brinell Hardness Number* (B.H.N.) is given as the load applied divided by the area of the curved surface of the indentation, that is,

$$\text{B.H.N.} = \frac{2W}{\pi D^2 [1 - \sqrt{\{1 - (d/D)^2\}}]}$$

where W = applied load, d = diameter of impression and D = diameter of ball.

Tables for converting the measured values of W, d, and D to hardness are given in B.S. 240.* The hardness, which has the dimensions of stress, is always expressed in Kg/mm^2.

In most cases the B.H.N. is not constant for a given specimen under test, but depends upon the load and size of ball used. It is found that for geometrically similar indentations in a homogeneous medium, whatever their size, the hardness number is constant. Thus if d/D for one indentation is the same as d/D for another indentation with a ball of different diameter and an appropriately different load, the same B.H.N. results. Hence it is always necessary to state the values of D and W used when quoting a B.H.N. It is usual to choose a value of W so that d/D lies between 0·25 and 0·5.

Balls of tungsten carbide are often used in place of steel balls when materials of high hardness are being tested, as these are much harder and deform less.

12.14. Diamond pyramid hardness

This method was introduced by Smith and Sandland in 1922 and developed by Vickers-Armstrong Ltd. For this reason it is often referred to as the *Vickers hardness.*

The indenter is a diamond in the form of a square pyramid, the angle between opposite faces being 136°. This angle was chosen by analogy

---

*B.S. 240: Part 1: 1937. *Method and Tables for Brinell Hardness Testing*

with the Brinell test in which the average d/D ratio is 0·375. When tangents are drawn from the edges of an impression with this d/D ratio, as in fig. 12.17, the included angle is 136°.

The impression is made by applying a suitable load, and the length d of its diagonal (fig. 12.18) is measured. The hardness (D.P.N.) H_D is defined as the load W divided by the area of the sloping sides of the impression:

$$H_D = \frac{2W}{d^2} \cos 22°$$

$$= 1 \cdot 854 \frac{W}{d^2}$$

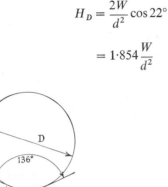

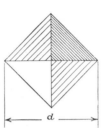

Fig. 12.17.—Relation of diamond indenter to Brinell indentation

Fig. 12.18.—Plan view of diamond impression

The loads used may be from 1 to 120 Kg, depending upon the hardness of the material under test. For most work the load is chosen to make the value of d lie in the range 0·5–1 mm.

Tables for converting d to D.P.N. are given in B.S. 427.* The D.P.N. is always quoted in Kg/mm².

Since all impressions are geometrically similar, the D.P.N. is independent of the load used, provided that the material is homogeneous in its mechanical properties as the depth below the surface varies.

At low hardnesses, the B.H.N. and D.P.N. for any one material are equal.

12.15. Rockwell hardness

This test is based on the measurement of the depth of penetration of the indenter. A load of 10 Kg is first applied to the indenter, and the depth of penetration then reached is taken as the zero for further measurements. A further load (called the major load) is then applied and removed

---

* B.S. 427: 1931. *Diamond Pyramid Hardness Numbers*

as in fig. 12.19, leaving only the minor load. The depth, d mm, of the indenter relative to the zero position (i.e. that before the application of the major load) is recorded on a suitable dial gauge.

Different scales of hardness, using different shapes of indenter and different major loads, are available.* The commonest are known as Rockwell B (R_B) and Rockwell C (R_C).

For softer materials, a $\frac{1}{16}$-in diameter steel ball is used, the major load is 90 Kg (100 Kg total load) and the hardness is

$$R_B = 130 - \frac{d}{0.002}$$

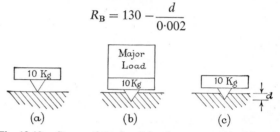

$$(a) \qquad (b) \qquad (c)$$

Fig. 12.19.—Stages of Rockwell hardness test; d is difference in indenter height between (a) and (c)

For harder materials, a conical-shaped diamond of 120° apex angle is used, the major load is 140 Kg (total load 150 Kg), and the hardness is

$$R_C = 100 - \frac{d}{0.002}$$

On the usual forms of hardness tester, the dial gauge is calibrated in divisions corresponding to intervals of 0.002 mm and numbered suitably for both R_B and R_C scales.

The conversion of Rockwell hardness values to D.P.N. and B.H.N. can be done by empirical curves. Tabular values from these curves are given in B.S. 860.†

12.16. Relationship of D.P.N. to yield stress

Since the deformation under the indenter is plastic, it should be possible to relate the hardness to the plastic properties of the material. The plastic flow is a three-dimensional problem and not amenable to

---

* A complete list is given in B.S. 891: 1940. *Direct Reading Hardness Testing (Rockwell Principle).*

† B.S. 860: 1939. *Approximate Comparison of Hardness Scales.*

Amendments to B.S. 240, 427, and 891 were issued in 1958 in which it was proposed that Brinell, Diamond Pyramid, and Rockwell hardnesses should be denoted by the standard abbreviations HB, HV, and HR respectively. HB should be followed by the ball diameter in mm and the load in Kg, HV by the load in Kg, and HR by the appropriate letter. The hardness value should precede the abbreviation. Examples are:

226 HB 10/3000
648 HV 30
60 HRA

simple treatment, particularly when work-hardening effects have to be con-sidered. It has been shown that for ideal plastic materials (see Section 12.9)

$$H_D \approx 2.9\,\sigma_y$$

where σ_y is the yield stress.*

Some experimental values for work-hardened materials which approxi-mate to an ideal plastic material are given in Table 12.1.

TABLE 12.1—HARDNESS AND YIELD STRESS OF SOME
WORK-HARDENED MATERIALS

Material	σ_y (Kg/mm^2)	H_D	H_D/σ_y
Aluminium	16·2	47·5	2·93
Copper	40·4	120	2·97
70/30 Brass	51·8	144	2·78
Mild steel	54·4	166	3·06

In a work-hardening material there will be different amounts of work hardening at different points under the indenter, so that the yield stress is not uniform. If the average amount of strain under the indenter were

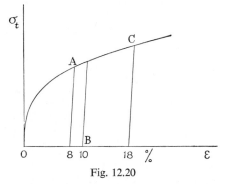

Fig. 12.20

known, it would be possible to say that the average yield stress would be the yield stress corresponding to that average value of strain. It is found by experiment that the average value of strain to be considered is about 8%, so we may say that the indentation takes the material on average to a state corresponding to 0·08 more strain than it had previously undergone.

Thus for virgin material O (fig. 12.20) the average condition under the indenter will be A which corresponds to a strain of 0·08. For material given 10% strain originally, B, the average condition under the indenter

* D. Tabor, *The Hardness of Metals* (Oxford University Press, 1951).

will be C, which corresponds to a strain of 0·18, etc. The stresses corresponding to A and C are the values of the representative yield stress Y_r such that

$$H_D \approx 2·9\,Y_r$$

The results of some practical tests on an annealed copper specimen which verify this are given in fig. 12.21.

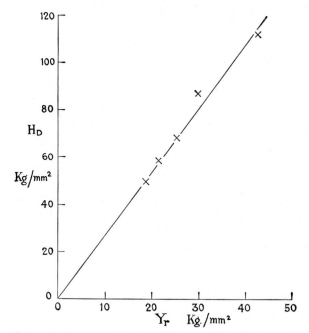

Fig. 12.21.—Hardness and representative yield stress under indenter for various stages of work hardening an annealed copper specimen

12.17. Relationship between U.T.S. and D.P.N.

For a material with a true stress-linear strain curve given by

$$\sigma_t = a\varepsilon^b$$

it has been shown (p. 167) that

$$\text{U.T.S.} = ab^b(1-b)^{1-b}$$

Now the diamond indenter produces an average strain of 8%, so that the representative yield stress is

$$Y_r = a(0·08)^b$$

and

$$H_D = 2·9a(0·08)^b$$

Therefore

$$a = \frac{H_D}{2 \cdot 9}(12 \cdot 5)^b$$

Substitution of this value in the expression for the ultimate tensile stress gives

$$\text{U.T.S.} = \frac{H_D}{2 \cdot 9}(12 \cdot 5b)^b(1-b)^{1-b}$$

In a class of materials which have stress-strain curves of similar shape, i.e. b is the same but a differs, there will be a constant relationship between U.T.S. and H_D.

For annealed steels $b \approx 0 \cdot 2$, so that

$$\frac{(12 \cdot 5b)^b(1-b)^{1-b}}{2 \cdot 9} = \frac{(12 \cdot 5 \times 0 \cdot 2)^{0 \cdot 2}(0 \cdot 8)^{0 \cdot 8}}{2 \cdot 9}$$

$$= 0 \cdot 346$$

i.e.

$$\text{U.T.S. (in Kg/mm}^2) = 0 \cdot 346\, H_D$$

But

$$1\ \text{Ton/in}^2 = 1 \cdot 5749\ \text{Kg/mm}^2$$

so that

$$\text{U.T.S. (in Tons/in}^2) = \frac{0 \cdot 346}{1 \cdot 5749}\, H_D$$

$$= 0 \cdot 22\, H_D$$

That is, the ultimate tensile stress measured in Tons/in^2 is approximately one-fifth of the diamond pyramid hardness. Such a result is useful in estimating the strength of a steel from a single hardness measurement.

QUESTIONS

1. Sketch curves connecting the nominal stress and linear strain obtained from tensile tests of (a) a typical ductile material, (b) a typical non-ductile material, (c) 0·2% carbon steel.

The following figures were obtained in a tensile test of a test piece with a 2-in gauge length and a cross-sectional area of 0·25 in^2:

Extension (in)	0·002	0·004	0·006	0·008	0·010	0·012	0·05	0·10	0·15	0·20	0·25	0·30
Load (Tons)	1·2	2·5	3·2	3·6	4·0	4·2	6·3	8·0	9·3	10·0	10·1	9·0

The elongation and reduction of area were 16% and 64% respectively.

Calculate the maximum allowable working stress if this is to equal (a) 0·25 × U.T.S., (b) 0·6 × 0·1% proof stress.

What would have been the elongation and reduction of area if a 6-in gauge length had been used? [P]

2. A tensile test on a specimen of annealed mild steel, 0·178 in diameter, gave the following data for a part of the load-extension curve:

Load (Tons)	0·45	0·50	0·55	0·60	0·65
Extension on 0·633 in (in)	0·007	0·012	0·020	0·030	0·052

Calculate the true stress σ_t and the linear strain e corresponding to each load. Show graphically that they are related by a law of the form $\sigma_t = ae^b$, and determine the values of the constants a and b.

Estimate the ultimate tensile stress of the material from the relationship

$$\frac{d\sigma_t}{de} = \frac{\sigma_t}{1+e} \qquad\qquad [S]$$

3. The following observations were made during a tensile test on a 0·560-in diameter specimen of pure aluminium:

Load (Tons)	Extension on 2-in gauge length (in)
0·4	0·0008
0·6	0·0050
0·8	0·025
1·0	0·060
1·2	0·19

By plotting on log-log graph paper, or otherwise, determine a mathematical relationship between true stress and linear strain. Hence determine the ultimate tensile stress for the material. [MST]

4. Show that the ultimate tensile strength of a ductile material is determined by the plastic properties of the material and not by rupture strength.

Calculate the ultimate tensile strength for a material whose true yield stress σ_t and linear strain ε are related by $\sigma_t = 27\,\varepsilon^{0.25}$. [P]

5. Calculate the ultimate tensile strength of a brittle material for which $a = 40$, $b = 0·25$, and the elongation to fracture on a 2-in gauge length is 25%. [MST]

6. What is work hardening in metals?

During tensile testing of a specimen of ductile metal originally 0·564 in diameter and 2 in gauge length, the diameter was found to have decreased to a uniform value of 0·530 in when the load was 5·5 Tons.

Calculate (a) the amount of true strain which the material has undergone in tension, and (b) the load required to cause the same amount of true strain in compression for a specimen of the same material and the same initial diameter. [P]

7. For a material with a true stress-linear strain relationship $\sigma_t = 40\varepsilon^{0.3}$ the elongation to fracture on a 2-in gauge length of a specimen of 0·564 in diameter was 56%. What would be the elongation to fracture using a 3-in gauge length on a specimen of the same diameter? What diameter of specimen would show an elongation of 56% on a 3-in gauge length?

8. Why are hardness tests frequently used in place of tensile tests to determine the mechanical strength of a metal?

It has been shown that $H_D = 2·9Y_r$, where H_D is the diamond pyramid hardness of a metal in any particular state of strain and Y_r is the yield stress measured at a strain 0·08 more than that at which the hardness is measured. A certain metal has a stress-strain curve given by $\sigma_t = a\varepsilon^{0.32}$, where σ_t is the true tensile stress, ε is the linear tensile strain, and a is a constant. Derive an expression for the ultimate tensile stress of a specimen of the metal in terms of the measured value of H_D for the specimen. [MST]

CHAPTER 13

Relationship of Mechanical Testing to the Design
of Engineering Structures

13.1. Introduction

One of the important considerations in the design of an engineering component or structure is that it shall not deform excessively or break under the loads or forces to which it will be subjected during its working life, that is to say, its mechanical strength shall be sufficient. For any particular design, the stresses at all points can be determined, by calculation or some experimental method of stress analysis, for the loads and forces to which that component will be subjected. The stresses must obviously not exceed the permissible stress for the material chosen and the factors governing the choice may vary. In some cases, limitations of space or weight may dictate the size and hence the stresses, the material being chosen accordingly; or the material may be chosen with some other factor in mind, such as cost or corrosion resistance, and the size of the component made to fit.

The maximum allowable stress in the component will be related to the minimum stress that will cause plastic deformation in the material. In practice, a value that is some fraction f of the yield-point stress or a proof stress is usually taken, and $1/f$ is known as the *factor of safety*.

13.2. Plastic flow under multi-axial stresses

In a tensile or compressive test the specimen is subjected to stress in one direction only—uniaxial stress. In many engineering components the shape is such that at a point there are stresses in more than one direction—a *multi-axial stress* system. At any point a stress system can be defined by normal stresses on three mutually perpendicular planes, the directions of these planes being chosen so that the shear stresses on them are zero. These normal stresses are known as the *principal stresses*. The normal and shear stresses on a plane in any other direction through the point can be calculated by formulae which are given in many textbooks on strength of materials.

The conditions for the onset of plastic deformation under multi-axial stressing has been the subject of extensive investigations. For a material with constant yield stress in uniaxial tension, i.e. no strain hardening, the most widely-accepted criterion is that the von Mises plasticity function

$$[(\sigma_1 - \sigma_2)^2 + (\sigma_2 - \sigma_3)^2 + (\sigma_3 - \sigma_1)^2]$$

reaches a constant value of $2\sigma_y^2$, where σ_y is the yield stress in simple tension and σ_1, σ_2, σ_3 are the three principal stresses.

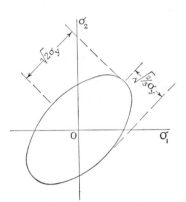

Fig. 13.1. — Boundary of yield under plane stress system according to von Mises plasticity function.

For the case when $\sigma_3 = 0$, the values of σ_1 and σ_2 for which yielding will just occur lie on an ellipse as shown in fig. 13.1. Addition of a hydrostatic stress σ_v to the three principal stresses does not alter any of the terms $(\sigma_1 - \sigma_2)^2$, etc., in the von Mises function. Hence for any value of σ_3 that is not zero, the boundary curve for yielding is an ellipse of the same shape but with its centre displaced along the line $\sigma_1 = \sigma_2 = \sigma_3$, the σ_3-axis being perpendicular to both the σ_1 and the σ_2-axes. The surface generated by the ellipse moving along this line is a circular cylinder of radius $\sqrt{(\frac{2}{3})} \cdot \sigma_y$.

13.3. Ductile fracture

It was shown in Chapter 12 that the maximum stress that a material can stand in simple tension, i.e. the ultimate stress, is a plastic property dependent only upon the plastic deformation law of the material. At that stress, necking commences and the cross-section decreases until the specimen separates into two parts. The fracture is described as a cup-and-cone fracture, having a flat central part surrounded by a sloping edge or lip which may be entirely on one part or partly on each. A typical break is shown in fig. 13.2.

If the two parts are fitted together and sectioned as in fig. 13.3 it will be seen that the cup portion had failed before the cone, and that in the cup the metal has drawn out into separate fibres, each of which finally fractures. It has been shown* that, in the last stages of deformation at the neck, holes develop in the material at impurities and open up so that there is an internal as well as an external reduction of area, and the net

---

* C. F. Tipper, *The Fracture of Mild Steel Plate*, Admiralty Ship Welding Committee, Report No. R3. (H.M.S.O., London, 1948).
    K. E. Puttick, *Phil. Mag.*, Vol. 4, 1959, p. 964.

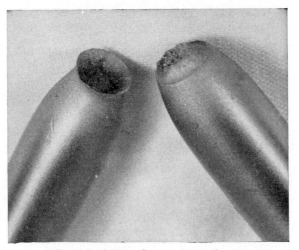

Fig. 13.2.—Views of cup-and-cone fracture

area just before separation of the two portions is probably very close to zero. Bridgman* has shown that for tensile tests conducted under externally-applied hydrostatic pressure the reduction of area at fracture is increased, mainly by reduction of the area of the cup. Under external

Fig. 13.3.—Section of cup-and-cone fracture ($\times$ 3)

* P. W. Bridgman, *Studies in Large Plastic Flow and Fracture* (McGraw-Hill, 1952)

pressure, there can be a shear stress causing deformation while the principal stresses are still compressive, so that there would be no tendency for holes to form at any impurities.

Also as purer and purer material is used, it is found that the observed reduction of area becomes greater, presumably because there is less opportunity for internal holes to be formed.

Hence ductile fracture is not really a fracture, but plastic deformation to the end.

13.4. Actual failures of engineering components

Components designed with the maximum stress criterion described in Section 13.1 modified as in Section 13.2 in cases of multi-axial stressing would be expected not to fail under the applied loads and forces. If these loads and forces were exceeded, plastic deformation would ensue, leading in cases of sufficient overload to ductile fracture.

Many components designed solely on the criterion that the stresses due to the applied loads shall not be sufficient to cause plastic deformation, nevertheless are found to fail in service. The causes of such failures are numerous, and their significance must be appreciated by designers and allowed for in appropriate cases. Among the more important are:

> brittleness or lack of toughness
> fatigue
> creep
> corrosion

The first three of these are considered in some detail in the following sections, together with testing methods used for assessing their relevant effects in various cases. Corrosion is discussed in Chapter 16.

It has been shown in the last chapter that the tensile, compression, and static indentation hardness tests can all be related to one another via the fundamental plastic law of the material. Thus from the results of a complete tensile test it would be possible to predict the results of a compression and a hardness test. No further fundamental information would therefore be gained by performing these two tests on material for which the results of a tensile test are already available.

The three types of mechanical tests now to be described bear no straightforward relationship to the tensile test and the results cannot be forecast from the tensile-test results.

TOUGHNESS

13.5. Brittle fracture

As mentioned in Section 12.1, brittleness is exhibited where a tensile specimen fractures without forming a neck.

Glass fractures with no previous plastic deformation and may be regarded as a typical brittle material.

Freshly-drawn glass fibres can withstand a very high tensile stress (about 200 Tons/in²) without fracture, but if a scratch is made on the surface (even a feather drawn lightly across the surface will produce a sufficiently deep scratch) the glass fractures under much lower stresses. Griffith has developed his crack theory that the crack acts as a stress concentration, so that at the tip of the crack the stress is above the fracture stress when the average stress is much lower. Hence the crack will extend and, the stress concentration being maintained at the new tip of the crack, fracture will continue. The larger the crack, the smaller is the stress necessary to cause fracture.

13.6. Toughness

The term *toughness,* which is not always used in a strictly defined sense, is usually taken in a metallurgical context to mean the converse of brittleness. In a quantitative manner it can be quoted as the energy consumed or work done in rupturing a specimen. Obviously the geometry of the specimen is one of the governing factors, and so a standard size and shape of specimen must be used for comparative purposes. Since work is the product of force and distance, the toughness is dependent upon both yield stress and ductility. If the test is not a simple tensile test on a parallel-sided specimen, the yield stress under conditions of multi-axial stress is important.

The toughness as determined from a test on a specimen which contains a machined notch, that is, the energy consumed in rupturing the specimen, should be more accurately described as the *notch toughness.*

It might be expected that it would be possible to calculate the result of any particular test by working from the tensile-test results, since by knowing the strain at any point we can get the stress. But it is found that this is not so. Two different specimens (even two different plain carbon steels) may give identical stress-strain curves in tension, but behave quite differently in a particular type of test known as a notch impact test (see

Section 13.7). For example, the following results for two steels may be compared:

	Yield point	U.T.S.	% El.	% R. of A.	Toughness
(a)	48·7 Tons/in²	55·5 Tons/in²	28·6	64·0	78 ft Lb
(b)	45·9	54·3	26·5	63·7	9

It will be observed that, although the tensile results are almost identical, the work necessary to cause fracture of one specimen is nearly nine times greater than the work to cause fracture of the other specimen.

Specimen (a), which would be classed as a tough specimen, would have deformed a lot, eventually tearing at the root of the notch and so absorbing a lot of energy. Specimen (b) would have deformed very little before

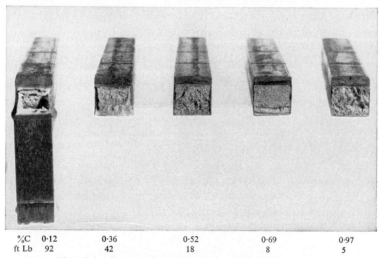

%C	0·12	0·36	0·52	0·69	0·97
ft Lb	92	42	18	8	5

Fig. 13.4.—Fractured Izod specimens. Plain carbon steels

snapping in a brittle manner, so absorbing little energy. When iron and steel fail in a brittle manner, they do so by splitting or *cleavage* along certain planes in the crystals and produce a bright *crystalline* appearance, easily distinguishable from the *fibrous* appearance of a ductile fracture. Some fracture surfaces are seen in fig. 13.4. This change from ductile to brittle fracture is brought about by the increase of the yield-point stress due to the triaxial conditions set up at the root of the notch. It will be seen later that other factors which also raise the yield point, viz. low temperatures and increased rates of strain will also cause a change of mode of fracture.

13.7. Notch impact tests

The number of tests for determining notch toughness is very large.*
The common ones in regular use are the Izod and the Charpy tests.†

The Izod specimen is a bar of square cross-section across which is machined a notch of standard size. The dimensions of the specimen and of the notch are shown in fig. 13.5. The Izod specimen is usually made with three notches, so that three measurements of toughness can be obtained from one specimen.

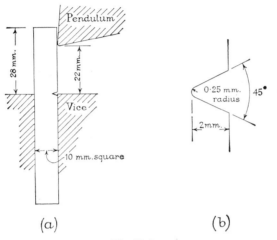

Fig. 13.5

(a) Izod specimen and mounting.   (b) Form of standard Vee notch.

The bar is clamped just below a notch and hit at a point 22 mm from the notch by a swinging pendulum, i.e. it is loaded as a cantilever. The pendulum is released from a height such that at the bottom of its swing, when it hits the specimen, its kinetic energy is 120 ft Lb. After hitting the specimen, the pendulum continues to swing to a height which gives a measure of the work done in bending or breaking the specimen. The greater the work done, the less high does the pendulum swing. The angle of swing or the energy absorbed is read off a calibrated scale.

Two of the standard Charpy specimens are shown in fig. 13.6. The Vee notch specimen is the one more commonly used in Great Britain. The specimen is fractured by a swinging pendulum as for the Izod test, but the specimen is loaded as a beam instead of as a cantilever.

* C. F. Tipper, " The Brittle Fracture of Metals at Atmospheric and Sub-Zero Temperatures," *Met. Rev.*, Vol. 2, 1957, p. 195.
† B.S. 131: 1933. *Notched Bar Test Pieces.*

13.8. Factors of Izod and Charpy tests

The notch impact bend tests (to give them their fully descriptive name) have three factors not present in a tensile test, each of which may have an effect upon the energy value. These are the notch, the bending, and the impact or high rate of strain. It is important to consider the relative importance of each.

It would be possible to do the tests on un-notched specimens. The standard impact test for cast iron is in fact performed on an unnotched bar,* but this is a material which is basically brittle. The notch, as already

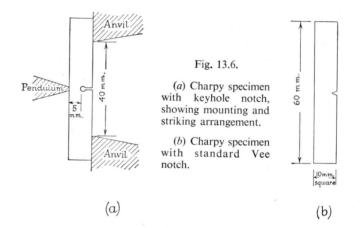

Fig. 13.6.

(*a*) Charpy specimen with keyhole notch, showing mounting and striking arrangement.

(*b*) Charpy specimen with standard Vee notch.

(a)   (b)

explained, has the effect of introducing multi-axial stresses, and in some cases causing brittle fracture. Hence the notch plays a very important part.

The bending is merely a geometrical factor, being the manner by which the tensile stress is introduced, and plays a very small part. A notch bend test does not discriminate steels in a different manner from a notch tensile test.

An increased rate of straining is found to raise the yield stress. In certain cases this effect may be sufficient to change the mode of fracture, when there will be a large decrease in the energy value. If the mode is not changed, then, since the work to fracture is a function of stress and strain, the higher speed of loading will raise the stresses and hence the energy. In a ductile fracture, where there is much plastic deformation, the raised yield stress may contribute as much as 40% of the total energy in an impact test. In a brittle fracture, where there is very little plastic flow, the contribution is much less.

---

* B.S. 1349: 1947. *Impact Test for Cast Iron.*

By straining notched specimens slowly in a suitable machine, the work to fracture can be evaluated from the area under the load-deformation curve and compared with the value for impact loading. Some actual tests on two steels gave the following results:

	slow loading	impact loading
Low-carbon steel	22·2 ft Lb	37·8 ft Lb
High-carbon steel	2·3	2·7

Thus the notch is the most important feature of the notch bent impact test.

13.9. Uses of notch tests

The Izod test was first devised for checking the suitability of different heat treatments applied to steels, but it has come into much greater prominence in recent years in the study of the low-temperature brittleness of mild steel. The effect of heat treatment upon the Izod value will be considered in Chapter 14.

The energy values given by a notch bend test cannot be used directly for design purposes. Hence the main purpose of the test is for sorting materials into an order of merit, either to choose the best for a particular application or to compare with others of proved value.

13.10. Notch brittleness of mild steel

If we perform Izod tests on a steel over a range of temperatures, it is found that there is a sudden change from high-energy and fully-fibrous

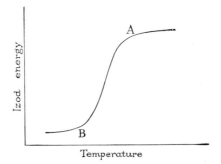

Fig. 13.7.—Typical curve for variation of Izod value
with temperature for a mild steel

fractures to low-energy and fully-crystalline fractures. The drop in energy is rapid over a small range of temperatures as may be seen from the typical curve in fig. 13.7. Points A and B which mark the limits of the transition range may be only 20 to 30° apart. A normal unnotched tensile test would, however, show only a small and gradual change over a 100° range, the yield point being raised as the temperature falls; but this increase, like the effect of the notch and increased rates of strain, promotes brittleness.

The form of curve so obtained is typical of all body-centred cubic and hexagonal close-packed metals, but the phenomenon is not shown by face-centred cubic metals.

13.11. Transition temperatures

The transition temperature which marks the region in which the energy value and type of fracture undergo their great change may be defined in one of several ways, and different ways may give somewhat different values of the temperature. Hence it is important to note the basis of definition for any quoted values of transition temperature. The most common bases of definition are:

The point of greatest slope of the energy-temperature curve.
The temperature at which the fracture appearance shows a definite percentage of crystallinity, e.g. 50%.
The temperature at which the energy has a definite value, e.g. 15 ft Lb.

13.12. Tests on large plates

When large plates are tested in tension and notches are deliberately placed in them, it is found that the plate tears if the temperature is above

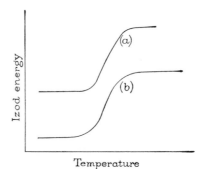

Fig. 13.8.—Comparison of transition curves for two hypothetical steels. The energy value of steel (b) for a fully ductile fracture is equal to that for an almost fully brittle fracture of steel (a).

a certain value, but breaks in a brittle manner if the temperature is below that value. The particular value, which varies from steel to steel, is found to correlate closely with the transition temperature as defined in either of the first two ways listed above. The actual energy value is of much less significance; what is a low-energy value for one steel may be a high-energy value for another steel as may be seen from the curves in fig. 13.8.

13.13. Casualties due to brittle fracture

Abnormal conditions not contemplated in design do occur and have brought about failures due to brittle fractures. Stress concentrations, rough edges, defective welds, etc., can all lead to small notches or cracks which, if the steel is below the transition temperature, may start a brittle fracture. The mean stress need not necessarily be high, because the stress concentration can raise it locally, and also, as has been shown by Wells* and Mylonas,† residual stresses due to welding or plastic deformation can add to small applied stresses to give local stresses equal to the yield stress. In a welded structure the fracture can pass through welds into neighbouring plates, and if these are likewise below their transition temperature the result may be a failure of large extent.

Many brittle fractures have occurred in ships, several welded vessels having broken completely in two. Other large-scale fractures have occurred in large oil-storage tanks and in welded pipelines.

Poor design and poor workmanship have contributed to these failures, but even when these factors have been largely remedied, casualties have occurred. If the steels used had had a much lower transition temperature, these failures would not have occurred. In a large number of cases which have been thoroughly investigated, it was found that the steel temperature at the time of the fracture was below the transition temperature, as shown by an Izod or Charpy test or a notch tensile test.‡

13.14. The effect of metallurgical factors

The transition temperature of a steel is found to be related to the composition—each element, even when present in small quantities, having an effect—and to the grain size. As both of these factors are dependent upon the practices adopted in steelmaking, a brief outline of the processes is necessary for an understanding of these effects.

Steel is made from pig iron (see p. 97) by refining, which is principally

* A. A. Wells, *Trans. Inst. Naval Arch.*, Vol. 98, 1956, p. 296.

† C. Mylonas, D. C. Drucker, and J. D. Brunton, *The Welding Journal*, Research Suppl., Vol. 23, 1958, p. 473S.

‡ J. F. Baker and C. F. Tipper, " The Value of the Notch Tensile Test," *Proc. Inst. Mech. Engrs.*, Vol. 170, 1956, p. 65.

the removal of the unwanted carbon and other elements by oxidation. Most mild steel is made by one of two processes, either (*a*) the Bessemer process, in which air is blown through the molten pig iron to oxidize the unwanted elements, the heat of reaction being sufficient not only to keep the steel molten, but also to raise its temperature; or (*b*) the open-hearth process, in which the molten metal is contained in a shallow hearth and heated by flames burning across the top, iron oxide being added to remove the carbon, etc. In each process any necessary additions of alloying elements are made at an appropriate stage.

The molten steel in the final stages of refining contains a considerable amount of iron oxide in solution. This may be removed by the addition of certain elements (usually manganese, silicon, or aluminium) to the metal just before pouring into the moulds. The process is known as *killing*. Unkilled steel is known as *rimming* steel. The major part of the steel used for structural purposes is *semi-killed*, i.e. de-oxidation is not carried to completion.

Finally, the steel ingots are hot-rolled to plates or sections, while the steel is at temperatures well above the A_3-temperature. During rolling, austenite grains are broken down. If rolling is completed at temperatures well above the A_3-temperature, grain growth may subsequently occur while cooling before the austenite transforms. Thick plates usually have a higher finishing temperature, unless special steps are taken to cool the steel between passes, and also cool more slowly to the A_{r3}-temperature, permitting more grain growth.

Bessemer steels generally contain a higher proportion of nitrogen, which gives higher transition temperatures in notch tests, and these steels have been forbidden for structural and shipbuilding purposes in the United Kingdom for many years.

The grain size of the steel is affected by the elements present, especially those used for de-oxidizing, aluminium in particular promoting fine grain size (see p. 58). Fully-killed and fine-grained steels have lower transition temperatures and are to be preferred where there might be a danger of brittle fracture.

Increased manganese content lowers the transition temperature and increased carbon raises it. The practice adopted has been to keep the Mn/C ratio high, thereby compensating for loss of strength due to less carbon by increase of strength due to added manganese. The ratio must not be too high, however, or trouble arises in welding.

Strain ageing (see p. 149), cold working, and any other process which normally raises the yield point of the steel and also reduces its ductility have the effect of raising the transition temperature. Fully-killed fine-grain steels show little or no strain ageing.

The high transition temperature of the steel used in a lot of the earlier welded ships was due to a low manganese content. Specifications for ship steel, which required that the steel should satisfy a tensile test, were in the course of time modified to demand a composition which would ensure a sufficiently low transition temperature. The need has since arisen for thicker plates, thicknesses of $1\frac{1}{2}$ to 2 in being needed instead of the customary maximum thickness of about 1 in. Hence the transition temperature of the plates has tended to rise again. This can be overcome, either by the use of expensive alloying elements, or by modifying rolling practice so that the plates have lower finishing temperatures, or by subjecting the rolled plates to a normalizing treatment (see p. 217) to reduce the grain size.

FATIGUE

13.15. Failure due to fatigue

Certain machine components and other structural parts subjected to loads which are repeated a large number of times, may break abruptly without any permanent deformation to herald the fracture, although these components will safely withstand even greater loads if applied once only in a steadily increasing manner, and under such conditions will show considerable plastic deformation.

As an example, a particular metal (the following values relate to a steel containing 0.5% carbon and 5% nickel) is found to have a U.T.S. of 54 Tons/in^2. Therefore it can be loaded in tension to a stress of 40 Tons/in^2 with no fear of fracture. If this load is applied repeatedly, it is found that fracture may occur after about 10^4 loadings. Or an even lower load of 30 Tons/in^2 may fracture the specimen if applied 10^5 times. This phenomenon is known as *fatigue*.

As repeated loading is encountered very frequently in engineering practice, it is necessary for a lot of attention to be paid to fatigue.

As in the case of toughness, the performance of a particular material in a tensile test is not a reliable guide to its behaviour under fatigue loading conditions. This is evident from the following results for two different types of alloy.

	Alloy	*U.T.S.*	*Stress to cause fracture after 10^8 loadings*
En 12	(1% Ni steel)	38 Tons/in^2	19 Tons/in^2
RR 88	(Al + 1% Cu, 2.7% Mg, 0.5% Mn, 5.3% Zn)	38	10

13.16. Characteristic of fatigue failures

The surface of a fatigue fracture often exhibits two zones, one a glossy smooth surface and the other a crystalline or fibrous surface as found in a broken Izod specimen. The crack usually has its origin in a minute fissure which progressively enlarges until insufficient sound metal remains in the section to support the applied load, whereupon sudden fracture occurs.

Fig. 13.9.—Fatigue fracture in circular shaft showing lines of arrest

The glossy smooth surface indicates that there has been rubbing or fretting of the surfaces of the crack against one another during its development. The crystalline or fibrous zone shows the area of the instantaneous final fracture. The crystalline appearance is more commonly found.

If the fracture has been brought about by a number of periods of application of stress separated by periods of rest, the surface of the fatigue crack is divided by a series of curved lines known as *lines of arrest*. These are thought to be due to plastic deformation due to the stress concentration at the bottom of the notch. Oxidation of the crack may also occur and help to distinguish the lines of arrest. Lines of arrest may be seen in fig. 13.9.

The pattern of the lines of arrest may assist in identifying the point of origin of the fatigue crack.

Fatigue cracks, which tend to originate from sharp corners, etc., follow a direction perpendicular to the maximum principal stress, typical paths in two components being shown in fig. 13.10.

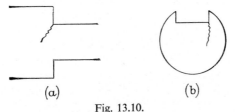

(a)   (b)

Fig. 13.10.

(a) Longitudinal section of shaft with sharp reduction in diameter

(b) Transverse section of splined shaft

Most probable path of a fatigue crack is shown in each case

13.17. Detection of fatigue cracks

If a fatigue crack can be detected before final failure has occurred, it may be possible to replace the damaged part and so avoid the consequence of a fracture.

The cracks, which are initially very fine, are detectable when about 85 to 90% of the total life of the component has been reached. Hence, once a crack is detected, it is expedient to replace the component at once. If the crack has reached the stage at which it can be seen by the naked eye, the life of the component is almost at an end.

A variety of methods for detecting cracks are available. Surface cracks may be rendered visible by painting the surface with a suitable liquid and then wiping off the excess. Any liquid which has penetrated the crack will subsequently emerge and may be observed in a variety of ways, for example, fluorescent liquids will show up in ultra-violet light. Acoustic and ultrasonic methods may detect both surface and subsurface cracks. An example of the acoustic method is the tapping of railway rolling stock wheels and listening to the " ring ".

13.18. Mechanism of fatigue failure

Under repeated stressing, it is thought that slip occurs in crystal grains, the slip planes of which are favourably oriented in or near planes of principal shear stress and which are so related to their neighbouring grains that slip is permissible under the applied stress. For example, grains which have a free surface on one side can slip more easily.

The repeated stressing will cause repeated reversal of slip so that work hardening occurs and eventually a crack will form.

191

It has been observed that slip bands develop during the cyclic stressing. Slip on adjacent slip bands may be in different directions, so that notches or peaks may form as in fig. 13.11. In certain cases, extruded tongues of

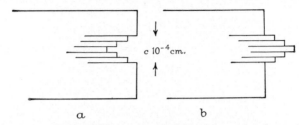

c 10^{-4} cm.

a   b

Fig. 13.11.—(a) Notch-like contour and (b) peak produced at surface by to-and-fro slip movements on adjacent slip planes. [Wood]

metal have been found by examination under the electron microscope and have an appearance which is shown schematically in fig. 13.12. The fatigue cracks develop at some of the slip bands, presumably at the bottom of the notches.

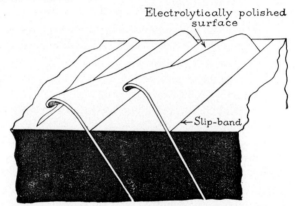

Electrolytically polished surface

←Slip-band

Fig. 13.12.—Diagrammatic representation of slip-band extrusions in aluminium-copper alloy. [Forsyth]

Orowan* has advanced a theory that at stress concentrations progressive work-hardening occurs with each reversal of stress until the local stress either reaches the rupture strength of the material after a certain number of cycles, when a crack will form, or, for a smaller amplitude of applied stress, reaches a maximum value less than the rupture stress, under which condition no fatigue failure will occur. This theory gives a relation-

* E. Orowan, *Proc. Roy. Soc.* A, Vol. 171, 1939, p. 79

ship between applied stress and number of reversals to fracture which is of the form found in practice.

This theory is founded on certain simplifying assumptions which are not completely valid, but nevertheless is considered by Pope* to be the best hypothesis yet expounded.

13.19. Fatigue testing

As components, in general, are subjected to more than one form of load at the same time, a complete range of fatigue testing must cover a large number of combinations.

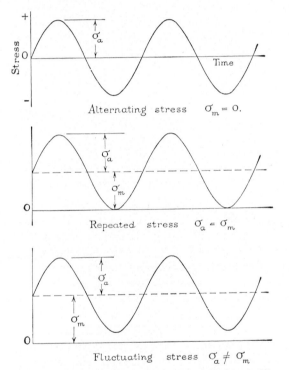

Fig. 13.13.—Forms of stress-time curves in fatigue loading

The simple type of testing would be the application of alternating tension and compression with or without a simultaneous static direct stress.

Possible forms of loading curves are shown in fig. 13.13. The first shows an alternating stress about a mean value of zero, and the other

* J. A. Pope (Ed.), *Metal Fatigue* (Chapman and Hall, 1959)

curves show a mean value that is not zero. If the semi-range of the alternating stress is σ_a and the mean stress is σ_m, then the stress varies between the limits of $\sigma_m + \sigma_a$ and $\sigma_m - \sigma_a$.

Similar series of tests can be carried out with torsional loading to give an alternating shear stress.

To simulate more closely actual conditions of service life, it might be necessary to carry out tests combining an alternating and a static stress of different types, e.g. alternating torsion with static tension. Again the two types of stress might be applied as alternating loads of different frequencies.

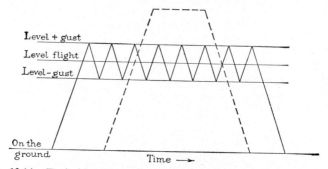

Fig. 13.14.—Typical loading curve for flight simulation in aircraft fuselage
——— wind load, – – – – cabin pressure

An example of this is the complicated series of loadings which are carried out on complete aircraft fuselages to simulate flight conditions. When on the ground the weight of the wings causes tension in their upper surfaces. When in flight, the weight of the aircraft is supported by the wings so that there is compression in the upper surface. This represents a static load to which must be added an alternating vertical load to simulate the effect of wind gusts while in flight. If the aircraft has a pressurized cabin, the pressure inside the fuselage is varied at a much lower frequency to represent the ascent into a rarified atmosphere once each flight. In certain regions of the fuselage, the stresses will be due to both these loadings. A typical simple cycle of loading is shown in fig. 13.14.

13.20. Fatigue testing machines

The principles of a few only of the more common types of machine for direct tension-compression testing are described in this section.*

* A large number of types of testing machines are described in *Manual on Fatigue Testing*, American Society for Testing Materials, Philadelphia, 1949

In the rotating bending machines, a specimen of circular cross-section is rotated while a bending moment is applied in a fixed plane through the axis of rotation. The moment may be applied as shown in fig. 13.15

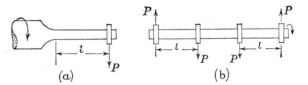

Fig. 13.15.—(*a*) Cantilever and (*b*) four-point loading for rotating bending fatigue tests. In each case the maximum bending moment is *Pl*

either as an end load to a cantilever or by four-point loading. In the latter case there is a uniform bending moment over a length of the specimen. The stress in the outer fibre will alternate between a tensile stress and a compressive stress about a mean value of zero once each revolution.

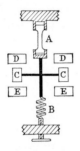

Fig. 13.16.—Haigh type fatigue machine. Specimen A given mean stress by tension spring B and alternating stress by attraction of iron C to alternately excited electromagnets D and E.

For the application of a static stress simultaneously with the alternating stress, a more complicated type of machine is needed. In the Haigh and Schenck machines (figs. 13.16 and 13.17), the static prestress is applied by a spring between the specimen and the fixed anchorage. The alternat-

Fig. 13.17.—Shenck type fatigue machine. Specimen A given mean stress by tension spring B using pre-tensioning wheel C. Unbalanced rotating masses D give oscillatory force.

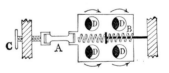

ing load is applied to the end of the specimen adjacent to the spring either by electromagnets in the Haigh machine or out-of-balance rotating masses in the Schenck machine.

The Losenhausen machine (fig. 13.18) works entirely by hydraulic pressure, an alternating pressure being applied to one side of a piston and a static pressure to the other side. The piston is connected to the specimen. The alternating pressure is derived from another cylinder in which is a driven piston, the stroke being varied to give the required stress amplitude on the specimen.

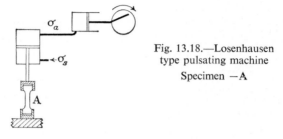

Fig. 13.18.—Losenhausen
type pulsating machine
Specimen —A

13.21. Results of fatigue tests

In completing a test cycle on a material, it is necessary to test different specimens with different values of alternating stress and for each value determine the number of cycles of stress that can be applied before fracture. The number of cycles to fracture is known as the *life N*. The

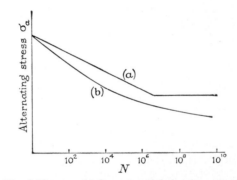

Fig. 13.19.—S-N curves (*a*) for a material showing a fatigue limit,
(*b*) for a material which does not show a fatigue limit

alternating stress is the *fatigue strength** or *endurance strength* for this life. As the stress range is reduced, for some materials a value is reached at which fracture will not occur. This value is known as the *fatigue limit* or *endurance limit*.

A plot of the semi-range of alternating stress σ_a against N on a logarithmic scale gives curves such as those in fig. 13.19, familiarly known

---

* There is some confusion in the literature over the meanings of these terms. The nomenclature used here is in conformity with that recommended in *Manual on Fatigue Testing*, with the exception of the use of σ in place of S for stress.

as *S-N* curves. Some materials represented by curve (*a*) have a well-defined fatigue limit. For components made from these materials, which are intended to have only a limited life, it is possible to use a higher permissible design stress than would be the case if the design stress were based on the fatigue limit.

Other materials, aluminium alloys for example, give a curve of the shape shown as (*b*) in fig. 13.19. With such materials it is possible to design for a limited life only.

The scatter of results in fatigue tests is relatively great, the curves shown in fig. 13.19 representing the mean value of the life at each stress range. It is found that the variation in life may be as much as 3:1 for identical polished specimens and as great as 10:1 for complete components. Due consideration must be paid to this statistical variation in accepting a stress value for a limited life.

13.22. Effect of mean stress

For any value of the mean stress σ_m, it will be possible to determine a similar *S-N* curve. As the value of σ_m is raised, the curve will appear lower on the diagram as in fig. 13.20*a*.

The variation of fatigue limit with mean stress is commonly represented on one of three types of diagram:

Goodman diagram on which $\sigma_{max} = \sigma_m + \sigma_a$ is plotted against $\sigma_{min} = \sigma_m - \sigma_a$.
Gerber diagram on which σ_a is plotted against σ_m.
Smith diagram on which both σ_{max} and σ_{min} are plotted against σ_m.

When σ_m is zero, the value of σ_a is the fatigue limit in the absence of a mean stress, and when σ_m equals the ultimate tensile stress, then σ_a is zero. The points A and B corresponding to these two values respectively are marked on the three types of diagram in fig. 13.21.

On a basis of certain experimental values for intermediate points, Goodman proposed that the intermediate values should lie on straight lines between A and B. From a study of other results, Gerber proposed that the relationship should be a parabola with its apex at A and passing through B. These curves are shown in the three diagrams in fig. 13.21. It will be noted that the Goodman diagram is merely the Gerber diagram rotated through 45°. Whereas some experimental results for mild steel follow closely the Gerber curve, and some for naval brass follow the Goodman line, in the majority of cases results lie between the two proposed curves.

For a material which does not show a fatigue limit, curves of the fatigue strengths for various lives can be shown on any of these diagrams. An example is given in fig. 13.20*b*.

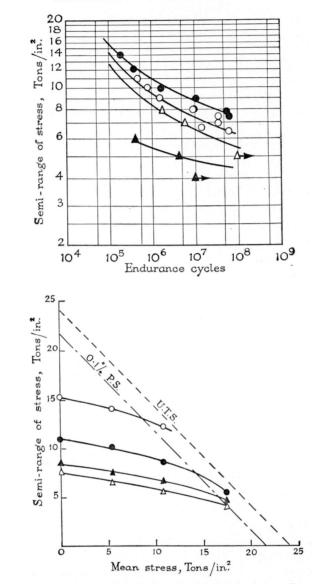

Fig. 13.20.—Results of fatigue tests on an aluminium alloy

(a) S-N curves for various values of σ_m: ● 0, ○ 5·75, △ 11·0, ▲ 17·5 Tons/in². Points with arrows signify that tests were discontinued at 10^7 and 10^8 cycles respectively, failure not having occurred.

(b) Gerber diagram showing curves for various lives ○ 10^5, ● 10^6, ▲ 10^7, △ 5 × 10^7 cycles. [Woodward, Gunn and Forrest]

198

13.23. Variation of fatigue limit

The lack of any close relationship between the fatigue limit and the ultimate tensile stress of different materials has already been mentioned (p. 180). An analysis of the results of a large number of tests has produced the frequency distribution curves shown in fig. 13.22. Although the endurance ratio (that is, the ratio of the fatigue limit to the U.T.S.) has a mean value of about 0·42, there is a considerable spread of values. The endurance ratio for any material must be determined by experiment. Its value cannot be guessed with any certainty.

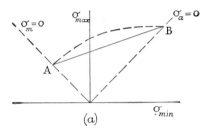
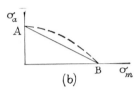

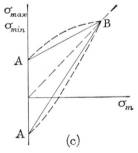

Fig. 13.21

(a) Goodman, (b) Gerber, (c) Smith diagrams for plotting fatigue test results. ———— and – – – – are Goodman's and Gerber's proposed curves. All diagrams are to the same scale.

13.24. Effect of notches

If the geometry of a component is such that there is a change of section, a hole, or a notch, which of itself will have a stress concentration factor, then the fatigue limit will be lowered.

The stress concentration factor is defined as the ratio of the maximum stress due to a hole or notch to the mean stress that would exist in the absence of the hole or notch. The theoretical value of this ratio assuming elastic behaviour is denoted by K_t.

It would appear probable that as plastic deformation is not generally observed at a fatigue fracture, there would be no reduction of stress concentration as far as the varying stress is concerned. Hence if σ_0 were the fatigue limit with no stress concentration present and σ_k the corresponding fatigue strength when a stress raiser is present, we would expect that

$$\frac{\sigma_k}{\sigma_0} = \frac{1}{K_t}$$

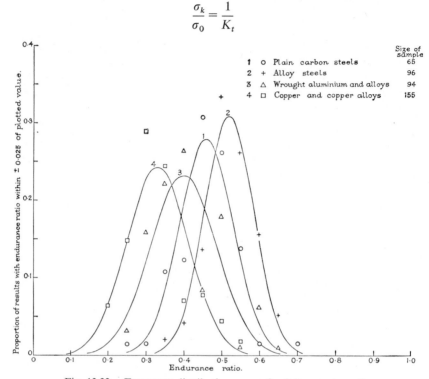

Fig. 13.22.—Frequency distribution curves for fatigue test results

[An analysis of collected data from *Fatigue of Metals and Structures* by H. J. Grover, S. A. Gordon and L. R. Jackson (Thames and Hudson, London, 1956). The curves are normal distribution curves with the same mean values and variances as the samples.]

In general this is not the case, σ_k/σ_0 being greater than $1/K_t$; that is, the reduction in fatigue strength is less than would be anticipated from theoretical considerations. The ratio σ_0/σ_k is called the *fatigue strength concentration factor* or the *fatigue strength reduction factor*, denoted by K_f. Now K_f may have any value between K_t and 1, the actual value depending upon the material, and the shape and size of the specimen. From this has been developed the *notch sensitivity index* which is defined as

$$Q = \frac{K_f - 1}{K_t - 1}$$

200

The value of Q will lie between 0 and 1, being 0 for a case which is not notch-sensitive, i.e. $\sigma_k = \sigma_0$, and 1 for a material which is 100% notch sensitive, i.e. $K_f = K_t$.

13.25. Effect of residual stress

Operations such as plastic straining, grinding, and case hardening may induce residual stresses. A tensile residual stress generally lowers the fatigue limit while a compressive residual stress is beneficial.

One method of introducing a compressive residual stress is by shot peening, and this is frequently used as a means of improving the fatigue life of components.* Shot peening is carried out by firing a stream of chilled cast iron or steel shot on to the surface.

13.26. Surface finish

A polished specimen has a higher fatigue limit than a rough turned one.

13.27. Corrosion fatigue

When a fatigue test is carried out in the presence of a corrosive medium, there is a reduction in the fatigue strength for any particular life, and the fatigue limit may disappear. Even fresh water is sufficiently corrosive to have an effect. The phenomenon will be dealt with at greater length in Chapter 16.

The usual protective coatings and corrosion inhibitors have a beneficial effect.

CREEP

13.28. Creep phenomena

In the preceding sections it has been assumed that there exists for any material a stress-strain relationship which is independent of time. In a tensile test, on applying a load in the plastic region, there is an immediate extension, but this is followed in time by further extension. In mild steel, for example, at room temperature after applying an increment of load, the strain varies rapidly at first and then at a decreasing rate. In lead, the strain can continue for a long time at a steady rate even under very low stresses. This is seen in the slow movement of lead on sloping roofs and the gradual sagging of unsupported lead pipes. The strain-time variation

---

* A. G. H. Coombs, F. Sherratt, J. A. Pope, *International Conference on Fatigue of Metals,* Inst. Mech. Engrs., 1956, p. 227

at constant load is known as *creep*. At high temperatures, steel and other materials show this steady creep, which becomes of importance in components which are exposed to high temperature during service.

13.29. Creep testing machines

Creep properties of materials are determined by keeping specimens under constant stress for long periods during which strain measurements are made by a suitable extensometer. The majority of the tests are conducted at high temperatures, necessitating a furnace surrounding the specimen and associated equipment to maintain the temperature constant within very close limits. Also to ensure constant loading, it is usual to house the apparatus in a temperature-controlled room.

The usual type of machine is a lever machine loaded by weights. One type of extensometer employed has two arms, one connected to each end of the specimen, which are parallel and long enough to extend beyond the furnace. The relative movement is determined, for example by the rotation of a small hardened steel rhomb carried between them, the rotation being measured by a telescope and scale.

13.30. Characteristics of creep curves

The extension with time during creep is greater at increased stress or temperature. A set of short-time creep curves for some lead specimens tested at room temperature is shown in fig. 13.23.

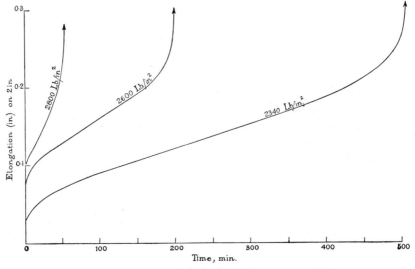

Fig. 13.23.—Creep curves for lead tested at room temperature

All creep curves are of the type shown idealized in fig. 13.24. There are four parts to the curve:

    (i) An initial instantaneous extension.
    (ii) A stage of creep at a decreasing rate.
    (iii) A stage of creep at an approximately constant rate.
    (iv) A stage of creep at an increasing rate ending in fracture.

Stages (ii), (iii), and (iv) are usually referred to as *primary*, *secondary*, and *tertiary* creep respectively.

Andrade found that the creep curves of all pure metals could be expressed by a single formula:

$$l = l_0(1 + \beta t^{1/3})e^{kt}$$

where l is the value of the length at time t, l_0 is a length, probably the length immediately after loading, and β and k are constants whose values depend upon the material, the temperature and the stress.

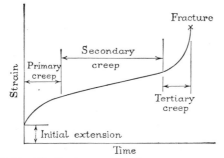

Fig. 13.24.—Idealized creep curve for test at constant load

For small values of t, this becomes

$$l \approx l_0(1 + \beta t^{1/3})$$

and the rate of extension is

$$\frac{dl}{dt} = \tfrac{1}{3}l_0\beta t^{-2/3}$$

which decreases as t increases, becoming asymptotic to zero.

For large values of t, the extension is

$$l \approx l_0\, e^{kt}$$

giving as the rate of extension

$$\frac{dl}{dt} = l_0\, ke^{kt} = lk$$

203

or

$$\frac{1}{l}\frac{dl}{dt} = k$$

Since *dl* is very small compared with *l*, *l* is almost constant, so that the creep rate in the second stage is approximately constant.

The two types of flow have been called *transient* and *quasi-viscous* flow.

If tests are conducted at constant stress, that is, the load is decreased as the cross-section decreases, the tertiary stage of increase of creep rate does not occur. In tests at constant load, the decrease of cross-section which accompanies the extension causes the stress to increase. The constant *k* is highly sensitive to small changes of stress, so that in the tertiary stage the strain rate increases rapidly.

13.31. The mechanism of creep

When a strain-hardened metal is heated above a sufficiently high temperature, recovery takes place and the metal is softened. Creep is a balance between strain hardening and thermal softening.

Various theories of creep have been proposed. The transient creep appears to be due to the movement of dislocations by thermal activation, while quasi-viscous creep at high temperatures also involves grain boundary flow.

13.32. Development of creep-resisting alloys

As creep is largely a matter of movement of dislocations, any form of obstacle used for blocking dislocations will reduce creep. Many of the obstacles used to give room-temperature strength do not remain at high temperatures. For example, in heat-treated plain carbon steels, martensite breaks down on tempering and the carbide, cementite, becomes less dispersed, producing softening; at higher temperatures eventually all the carbide dissolves in the austenite, so that these have poor creep resistance. In alloy steels containing strong carbide-forming elements such as chromium, tungsten, vanadium, and molybdenum (see Chapter 15) the carbides remain in a finely dispersed condition to much higher temperatures, and creep-resistance properties are satisfactory up to about 550° C in low-alloy steels and to higher temperatures in some high-alloy steels. For use at higher temperatures, the type of steel used must also be resistant to oxidation.

The most successful creep-resistant alloys developed for gas turbines, etc., are the Nimonic series. These are based on an 80/20 nickel-chromium alloy which has excellent resistance to oxidation at high temperatures.

Addition of alloys which by suitable heat treatment will give dispersed precipitates stable at high temperatures give the desired creep-resistant properties. One of the more important is a titanium-aluminium phase which is obtained by a prolonged solution treatment at about 1100° C followed by air cooling and precipitation treatment at 700° C.

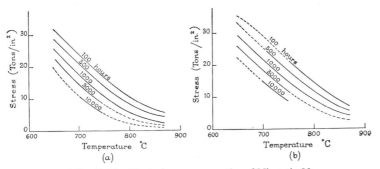

Fig. 13.25.—Typical creep properties of Nimonic 90
(*a*) Stress to produce 0·2% creep strain, and (*b*) stress to produce rupture
in certain times at various temperatures

13.33. Presentation of creep results

The variables involved are the strain, stress, temperature, and time. In two dimensions data are presented as:

(i) variation with temperature of the stress to produce a stated amount of strain or rupture in various times, and

(ii) variation with time of the stress to produce various amounts of strain or rupture at a stated temperature.

Examples for Nimonic 90 are shown in figs. 13.25 and 13.26.

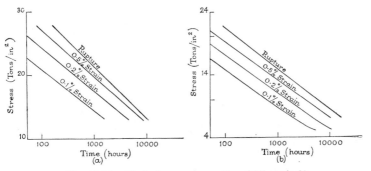

Fig. 13.26.—Typical creep properties of Nimonic 90
Stress to produce certain strains or rupture in various times at (*a*) 700° C, (*b*) 750° C.

[Figs. 13.25 and 13.26 redrawn from *The Nimonic Alloys: Design Data* (Henry Wiggin and Co. Ltd., Birmingham).]

205

13.34. Creep and design

Creep tests that reproduce operating conditions of load and temperature are necessarily long-term, so that it would be desirable to predict behaviour from more short-term tests. This would involve determining the dependence of β and k upon temperature and stress, and extrapolation of the results—a rather unreliable procedure. However, comparison of short-term tests with those of already proved materials will indicate whether a newly developed material is likely to show promise.

It will be seen from fig. 13.26 that a small increase of temperature can greatly increase the creep rate; for example, the creep rate between 0·1 and 0·2% strain is increased by twenty times when the temperature is raised from 650° to 700° C or from 700° to 750° C.

In gas turbines, blades are designed within close creep limits for a limited life.

CHAPTER 14

Heat Treatment of Steel

14.1. Introduction

Heat treatment is the term that describes in a general manner an operation or series of operations which involve the heating and cooling of a metal or alloy in the solid state, carried out for the purpose of obtaining certain desired properties.

The properties of steels can be varied over a very wide range by heat treatment, which is one of the reasons for the great usefulness of steels. The heat treatment of steels is generally taken to embrace the martensitic change which occurs on quenching from the austenitic state and the softening which results from the subsequent tempering. These changes have already been mentioned in Section 11.7. The actual heat treatment employed depends upon the values of mechanical properties desired. Thus if high hardness is needed, the treatment may consist solely of quenching, but if high toughness is needed, then a high-temperature tempering must also be given. Generally, a full heat treatment is employed to give an all-round improvement in properties.

The behaviour of pure iron-carbon alloys will be discussed in this chapter, the effect of alloy additions being considered in Chapter 15. The transformations that occur on heating and cooling are first considered separately.

14.2. Transformations on heating

A hypoeutectoid steel which has been slowly cooled under almost equilibrium conditions consists at room temperature of grains of pro-eutectoid ferrite and grains of pearlite as in fig. 8.11*a–b*. If the steel is heated to any temperature below the A_{c1}-temperature and then cooled, no alteration of structure will occur, but if it is heated to just above this temperature, the pearlite will transform to austenite.

The mechanism of the change is one of nucleation and growth, the nucleation occuring at points on the ferrite-cementite interfaces in the eutectoid. Once formed, these nuclei of austenite grow by absorbing both ferrite and cementite until each pearlite grain has completely changed to austenite. As the change is proceeding, the carbon diffuses from the original cementite regions until it is homogeneously distributed within each austenite grain. Because the diffusion of carbon is not instantaneous, but occurs at a finite rate, time plays a part and the transformation

$$\text{ferrite} + \text{FeC}_3 \rightleftharpoons \text{austenite}$$

is slow compared with the allotropic change from α to γ-iron when carbon is absent.

As the temperature is slowly raised above the A_{c1}-temperature, the pro-eutectoid ferrite becomes absorbed by the growth of the austenite grains, the transformation being complete at the A_{c3}-temperature.

In hypereutectoid steels, a similar process occurs, the pearlite being transformed to austenite at the A_{c13}-temperature and the pro-eutectoid cementite dissolving in the austenite between the A_{c13} and the A_{cm}-temperatures.

Each pearlite grain may give rise to several austenite nuclei, so that the austenite grain size just above the A_{c3}-temperature is smaller than the previous ferrite-pearlite grain size. On heating the austenite to higher temperatures, the grain size increases by a process of absorption of some grains by others. The character of the grain-size/temperature relationship is discussed in Section 14.10.

14.3. Transformations on cooling

As a hypoeutectoid steel is slowly cooled from above the A_{c3}-temperature, pro-eutectoid ferrite will begin to separate from the austenite at the A_{r3}-temperature. Since the α-iron dissolves only a very small amount of carbon, most of the carbon diffuses into the remaining austenite, thereby lowering the temperature for further change, until the eutectoid composition is reached. The remaining austenite then transforms to pearlite at the eutectoid temperature. As the pro-eutectoid ferrite separates, it migrates to the austenite grain boundary.

When the eutectoid temperature is reached, nuclei of cementite form at the austenite grain boundary. These contain a higher proportion of carbon than the eutectoid austenite, so that carbon diffuses from the adjacent austenite, which immediately transforms to ferrite. Alternate layers of cementite and ferrite thus form and grow edgewise into the austenite grain. The method of growth is shown diagrammatically in fig. 14.1.

A hypereutectoid steel cooled from the austenite region will first precipitate cementite which migrates to the grain boundaries and forms a network structure which is visible at room temperature (fig. 8.11d). As this proceeds, the carbon content of the remaining austenite decreases until it is of eutectiod composition, when it transforms at constant temperature to pearlite.

The pearlite that forms from the eutectoid austenite does so by separation of ferrite and cementite, which involves diffusion of carbon, and therefore its formation takes a finite time. If the steel is cooled more rapidly, a lower temperature is reached before the change is complete. At lower temperatures, diffusion is less rapid, so that the spacing of the pearlite lamellae is smaller. The finer distribution results in a modification of the physical properties.

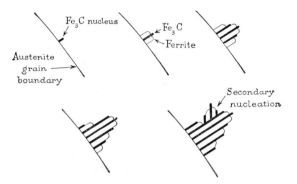

Fig. 14.1.—Diagrammatic representation of pearlite formation

14.4. Quenching temperature and rate

When austenite is cooled extremely rapidly, the change to ferrite and cementite is suppressed and martensite is formed. As stated on p. 153 this is extremely hard and brittle and may be softened by tempering. If the steel is quenched from a temperature at which it is not 100% austenite, then the ferrite or cementite present at that temperature will be unchanged on quenching, and during any subsequent tempering. Hence to get the best effects from heat treatment the quenching should be carried out from above the A_{c3}-temperature for hypoeutectoid steels and above the A_{cm}-temperature for hypereutectoid steels. The cementite present in hypereutectoid steels between the A_{c13} and A_{cm}-temperature is, however, hard and can contribute significantly to the final hardness in the quenched and in the tempered states. The danger of cracking on quenching high-carbon steels is great and is reduced by quenching from lower temperatures. It is usual to quench hypereutectoid steels from just above the A_{c13}-temperature. In practice, to ensure that the temperature throughout the test piece has reached the required value and that the desired changes on heating have been completed, it is usual to quench from a temperature about 50° above the A_{c1} or A_{c13}-temperature as shown in fig. 14.2.

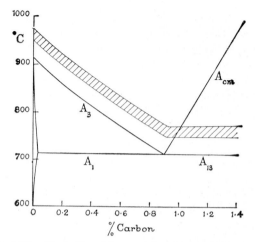

Fig. 14.2.—Shaded band is approximate temperature range used for austenizing carbon steels prior to quenching

In order to transform the austenite present at the quenching temperature to 100% martensite, it is necessary to cool the steel faster than some minimum rate—the *critical cooling rate*. The critical cooling rate depends upon the carbon content, varying in the manner shown in fig. 14.3.

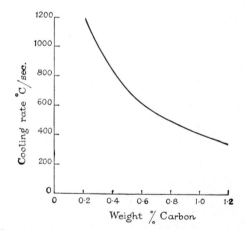

Fig. 14.3.—Variation of critical cooling rate with carbon content of carbon steels

If the rate of cooling is less than the critical cooling rate, the structure may contain some martensite together with either ferrite or pearlite, or bainite (see p. 212), or a mixture of these.

14.5. Isothermal transformation diagrams

In cases where the austenite is not transformed completely to martensite, the other changes involve nucleation and grain growth processes
which occur at varying temperatures. As both nucleation and grain
growth rates are temperature-dependent, a fundamental investigation
should study the rates at which the changes would occur at a constant
temperature.

Isothermal investigations involve the study of the times required for
initiation and completion of changes at various sub-critical temperatures,
and the nature of the transformation products.

The method originally used by Davenport and Bain* was to study the
progress of transformation microscopically. Small pieces of the steel
under investigation (about the size of a sixpence is reasonable) are used
so that their temperature can be changed rapidly. These are heated to a
temperature above the upper critical temperature for long enough to be
austenized, and then in turn cooled instantaneously by quenching in a
suitable liquid bath held at the temperature under investigation. Each
piece is held at this temperature for a different length of time and then
quenched in cold water. The liquid bath may be a molten metal such as
lead, or a neutral salt of the type used for tempering baths. This procedure
is carried out over a range of sub-critical temperatures.

At the sub-critical temperature, some or all of the austenite may
transform to the transformation products appropriate to that temperature.
Upon quenching in water, any unchanged austenite will form martensite,
while the transformation products do not change. The final structure of
the specimen can be found by suitable etching and examination under a
microscope.

It is found that definite times are required for the initiation and completion of the transformation and that these times vary with the temperature. The progress of the transformation can also be studied and times
for (say) 10%, 50% and 90% transformation found.

Any other property that changes with proportion of austenite can also
be used as a guide to the progress of transformation, although the nature
of the transformation products cannot be identified other than by microscopic examination. In an investigation utilizing the method of Davenport
and Bain, it is convenient to follow the progress of the transformation by
hardness tests. A hardness test is quickly carried out on each specimen as
it is quenched. The results obtained can be used to indicate whether
transformation has started, is continuing, or has completed at the trans-

---

* E. S. Davenport and E. C. Bain, *Trans. Amer. Inst. Min. Met. Engrs.*, Vol. 90, 1930, pp. 117–154.

formation time investigated, and guidance can be immediately obtained as to the next time of quench required without awaiting the laborious preparation for microscopic examination, which can follow later. A typical set of results is given in fig. 14.4.

Dilatation (see p. 92) is another property which is commonly used for transformation studies,* particularly for transformations taking longer times, such as one hour or more.

The complete diagram for a eutectoid steel is shown in fig. 14.5. As the transformation temperature is lowered from the A_{13}-temperature to about 550°, the nucleation and completion time decrease and the pearlite lamellae become finer.

From about 550° to 250° C, the nucleation and completion times increase and the transformation product is *bainite*. Bainite is composed of the two equilibrium phases, ferrite and cementite, but differs from pearlite in appearance and in the method of growth. Two theories have been put forward for the formation of bainite.† In both it is postulated that the ferrite nucleates first, in contrast with pearlite where cementite nucleates first. The microstructure appears somewhat different at the upper and lower ends of the temperature range. Fig. 14.6 shows the development of a lower bainite structure during isothermal transformation.

The point of minimum nucleation time is known as the *nose* or *knee*.

Below about 250° C, martensite is formed. This is not a nucleation process and takes place almost instantaneously, but the amount formed depends upon the temperature. The upper and lower limits of the martensite transformation range are called the M_S and M_F-temperatures. The experimental procedure for determining these temperatures, introduced by Greninger and Troiano‡ is as follows. The specimen is quenched to the temperature being investigated, then reheated to some elevated temperature that is below the A_{13}-temperature and held for a time to temper the martensite already formed. It is then quenched in cold water, when the unchanged austenite transforms to martensite. When etched and examined under the microscope, the tempered and untempered martensite are readily distinguished. Care must be taken that the tempering temperature and time are chosen so that no other transformation products are formed. The temperature-time cycle is shown in fig. 14.7.

The complete isothermal transformation diagrams are also known as

---

* N. P. Allen, L. B. Pfeil, W. T. Griffiths, *Second Report of the Alloy Steels Research Committee*, Iron and Steel Institute, Special Report No. 24, 1939, Section XIII, pp. 369–390.

† A. Hultgren, *Trans. Amer. Soc. Metals*, Vol. 39, 1947, pp. 915–985. T. Ko and S. A. Cottrell, *Iron and Steel Inst.*, Vol. 172, 1952, pp. 307–313.
See also K. J. Irvine and F. B. Pickering, *J. Iron and Steel Inst.*, Vol. 188, 1958, pp. 101–112 for further work confirming the theory of Ko and Cottrell.

‡ A. B. Greninger and A. R. Troiano, *Trans. Amer. Soc. Metals*, Vol. 28, 1940, pp. 537–562.

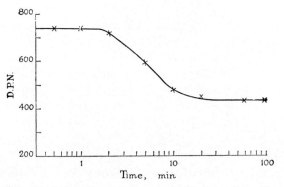

Fig. 14.4.—Typical hardness-time curves for isothermal transformation of En 26 steel at 340° C. Microstructures (fig. 14.6) show more bainite and less martensite for longer transformation times.

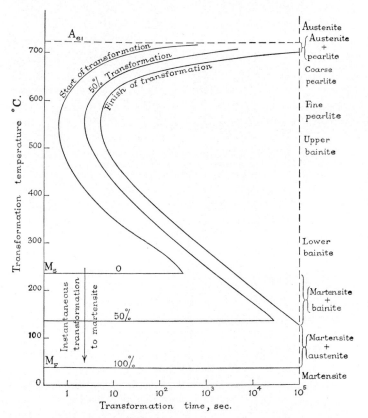

Fig. 14.5.—Isothermal transformation diagram for a eutectoid steel. Structures present after 10^5 seconds are given on the right-hand side

213

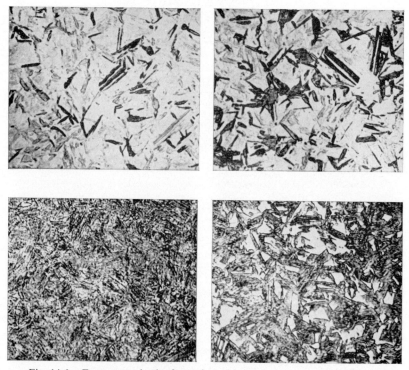

Fig. 14.6.—Four stages in the formation of lower bainite in a $2\frac{1}{2}\%$ Ni-Cr-Mo high-carbon steel (En 26), austenized at 835° C, and isothermally transformed for the times indicated at 340° C. ($\times$ 850). [International Nickel]

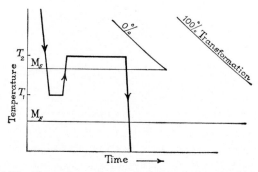

Fig. 14.7.—Temperature-time cycle for determination of martensite transformation temperatures. Martensite formed at temperature T_1 is tempered at temperature T_2 and can be distinguished from martensite formed in final quench.

Time-Temperature-Transformation diagrams, TTT or triple-T diagrams and, because of their shape, S-curves.

14.6. Isothermal transformation diagrams for hypoeutectoid and hyper-eutectoid steels

The isothermal transformation diagram for a typical hypoeutectoid steel is shown in fig. 14.8. Between the A_3 and A_1-temperatures, ferrite nucleates and grows, and austenite transforms to the extent indicated by

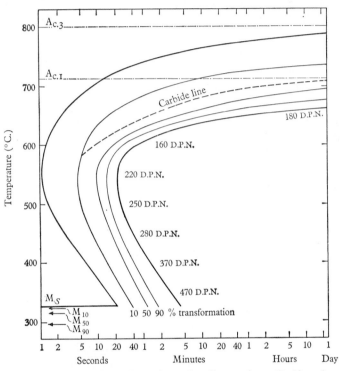

Fig. 14.8.—Isothermal transformation diagram for an En 12 steel (0·34% C, 1·06% Mn, 0·75% Ni). The hardness values are those of the fully transformed steel. [after International Nickel]

the equilibrium diagram. Below the A_1-temperature, ferrite nucleates first, followed by pearlite. The time at which pearlite starts to form at any particular temperature is shown by the *carbide* line. The start of the pearlite formation does not mean the end of proeutectoid formation, but is a close approximation to it. Thus at lower temperatures, the amount of pro-eutectoid ferrite decreases, and the ratio of ferrite to cementite in

215

the pearlite alters, so that the microstructure suggests that the steel has a higher carbon content. The bainite formation is not preceded by ferrite formation.

The diagram for a hypereutectoid steel would be similar, only cementite being nucleated at first and pearlite later.

14.7. Separation of pearlite and bainite knees

From the diagrams for plain carbon steels, it is not clear why the formation of pearlite should become more *rapid* as the sub-critical temperature is lowered, whilst the formation of bainite becomes *slower*

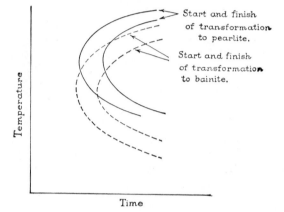

Fig. 14.9.—Nucleation and transformation time for pearlite and bainite structures

as the temperature is lowered, or why there is a change in the transformation product. The diagrams for some alloy steels help to clarify these points.

Each type of transformation has its own knee or temperature of maximum rate of nucleation as shown in fig. 14.9. At any sub-critical temperature, the mechanism which has the shorter nucleation and growth time will give the product. In alloy steels, the knees become much more separated than in plain carbon steels, giving curves of the type shown in fig. 14.10.

14.8. Continuous cooling transformation

In a similar manner it is possible to plot on a temperature-time graph points marking the beginning and end of transformation in the case of continuous cooling of steels. The results so obtained cannot be derived quantitatively from an isothermal transformation diagram, but a qualitative correlation is possible and helpful. A set of typical continuous cooling transformation curves is shown in fig. 14.11. A slow cool in the furnace, such as curve (*a*) would yield coarse pearlite, while slightly faster cooling in air such as curve (*b*) would give fine pearlite. Such treatments

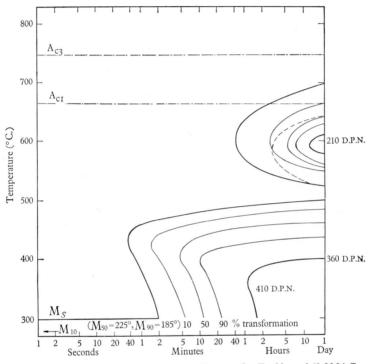

Fig. 14.10.—Isothermal transformation diagram for En 23 steel (0·33% C, 0·57% Mn, 3·26% Ni, 0·85% Cr). [after International Nickel]

are known as *annealing** and *normalizing* respectively. At faster rates of cooling, the transformation occurs at lower temperatures, that is, the A_r-temperatures fall as the cooling rate is increased.

Curve (*c*) would correspond to a cooling rate such as that obtained on quenching a large piece of steel in oil. Some of the austenite would transform to fine pearlite, but when the temperature had fallen below that of the pearlite knee, pearlite formation would cease. There is insufficient time for bainite to form, and the remaining austenite will transform to

---

* This is not the same as *process annealing*, which is heating to a temperature just below A_{c1}. No phase change occurs, but internal stresses due to mechanical working are relieved, producing some softening.

martensite between the M_S and M_F-temperatures. This is called a *split transformation* and occurs at cooling rates just slower than the critical cooling rate.

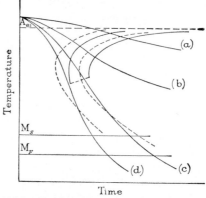

Fig. 14.11.—Continuous cooling transformation curves and cooling curves. Dashed lines show relative position of isothermal transformation curves.

Curve (d) corresponds to the critical cooling rate and is tne slowest rate at which only martensite is formed.

The continuous cooling curves lie at somewhat longer times and lower temperatures than the isothermal transformation curves for the same steel.

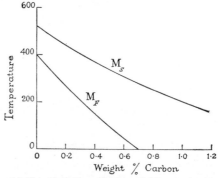

Fig. 14.12.—Variation of M_S and M_F-temperatures with carbon content

From Donald S. Clark and Wilbur R. Varney, *Physical Metallurgy for Engineers*. Copyright 1952, D. Van Nostrand Co., Inc., Princeton, New Jersey.

14.9. Retained austenite

The variation of the M_S and M_F-temperatures with carbon content is shown in fig. 14.12. Above 0·7% carbon the M_F-temperature is below 0° C, so that quenching higher-carbon steels into ice-cold water will not produce 100% martensite. The *retained austenite* is much softer than martensite and is an undesirable factor in the usual heat treatment cycle.

It has been found that if cooling is interrupted between the M_S and M_F-temperatures, not only does the transformation to martensite cease, but the remaining austenite acquires an increased stability, so that on subsequent cooling, the transformation does not start until the temperature has been lowered by a distinct amount. The extent of this *stabilization of austenite* depends upon the temperature and on the duration of the interruption.

A large-sized specimen, even with the most severe quenching, may not cool faster than the critical cooling rate, so that it may not be possible to get 100% martensite. This *mass effect* and related phenomena are dealt with further in Sections 14.15–14.20.

14.10. Grain size of steel and its effects

The rate of transformation of a steel at any given temperature is also dependent upon the grain size of the austenite. The transformation to ferrite and cementite structures involves the growth of the new structures from the austenite grain boundary, and the rate of growth normal to the grain boundary is dependent upon the diffusion rate of carbon. At any constant temperature the diffusion rate is constant, and so it is to be expected that the transformation time is longer for coarse-grained austenite. It is found that this is so and also that the time for transformation to start is longer. Isothermal transformation diagrams for two grain sizes of the same steel are compared in fig. 14.13. The coarser-grained steel has the lower critical cooling rate.

The grain size of the ferrite-pearlite structure at room temperature is dependent upon the austenite grain size, a coarser-grained austenite giving a coarser room-temperature structure. The relationship is, however, only qualitative, and for hypoeutectoid steels the austenite grain size cannot be determined directly from the ferrite grain size.

As stated on p. 208 each pearlite grain gives several austenite grains when heated through the critical temperature range, so that the grains are refined. Grain refinement of a steel is normally done by heating and cooling through the critical range a sufficient number of times. There is a limit to the smallness of grain that can be attained by this means, the A.S.T.M. value being about 5 to 8.

On heating further into the austenite region, the equilibrium grain size increases by the process of large grains absorbing the smaller ones. There are two distinct patterns to the grain-size/temperature relationship which are shown in fig. 14.14. An *inherently coarse-grained* steel shows

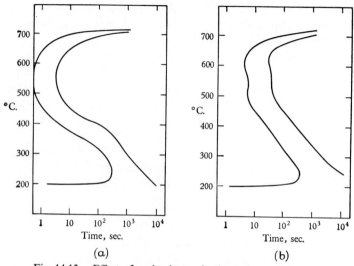

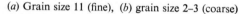

Fig. 14.13.—Effect of grain size on isothermal transformation
diagram of a eutectoid steel

(a) Grain size 11 (fine), (b) grain size 2–3 (coarse)

From Donald S. Clark and Wilbur R. Varney, *Physical Metallurgy for Engineers.* Copyright 1952, D. Van Nostrand Co., Inc., Princeton, New Jersey.

grain growth in a steady manner from the A_{c3}-temperature, upwards, whereas an *inherently fine-grained* steel remains at constant grain size for 100° to 200° above the upper critical temperature, after which the rate of growth is high.

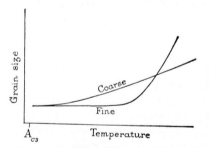

Fig. 14.14.—Grain growth of inherently
fine and coarse-grained steels

The difference in the grain-growth tendency of different steels has been found to depend upon small alloy additions, particularly those used in killing (see p. 185). Aluminium produces fine-grained steels and silicon gives coarse-grained steels.

As the austenizing of steels is usually carried out at about 50 to 100° C above the upper critical temperature, the inherent grain size of the steel is important because of the relationship of various properties to grain size.

Although coarse-grained austenite gives a lower critical cooling rate, small austenitic grain size produces steels which are tougher and more favourable for heat treatment, being non-warping and having less possibility of cracking and less retained austenite on quenching. Hence for heat treatment and general purposes, fine-grained steels are favoured, while lower critical cooling rates, when required, are obtained by other means (see p. 236).

14.11. Determination of austenite grain size

As the size of austenite grains cannot be observed directly, indirect methods have to be used, that is to say, by observing the transformation products. The method used depends upon the carbon content.

A *hypoeutectoid steel* is either cooled slowly for sufficient time for ferrite separation to start and then quenched, or else cooled at a steady intermediate rate which gives a split transformation. The ferrite formed will have migrated to the austenite grain boundaries before the remainder changes to martensite, and so outlines the original austenite grains.

During the slow cooling of *near-eutectoid* and all *hypereutectoid steels*, pro-eutectoid ferrite or cementite forms at the grain boundaries before the remainder changes to pearlite.

When *eutectoid steels* are quenched at a rate slightly less than the critical cooling rate, transformation to pearlite begins at the grain boundaries before the remainder changes to martensite. An alternative method for eutectoid steels is to quench to 100% martensite, temper at about 300° C, and quench in water, after which etching with a special solution developed by Vilella will reveal the former austenite grain boundaries.

14.12. Tempering

In the tempering cycle, the structure and mechanical properties are determined by the tempering temperature and the time at that temperature. The changes proceed rapidly at first and then slow down, the rate of change being very slow after about 30 minutes. At the tempering temperature the carbon atoms are able to diffuse and give a precipitate of cementite, leaving areas of ductile ferrite. The size of the cementite particles increases, and their number decreases as the tempering temperature is raised, so that there are fewer obstacles to dislocation movement. The structure is called tempered martensite (see fig. 14.15b), but may also be known as *troostite* or *sorbite*, or (for tempering temperatures just below the A_1-temperature) *spherodite*.

Recent research work using electron-microscope techniques[*] has shown that the initial precipitation of carbide is a hexagonal close-packed ε-carbide, which then forms thin platelets of orthorhombic cementite.

[*] E. D. Hyam and J. Nutting, *J. Iron and Steel Inst.*, Vol. 184, 1956, p. 148

The structure of the ε-carbide has not been definitely established, but it has a composition between Fe_3C and Fe_2C. From the platelets of cementite a microstructure of spheroidal cementite develops which then

(*a*)

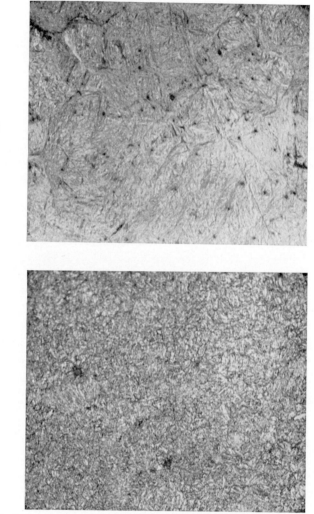

(*b*)

Fig. 14.15.—Microstructures of (*a*) martensite ($\times$ 200), (*b*) 0·53% C steel, water quenched and tempered at 350° C ($\times$ 200)

coarsens by diffusion of carbon from the smaller spheroids to the larger spheroids. Thus large particles grow at the expense of the small. The process gets slower and slower, but changes are still occurring after 100 hours at the tempering temperature. However, raising the temperature by about 50° produces the same mechanical properties in 1 hour as would 100 hours at the lower temperature. In practice, tempering times of ½ to 2 hours are used.

14.13. Mechanical property changes with tempering

Tempering increases the ductility and toughness above that of the as-quenched structure and decreases the hardness. As the tempering temperature is raised, all the mechanical properties alter. It is usual to show these changes in a *tempering diagram* or *property chart*, a typical example of which is shown in fig. 14.16.

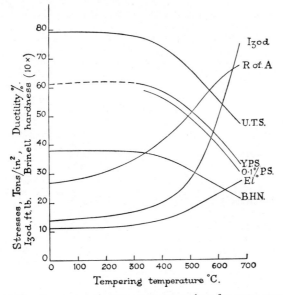

Fig. 14.16.—Tempering diagram or property chart for water-quenched 1⅛-in diameter bars of En 12 steel. [after International Nickel]

The general features are that increasing the tempering temperature increases ductility and toughness, while decreasing strength and hardness. The tempering temperature is chosen to give a desired combination of properties.

In certain cases, tempering can produce brittleness as shown by an Izod test. Some steels show an increase of Izod energy with tempering temperature up to 200° C and then a drop in the range up to 450°, after which it rises in the normal way. This is known as *brittle temper*, and for successful heat treatment the brittle tempering range must be avoided.

The cause is not fully understood. It may be due to the conversion of retained austenite to martensite or bainite. It is more pronounced in alloy steels.

Temper brittleness is a trouble found with many alloy steels. After tempering at 550 to 600° C, a slow cool leads to a low Izod value, but a rapid quench from the tempering temperature gives a satisfactory value. In steels where this is likely to occur, it can be prevented by incorporating $\frac{1}{2}\%$ of molybdenum in the composition. The reason for it is unknown.

At about 300° C mild steel shows a loss of toughness and ductility, and so is unsuitable for working at this temperature. This is *blue brittleness* and is not connected with tempering.

14.14. Special heat treatments

Two special heat treatments have been devised for cases involving large sections, where a water quench would be likely to produce cracking and a slower quench would not produce sufficient martensite. On

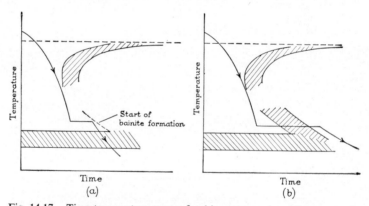

Fig. 14.17.—Time-temperature curves for (*a*) martempering, (*b*) austempering

quenching a large specimen to room temperature, the outside cools rapidly and transforms to martensite. The centre cools more slowly and transforms later, accompanied by dilatation, which can crack the brittle outer skin. The treatments which avoid this cracking are based on the isothermal transformation diagram.

In *martempering* (fig. 14.17*a*), the steel is cooled rapidly to a temperature just above M_S and held until the temperature becomes uniform through the specimen. As the time for initiation of bainite formation is so long at this temperature, there will be no transformation, and hence no stresses set up which could cause cracking. The steel is then allowed to cool slowly to room temperature during which process martensite forms uniformly through the specimen. The steel can then be tempered if desired.

In *austempering* (fig. 14.17*b*), the steel is also quenched to a temperature just above M_S and is then held at that temperature until transformation to lower bainite is complete. The properties of lower bainite are almost as good as, and in some cases superior to those of tempered martensite.

14.15. Hardenability

The ability to form martensite in a steel is dependent upon the critical cooling rate as well as on the size of the specimen and the manner in which it is quenched. If a series of bars of the same steel but of different diameters are quenched and sectioned, the variation in hardness across

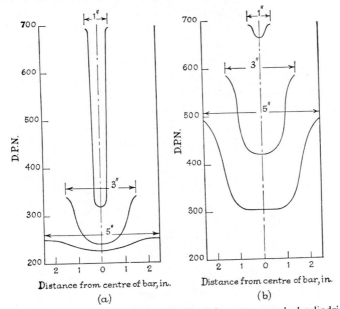

Fig. 14.18.—Variation of hardness with depth in water-quenched cylindrical bars of (*a*) a plain carbon steel, (*b*) a 1% Cr-V alloy steel

the section changes with size. A typical set of results is shown in fig. 14.18*a*. For the smallest bar, the centre is considerably softer than the outside. As the bar size increases, the centre gets softer, and eventually the outside also. This is because the rate of cooling is lower towards the centre of each bar and also decreases as the size of bar is increased, so that a smaller proportion of martensite is formed. A similar series of results for a steel of lower critical cooling rate is shown in fig. 14.18*b*. The hardness is more uniform across the smallest bar, and there is less decrease of hardness as the size of bar is increased.

The effect of size of specimen on the as-quenched hardness of a steel is known as the *mass effect*. The ability of a steel to form martensite when cooled at various rates is measured by its *hardenability*. A material with a higher hardenability will form martensite in larger sections on quenching. It is not related to the actual hardness of the martensite formed, which is almost solely dependent upon the carbon content of the steel. Hardenability is in effect the reciprocal of the critical cooling rate.

The properties of a tempered steel as shown in a property chart usually refer to the effect of tempering a structure that is 100% martensite. If the cooling rate during the quench is less than the critical cooling rate, so that the structure is only partly martensite—a *slack-quenched* structure—only the martensite portion will be affected on tempering. The resulting combination of properties is not so good as that obtained by tempering a structure of 100% martensite. Hence the potential mechanical properties of a steel are not fully exploited if the size of a component and the manner of quenching are such that the as-quenched structure is not 100% martensite. The steel to be chosen for a particular application should therefore be one with a sufficient hardenability.

14.16. Measurement of hardenability

Two types of test for the measurement of hardenability will be described here. They are both appropriate for use with steels of medium hardenability. The first is the cylinder series test which gives a single value for hardenability, that being the diameter of the bar which gives a certain percentage of martensite at the centre when quenched in a certain manner, and the second is the Jominy end quench test which gives a curve.

14.17. Cylinder series test

In the cylinder series test devised by Grossmann and others,* a series of round bars of different diameters are austenized and quenched in oil or water. The length of each bar must be sufficiently large for the cooling effect at the mid-length to be unaffected by the ends. After quenching,

---

* M. A. Grossmann, M. Asimow, and S. F. Urban, " Hardenability, Its Relation to Quenching and some Quantitative Data," *Hardenability Symposium*, Amer. Soc. for Metals, Cleveland, Ohio, 1938, pp. 124–196.

each bar is cut in half and a hardness survey made along a diameter, or the microstructure examined after etching. Fig. 14.18 shows typical hardness traverses for two steels. As it is not possible to identify with any precision the depth to which 100% martensite is formed, the hardened zone is specified as that region in which the martensite forms more than a certain percentage of the microstructure. The value usually specified is 50%. From a graph in which the diameter at which 50% martensite occurs is plotted against bar diameter, we can estimate the diameter of bar that would show 50% martensite at the centre. This is called the *critical diameter* for that quenching medium. Because the rate of cooling is less for an oil quench than for a water quench, the critical diameter of any steel will be less for oil quenching than for water quenching.

The quenching condition can be denoted quantitatively by the severity of quench H which is given by

$$H = \frac{\text{heat transfer coefficient between steel and quenching fluid}}{\text{thermal conductivity of steel}}$$

The most severe quench would be one with an H-value of infinity, corresponding to the surface layer of the bar immediately reaching the temperature of the quenching medium. The critical diameter for such an idealized and unrealizable condition is called the *ideal critical diameter*. By considering the thermal flow problem involved in the cooling of a quenched bar, the sizes of bar that would give the same rate of fall of temperature at the centre under quenches of different H, the relation between critical diameter, ideal critical diameter, and severity of quench can be determined. Some of the results obtained by Grossmann and others are shown in fig. 14.19. The values of severity of quench for different quenching conditions referred to a still water quench as unity are given in Table 14.1.

TABLE 14.1

Agitation of quenching medium	Movement of piece	Severity of quench			
		Air	Oil	Water	Brine
None	None	0·02	0·3	1·0	2·2
None	Moderate	—	0·4–0·6	1·5–3·0	—
None	Violent	—	0·6–0·8	3·0–6·0	7·5
Violent or spray		—	1·0–1·7	6·0–12·0	—

The relationship between ideal critical diameters for different specified percentages of martensite is shown in fig. 14.20.

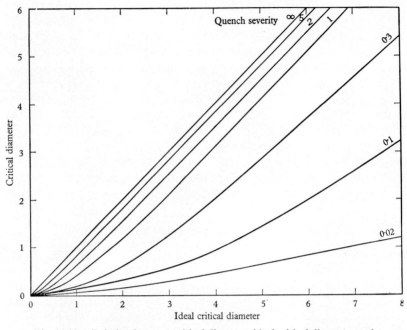

Fig. 14.19.—Relation between critical diameter, ideal critical diameter, and severity of quench

From Donald S. Clark and Wilbur R. Varney, *Physical Metallurgy for Engineers.* Copyright 1952. D Van Nostrand Co., Inc., Princeton, New Jersey.

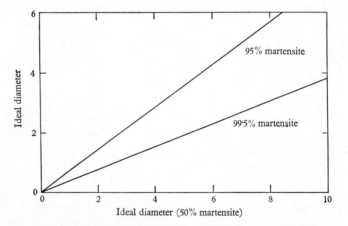

Fig 14.20.—Relationship between ideal critical diameters for different martensite microstructures. [after *Metals Handbook*]

14.18. Jominy end-quench test

This is a simpler test requiring one specimen only. A specimen of standard dimensions, as shown in fig. 14.21, is austenized and then transferred very quickly from the furnace to an apparatus in which it is supported by one end and the other end is subjected to a jet of water which

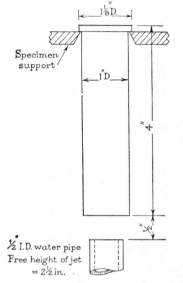

Fig. 14.21.—Jominy end-quench specimen mounted in quenching rig

can be supplied via a quick-acting valve immediately the specimen is in place. The specimen is cooled, the rate of cooling varying along the length of the bar. When the specimen is cold, a flat, 0·015 in deep, is ground along the length of the specimen. Hardness measurements are made along this flat and presented in a graph plotted against distance from the quenched end. Some typical curves are shown in fig. 14.22.

14.19. Relation of ideal critical diameter to end-quench curve

The rate of cooling at any point along the length of a Jominy bar can be determined either by thermal flow calculations or by measurement. Also the rate of cooling during quenching at various points on sections of round bars can be determined. It may be assumed that points that have the same rate of cooling will develop the same hardness, and hence the hardness variation across the section of a round bar can be predicted from the end-quench curve. Because the cooling-curve shapes differ in

229

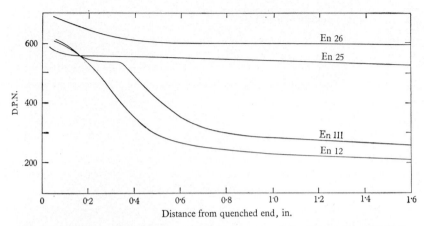

Fig. 14.22.—Some typical Jominy end-quench curves. [after International Nickel]

the two cases, the relationship depends on the cooling-rate criterion used. For equal average rates of cooling over the temperature range 700° to 500° C, the curves in fig. 14.23 apply.

If the position on the Jominy bar at which the structure is 50% martensite can be identified, the size of round bar that would give this structure at its centre can be deduced from fig. 14.23. This value is the critical diameter for oil quenching. The 50% martensite point can be

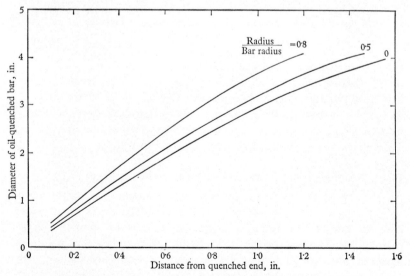

Fig. 14.23.—Positions on oil-quenched round bars and on Jominy specimen having the same cooling rates. [after International Nickel]

taken as the point of inflexion of the end-quench curve or may be found by use of fig. 14.24, which shows the relationship between hardness value and percentage of martensite. The hardness at the water-quenched end would be taken as the hardness of 100% martensite.

Other factors make the relationship not entirely quantitative, as for example the inhomogeneities that exist in all steels, particularly between the surface and centre of round bars.

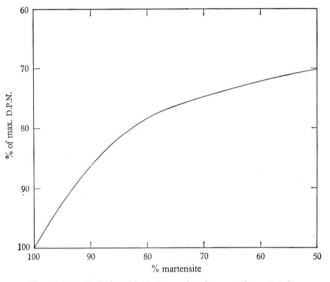

Fig. 14.24.—Relationship between hardness and martensite content of microstructure

14.20. Ruling section

It is possible to assess hardenability in terms of mechanical properties, the critical diameter then being the largest diameter of bar which can be hardened and tempered to develop a selected combination of mechanical properties in specimens machined from the axis of the bar. The critical diameter is referred to as the maximum *ruling section*. Thus, in an actual machine part, the portion that is most difficult to harden will be that which will cool most slowly on quenching, i.e. the part with the largest dimension that limits cooling. That diameter of a round bar that would have the same cooling rate at its centre is known as the *equivalent ruling section*, and under similar quenching and tempering treatment should produce the same mechanical properties as the worst in the actual machine part. Hardenability assessment and control in terms of ruling section is commonly used in Great Britain, as for example in the British Standard

Specification* that relates to wrought steels. For each steel, several maximum ruling sections and the associated mechanical properties are quoted. A knowledge of the percentage of martensite obtained on quenching is not involved in this method.

The relationship between cooling rates of plates and rectangular sections and those of round bars can be assessed from sets of conversion curves given in B.S. 971.†

QUESTIONS

1. Sketch and explain the isothermal transformation diagram for a hypoeutectoid carbon steel.

With the help of this diagram, explain *austempering* and *martempering*.　　[S]

2. What is an *isothermal transformation diagram*, and how is it used to determine the appropriate heat treatment for a carbon steel in order to obtain the desired properties in the heat-treated condition?

Discuss the influence on the diagram and on the corresponding heat-treatment procedure of (*a*) grain size, and (*b*) carbon and alloy content.　　[MST]

3. What is meant by (*a*) austenitic grain size, and (*b*) ferritic grain size? Why is the austenitic grain size important, and how may it be evaluated for a 0·2% carbon steel?

Distinguish between an inherently fine-grained steel and an inherently coarse-grained steel. Show how the former may develop a coarser grain size than the latter. What method can be used for refining the grain size of metals which are not polymorphic?　　[MST]

4. Describe the structures produced in a small sample of En 12 steel at the end of each stage of the following treatment, giving quantitative results where possible:

(*a*) Heat to 830° C for ½ hr.
(*b*) Quench to 600° C and isothermally transform for 5 sec.
(*c*) Continue isothermal transformation for 15 sec. (20 sec. total time).
(*d*) Quench to room temperature.
(*e*) Heat to 500° C for 15 min. and cool to room temperature.　　[MST]

5. Describe the effects of different heat treatments upon the mechanical properties of a plain carbon steel containing about 0·5% carbon.

What are the relative merits of the structures obtained by tempering slack-quenched and fully-quenched samples of a steel to give the same ultimate tensile stress?　　[S]

6. Discuss the influence of carbon content, heat treatment, and the temperature of test upon the results of Izod tests on plain carbon steels. Why has the effect of the last variable received much notice in recent years?　　[MST]

7. Define the terms *critical diameter* and *ideal diameter* as used in relation to the hardenability of steels.

A steel bar, of 6 in diameter, quenched in still water, was found to give 50% martensite and a hardness of 360 D.P.N. at the centre. What diameter bar of the same steel would be expected to give 95% martensite at its centre on air cooling? What would be the probable hardness at the centre of this bar?　　[MST]

8. In certain steels martensite can be produced by moderate rates of cooling. Under what circumstances may this be advantageous?

Describe an experiment whereby the effect of different cooling rates can be investigated by a test on a single specimen, and discuss the application of the results of such a test.　　[MST]

* B.S. 970: 1955. *Wrought Steels.*
† B.S. 971: 1950. *Commentary on British Standard Wrought Steels En Series*

CHAPTER 15

Alloy Steels

15.1. Purposes of alloying

Carbon steels, as made commercially, always contain certain amounts of other elements which are present in the ore and complete removal of which would be extremely difficult and expensive. Sulphur and phosphorus, when more than 0·05% of either is present, tend to make steel brittle, so that during steel making the amounts present are reduced at least to this value. Silicon has little effect up to 0·2%, after which it can strengthen the metal without decreasing the ductility; but above this quantity it causes a decrease in ductility. Silicon is frequently used as a deoxidizer in steel making, and the fraction that does not form silicon dioxide, which passes into the slag, will remain in solution in the steel. The quantity of silicon used has to be controlled so that, except in special cases, there is not more than a total of 0·4% left in the steel finally.

Manganese has a strengthening effect, but in quantities greater than 1·5% reduces the ductility. As mentioned on p. 188 the manganese/carbon ratio has an important effect on the notch ductile-brittle transition temperature. Because of its beneficial effect, excess manganese is usually added to the molten metal to bring the content up to the desired value, as well as being used as a deoxidizer.

By intentionally adding further elements to iron-carbon alloys, the structure can be modified to improve the properties in a number of ways. The same effect may be obtained in different ways by using different alloying elements or by different combinations of elements. Steels to which these intentional additions have been made (including those steels with manganese in excess of 1% or silicon in excess of 0·3%) are known as *alloy steels*.

15.2. Effect of alloying elements on iron-carbon equilibrium diagram

The body-centred cubic metals when alloyed with steel (chromium, tungsten, vanadium, and molybdenum are amongst the more important) tend to form carbides which may rob the iron of some of its carbon, so that the proportion of Fe_3C is changed.

The face-centred cubic metals (nickel, aluminium, zirconium, and copper) do not form carbides. As would be expected, the b.c.c. elements are more soluble in α-iron and the f.c.c. elements more soluble in γ-iron (except aluminium). In all these cases, the element forms a substitutional solid solution.

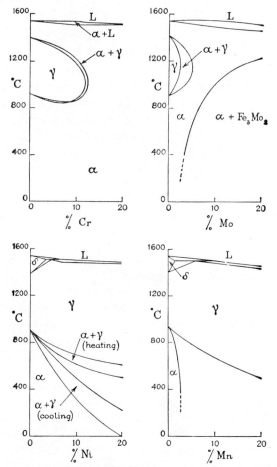

Fig. 15.1.—Iron-rich end of the equilibrium diagrams of iron with chromium, molybdenum, nickel and manganese

Manganese is allotropic and has three complex forms. It forms carbides readily and is more soluble in γ-iron than in α-iron.

An element that is more soluble in γ-iron will tend to stabilize the γ-phase by lowering the γ-α change temperature, and raising the γ-δ change temperature. An element that is more soluble in α-iron will have the reverse effect. With the exception of chromium, this is found to be so, as may be seen from the binary equilibrium diagrams in fig. 15.1.

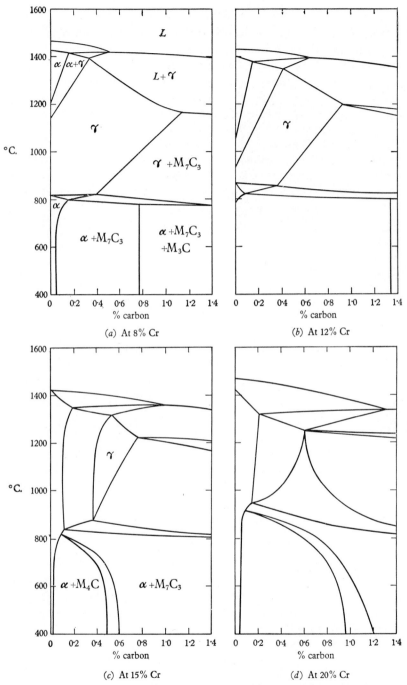

(a) At 8% Cr

(b) At 12% Cr

(c) At 15% Cr

(d) At 20% Cr

Fig. 15.2.—Sections of the iron-chromium-carbon equilibrium diagram
at various chromium contents

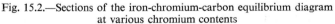

From Robert H. Heyer, *Engineering Physical Metallurgy.* Copyright 1939, D. Van Nostrand Co., Inc.
Princeton, New Jersey.

Chromium lowers the γ-α change temperature slightly when present in amounts up to 8%, but above that amount the temperature is raised sharply. It will be noticed that for more than 13% chromium or 5% molybdenum the γ-phase does not exist. The α-γ changes in iron-nickel and iron-manganese alloys are extremely sluggish, so that for all practical heating and cooling rates the change temperatures are different.

When carbon is present, the transformation temperatures are similarly affected, but the eutectoid has a lower carbon content. The size of the austenite region is increased by γ-stabilizing elements and decreased by α-stabilizing elements. The latter effect may be seen from fig. 15.2, which shows vertical sections of the Fe-C-Cr ternary equilibrium diagram. Although the γ-phase does not exist in pure iron-chromium alloys for more than 13% chromium, in the presence of carbon a γ-phase can exist up to 20% chromium.

15.3. Effect of alloying elements on isothermal transformation diagram*

The general effect of alloying elements is to reduce the diffusion rate of carbon and so slow down the transformation of austenite to ferrite and pearlite structures, so that the isothermal transformation curves are moved to longer times as illustrated in fig. 15.3. There is also a tendency to separate the pearlite and bainite knees as mentioned on p. 216. Because of the slowing down of transformations, the critical cooling rate is reduced and hardenability increased. This effect is only fully realized when the alloying element is dissolved in the austenite. When alloys containing carbide-forming elements are austenized prior to quenching, the treatment must be sufficiently prolonged for the carbides to have dissolved in the austenite. This may involve a higher soaking temperature and a soaking time of two to three hours in place of the half to one hour sufficient for plain carbon steels.

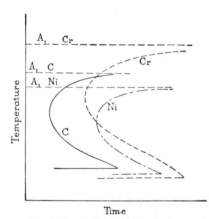

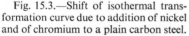

Fig. 15.3.—Shift of isothermal transformation curve due to addition of nickel and of chromium to a plain carbon steel.

Any added element lowers the M_S-temperature.

---

* The isothermal transformation diagrams of various alloy steels can be found in " Atlas of Isothermal Transformation Diagrams of B.S. En steels," 2nd Ed. Special Report No. 56, Iron and Steel Inst., 1956.

15.4. Effect of alloying elements on tempering

Because the presence of alloy elements tends to reduce the diffusion rate of carbon, processes are also slowed down in tempering. Higher tempering temperatures and longer times may therefore be necessary when heat-treating alloy steels.

15.5. Effect of alloying elements on mechanical properties

In the normalized condition the alloy elements dissolved in the ferrite have a strengthening effect, and any carbides present also increase strength and hardness. In a quenched condition, the hardness is solely dependent upon the carbon content if 100% martensite is present. After tempering, elements dissolved in the ferrite will again have a strengthening effect.

15.6. Classification of alloy steels

Alloy steels can be classified according to the elements they contain (e.g. nickel steels, chromium-vanadium steels, etc.) or according to their uses (e.g. high-tensile structural steels, stainless steels, etc.) or according to the structure produced by the heat treatment usually employed (e.g. pearlitic, martensitic, austenitic). The most reasonable classification, which is adopted in the following summary, is that based primarily on use.

15.7. High-tensile structural steels

High-tensile structural steels are steels of low carbon content which are used in the normalized or as-rolled condition. They are thus in a pearlitic state, and the improved properties are due to the strengthening of the ferrite by substitutional solid solution, and due to the presence of carbides which tend to be much more finely divided than the cementite in plain carbon steels. The solid solution strengthening of the ferrite is obtained without loss of ductility. Ultimate tensile strengths of the order of 40 Tons/in^2 are common in this group, compared with 30 Tons/in^2 for mild steel.

The general object of using these stronger steels is to give a reduction of weight, which can be an important factor in structures such as ships and bridges. The saving of weight has to be balanced against the increased cost of using more expensive materials.

15.8. Alloy steels used in a fully heat-treated condition

This group, which accounts for the greatest part of the tonnage of alloy steels, owes its importance to the high hardenability and to better all-round properties in the fully heat-treated condition. Because of the former reason, large sections can be fully quenched and slower cooling rates can be used. The latter is important where there is danger of cracking in a water quench. For *air-hardening steels*, the critical cooling rate is so low that a quenching bath is unnecessary for smaller sections. Thus En 30, a steel containing 3·9–4·3% nickel and 1·1–1·4% chromium, whose isothermal transformation diagram is shown in fig. 15·4, can be

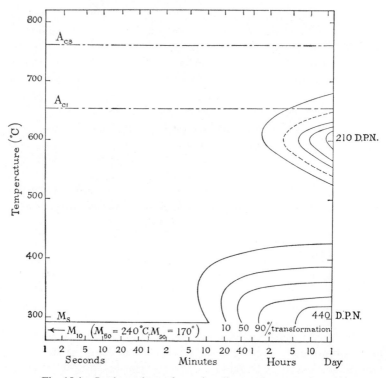

Fig. 15.4.—Isothermal transformation diagram for an En 30 steel (0·35% C, 4·23% Ni, 1·43% Cr). [after International Nickel]

air-hardened in sections up to about 2½-in diameter. This treatment may give a little lower bainite with the martensite, but not sufficient to impair the final properties. Fig. 15.5 shows a property chart for this steel. En 30 is intended for use as-cooled or tempered at a temperature not exceeding 250° C. In this condition it will show an ultimate tensile strength of 100 Tons/in².

There are a very large number of steels manufactured that fall into this group of heat-treated steels. Selection of the correct steel, after the required hardenability and mechanical strength are met, will then depend upon secondary requirements, such as suitability for welding, when a low carbon content is desirable, or low-temperature notch toughness when a nickel steel is needed, or wear resistance, which can be given by the carbides in chromium steel, etc. Such selection is a matter of consulting the manufacturers' lists of available steels and a matter of experience and is beyond the scope of this text.

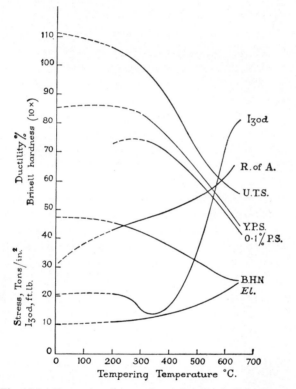

Fig. 15.5.—Tempering diagram for air-hardened, 1⅛-in diameter bars of En 30 steel. [after International Nickel]

15.9. Boron steels

Although not a separate class, these steels are of special note. Boron is used as an alloying element in low-carbon steels in quantities of about 0·002–0·004%, producing higher strengths in air-cooled parts and a higher hardenability.

When molybdenum is present, boron affects the isothermal trans-

239

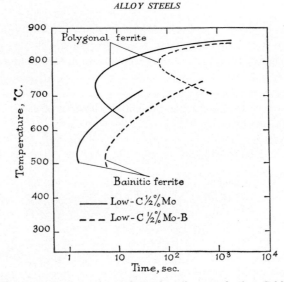

Fig. 15.6.—Isothermal transformation diagrams for low-C $\frac{1}{2}\%$ Mo steels with and without boron (showing start of transformation only). [Irvine, Pickering, Heselwood and Atkins]

formation diagram in the manner shown in fig. 15.6.* Air cooling thus gives a bainite structure with its superior strength. The effect of variation of boron content on mechanical strength is shown in fig. 15.7. It is thought that the boron, which forms an interstitial solid solution, segre-

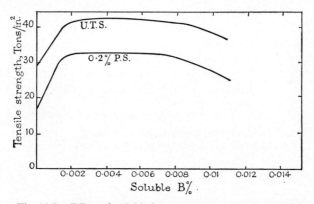

Fig. 15.7.—Effect of soluble boron content on steels containing 0·13–0·15% C and 0·40–0·60% Mo. [Irvine, Pickering, Heselwood and Atkin]

* K. J. Irvine, J. B. Pickering, W. C. Heselwood, M. Atkins, "The Physical Metallurgy of Low-carbon Low-alloy Steels containing Boron," *J. Iron Steel Inst.*, Vol. 186, 1957, pp. 54–67

gates to the grain boundaries where, by occupying the most favourable interstices, it retards the interstitial diffusion of carbon, thereby retarding the formation of pro-eutectoid ferrite during cooling.

The carbon content in these bainitic boron steels can be considerably less than that of a mild steel and yet give greater mechanical strength. This makes such steels eminently suitable for welding.

At higher boron contents, Fe_2B is precipitated at the austenite grain boundaries, and for more than 0.007% boron forms continuous films which have a bad effect upon hot workability.

15.10. Corrosion and heat-resistant steels

Stainless steels have corrosion-resistant properties due to a high proportion of chromium, which forms an oxide film that is impervious to oxygen and highly resistant to the passage of ions. Thus once the film is formed, the metal ions and the oxygen of the atmosphere cannot continue to meet, and further oxidation is prevented. The corrosion resistance is improved as the chromium content increases, provided that the chromium is in solid solution in the iron and not combined as carbides. The corrosion resistance is enhanced by the presence of a certain amount of nickel. These steels may be sub-divided according to the structure obtainable at room temperature. If chromium is the only alloying element and more than 13% is present, in the absence of carbon the alloy will be α-phase at all temperatures. With carbon present, more chromium is necessary to give an α-structure at all temperatures. Such steels are known as *ferritic stainless steels*.

When alloys contain at least 24% chromium and nickel combined, and not less than 8% of either element, the γ-phase is retained on cooling at normal rates. This is not immediately obvious from the ternary equilibrium diagram section in fig. 15.8, but the separation of the α-phase occurs only on very slow cooling. These are *austenitic stainless steels*, the most well known being the 18/8 stainless steel which contains about 18% chromium and 8% nickel.

Neither of the above groups are heat-treatable. Any steel which contains chromium and nickel in such proportions that it has a γ-phase at high temperatures and an α-phase on cooling at normal rates can be quenched to give a martensitic structure. Such heat-treatable steels are known as *martensitic stainless steels*, even when not in a heat-treated condition. Whereas the mechanical properties of a martensitic stainless steel can be changed by heat treatment, austenitic and ferritic stainless steels can be strengthened only by cold working.

Heating a stainless steel in the region of 500 to 700° C can lead to the precipitation of carbides at the grain boundaries. The chromium is removed from the adjacent solid solution, resulting in a lessening of the corrosion resistance. This can be particularly troublesome in the heat-affected zone (see p. 258) of welds in these materials, when the subsequent corrosion is known as *weld decay*. The defect can be cured by reheating the steel after welding to a sufficiently high temperature to redissolve the carbides—about 900–1000° C dependent upon the steel—and quenching.

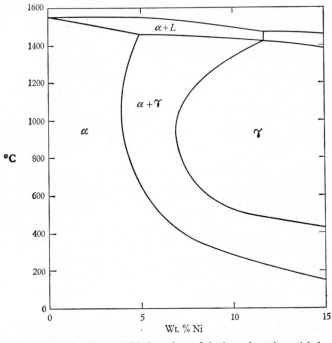

Fig. 15.8.—Section at 18% chromium of the iron-chromium-nickel diagram

Metals Reference Book, second edition edited by Smithells, Butterworth.

If such a treatment is impracticable, as for example due to size, it is necessary to use a *stabilized stainless steel*, that is, one which has niobium or titanium included in its composition. These elements have stronger carbide-forming tendencies than chromium, so that the chromium is not removed from the solid solution.

Steels which are to be used at high temperatures require resistance to oxidation and high strength at the working temperature. Chromium is again the principal alloy element used, with several other elements which help to give the desired resistance to creep (see Section 13.32).

15.11. Case hardening steels

Some equipment parts are required to have hard wear-resisting surfaces, and also toughness. The two are not possible in the same heat-treated steel, as if it is treated to give the greatest surface hardness, it will be martensitic and hence brittle, while if treated to develop maximum toughness, it will not be hard enough. The desired combination can be obtained by *case hardening*.

The surface layers of a low-carbon steel are *carburized*, that is, the carbon content is increased by heating in a suitable atmosphere, which causes carbon to diffuse into the surface layers. Afterwards, the part has to be heat-treated to give a martensitic structure in the high-carbon surface layers, and a tough ferritic structure in the core.

In nitriding, the nitrogen content of the surface layers is similarly increased, giving iron nitrides, which are extremely hard and require no further heat treatment.

Certain combinations of alloy elements are found to produce steels which are more suitable for carburizing and for nitriding.

15.12. Tool steels

Metal-cutting tools require high hardness and resistance to wear. For this purpose, steels containing carbides are necessary, but there must be a matrix tough enough to hold the hard carbide particles. During use, the tool tips may become hot due to friction, and steels are needed which do not soften appreciably with a rise in temperature.

For many purposes, near-eutectoid and hyper-eutectoid plain carbon steels suffice, but these are not suitable under more severe service conditions. In particular they must not be allowed to run hot.

Low-alloy tool steels have the advantage that they can be hardened by oil quenching or air-hardening and would be less likely to crack than would plain carbon steels when used for intricate tools.

For high-speed steels, which can be used at temperatures up to 500° C, tungsten, chromium, and vanadium, with sometimes cobalt, are used. These are carbide-forming elements and give mainly Fe_4W_2C, with the other elements sometimes replacing the iron or tungsten. A typical composition is 18% tungsten, 4% chromium and 1% vanadium (an 18/4/1 steel).

15.13. Special-purpose steels

Special-purpose steels are mainly steels employed for magnetic purposes. Alloys for use as transformer cores, etc., should have a high permeability with little hysteresis loss, while those to be used as permanent magnets should have a high remanence and coercive force.

QUESTIONS

1. Describe some ways in which alloying elements vary the properties of steels.
For what purposes are (*a*) manganese, (*b*) nickel, (*c*) chromium, and (*d*) molybdenum used in low-alloy steels?

[S]

2. For what purposes may chromium be used as an alloy element in steels?

[MST]

3. Discuss the primary function of the alloying elements in alloy steels of the machine steel group.
Determine the hardness at the centre and at $0.8 \times$ radius of a $1\frac{1}{4}$-in diameter bar of En 12 steel after oil quenching. Is oil quenching sufficiently rapid if a minimum of 50% martensite is specified?

[MST]

4. Distinguish between *hardness* and *hardenability*. What factors affect these properties in steels?
The figure shows the curves obtained in a Jominy end-quench test for two low-alloy steels which are of identical composition except that one contains 0·003% boron.
Determine the size of bar of each steel that will give a structure of 80% martensite at the centre after a still water quench.
Explain each step of your method.

[MST]

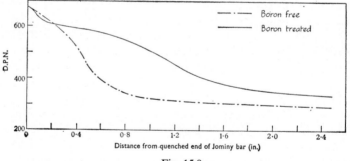

Fig. 15.9

CHAPTER 16

Corrosion

16.1. Introduction

Corrosion is a chemical or electrochemical reaction between a metal and its environment, which involves removal of the metal or its conversion to an oxide or other compound. It may also be defined as the passage of the metal atoms from the metallic to the ionic state. In some cases the compound will form a protective layer which reduces and prevents further corrosion, but in others this is not so and further corrosion is not inhibited.

The effects of corrosion are of serious importance in the engineering world. The cost of replacement of damaged material and of protective measures, such as painting and plating, is substantial and has been estimated at not less than £200,000,000 annually* in Great Britain alone.

Many of the basic principles of corrosion are now understood, and although corrosion theory cannot be applied rigorously to all practical problems, the basic principles can frequently give a guide to corrosion control.

16.2. Oxidation and reduction

As many corrosion processes are closely linked with oxidation, either directly or indirectly, it is as well to consider more closely the meanings of these chemical terms.

When charcoal burns in air, it forms carbon monoxide and carbon dioxide.

$$2C + O_2 \rightarrow 2CO$$
$$C + O_2 \rightarrow CO_2$$

Also when hydrogen burns in air, it forms water, and magnesium strip will burn rapidly when ignited to form magnesium oxide.

$$2H_2 + O_2 \rightarrow 2H_2O$$
$$2Mg + O_2 \rightarrow 2MgO$$

These and any other reactions in which the element combines with oxygen are termed *oxidation*.

* W. H. J. Vernon, *The Conservation of Natural Resources*, Inst. of Civil Engrs., London, 1957, p. 105

When these elements react with certain other non-metallic elements, the processes closely resemble that of burning in oxygen, and are also known as oxidation. Examples are the burning of carbon in fluorine.

$$C + 2F_2 \rightarrow CF_4$$

and the combination of iron with sulphur when heated

$$Fe + S \rightarrow FeS$$

In converting a metal to its oxide, the atom of the metal is changed to a positive ion, the electron passing into the oxygen atom. Thus oxidation may also be considered as a removal of electrons.

The reverse process to that of oxidation is known as *reduction*. Metallic ores, usually the oxides of metals, are reduced to the metals by removal of the oxygen or some other combined element by providing another element which has a higher affinity for the oxygen or other element. Thus iron ore is reduced to iron in the blast furnace by heating with carbon. The carbon forms carbon monoxide or dioxide which passes off as a gas, leaving behind the uncombined metal.

Reduction is the addition of an electron to the atom. This occurs directly in the electrolytic extraction of aluminium from its oxide by passage of a current through a solution of aluminium oxide in molten cryolite (Na_3AlF_6)

$$Al^{+++} + 3e^- \rightarrow Al$$

Oxidation or reduction of a substance could be carried out without simultaneous reduction or oxidation of another substance only if a large store of or reservoir for electrons is at hand. Accordingly, oxidation of one substance is always accompanied by reduction of another.

An element or compound which takes up the electrons removed from the oxidized material, thereby itself being reduced, is called an *oxidizing agent*, and one which liberates electrons is a *reducing agent*.

Some elements exhibit more than one valency, for example, iron is divalent in ferrous compounds such as ferrous chloride ($FeCl_2$), and trivalent in ferric compounds such as ferric chloride ($FeCl_3$). Tin is divalent in stannous compounds ($SnCl_2$) and tetravalent in stannic compounds ($SnCl_4$). A change of the -ous to the -ic compound is in effect

$$Fe^{++} \rightarrow Fe^{+++} + e^-$$

or
$$Sn^{++} \rightarrow Sn^{++++} + 2e^-$$

and so is an oxidation process. Conversely the -ic compounds can be reduced to -ous compounds.

246

16.3. Direct chemical corrosion by dry gases

Direct chemical corrosion is the reaction of the metal with dry oxygen or other gas. In the case of direct oxidation, the metal reacts to form an oxide, there being at the same time a decrease of the free energy, which acts as a driving force. Thus

$$M + \tfrac{1}{2}O_2 \rightarrow MO - \Delta G$$

where M is the metal atom and ΔG is the change in the free energy (see Appendix II). In the case of the noble metals such as gold and platinum, oxidation would involve an increase of free energy. Hence the metal is the stable form, which is why these metals occur in nature in an uncombined state.

The main feature of reactions of this type is not the driving force, but the rate at which it proceeds. Whereas aluminium has a large driving force, a very thin layer of the oxide is protective, and once a film of about half a millionth of an inch thickness has formed, further corrosion in air at room temperature ceases.

16.4. Growth of oxide layer

The oxide can continue to form only where oxygen and metal atoms meet. Once a layer has started, it grows by a diffusion mechanism; the metal and oxygen form ions at the respective surfaces and the ions then diffuse through the film as shown diagrammatically in fig. 16.1. This

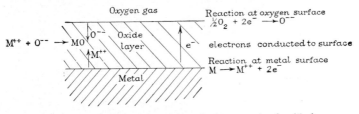

Fig. 16.1.—Movements and reactions during growth of oxide layer on a metal surface

mechanism requires the presence of lattice defects, such as vacancies, in the film, and such vacancies usually arise during film growth. The rate of oxidation is then controlled by the sum of the diffusion rates of the metal and oxygen ions, and these depend upon the size of the hole in the lattice of the ions of opposite sign. With a monovalent metal, e.g. sodium, there are two sodium ions to every oxygen ion, so that the hole in the oxygen lattice is much larger than that in the metal lattice and the metal atoms will diffuse easily, while the oxygen ions will diffuse very little. For a metal of high valency such as titanium (TiO_2) or tungsten (WO_3), the oxygen ions will diffuse relatively easily. Metals ions are smaller than oxygen ions to such an extent that, in oxides of trivalent metals, the two diffusion rates are approximately equal and the sum of the rates is less than for other metals. This helps to explain the high oxidation resistance of aluminium and chromium.

An increase of temperature will cause an increase of diffusion rates in accordance with Arrhenius' rate law (see p. 119). A thicker film must therefore develop to give protection. This may be seen in the films that form on iron when it is heated in the temperature range 200–300° C. As the temperature is raised, the thin film of ferric oxide (Fe_2O_3) gives various colours due to optical interference effects, and the top temperature reached may be judged from the final *temper colour*.

On many metals the film breaks down before protection is complete. This may be due to evaporation, as occurs with the oxides of arsenic at 200° C, and molybdenum and tungsten at high temperatures. Although the surface of these metals will continue to appear bright, corrosion continues at a constant rate.

The more usual cause of film failure is by cracking. If the volume of the oxide film is different from that of the metal from which it is formed, then stresses will be set up in the film. If the film is sufficiently plastic, the stresses can be relieved by plastic flow, and the protection is maintained. If, however, the film is more brittle, it will crack, and protection will be lost because the oxygen will then have direct access to the metal surface. Film growth in these cases will continue at an approximately uniform rate. Since the plasticity of a substance varies with temperature, the liability to film breakdown is temperature-dependent. In uranium, for example, the oxide film does not crack at high temperatures, and the protection is better than at low temperatures.

16.5. The ionization of water

The other form of corrosion—electrochemical corrosion—occurs only in the presence of water or aqueous solutions, and is dependent upon the concentration of ions present in the solution.

Pure water ionizes into positive hydrogen ions and negative hydroxyl ions.

$$H_2O \rightleftharpoons H^+ + OH^-$$

It is found that the degree of ionization is such that pure water contains

10^{-7} gm ions of each sort per litre. By application of the laws of chemical equilibrium it can be shown that the product of the concentrations of the two sorts of ions will be constant for all aqueous solutions at the same temperature. Thus in any solution, the *ion product*

$$[H^+] \times [OH^-]$$

where $[H^+]$ and $[OH^-]$ are the concentrations of the two sorts of ion measured in gm ions per litre, will have the same value as for pure water, i.e. 10^{-14}.

When acid is added to water, the concentration of H^+ ions will increase and so that of hydroxyl ions will decrease to keep the ion product constant. If hydrogen ions are removed from an aqueous solution in a corrosion process then more water will ionize and the $[OH^-]$ will increase so that the solution becomes more alkaline.

The acidity or alkalinity of a solution can be expressed solely in terms of its $[H^+]$ value and is usually given as the *pH value*, which is x where

$$[H^+] = 10^{-x} \text{ gm ions per litre}$$

A neutral solution has a pH value of 7. A smaller value denotes acidity and a larger value denotes alkalinity.

16.6. Electrochemical corrosion

Corrosion at room temperature occurs mostly in the presence of water or aqueous solutions of ionic compounds (acids, bases, and salts). The reactions in these cases are electrochemical, that is, electric currents flow through those parts of the metal not actually being corroded.

The passage of the metal into the ionic state is an anodic reaction which is represented by

$$M \rightarrow M^{++} + 2\,e^-$$

The electrons left behind in the metal must be satisfied if the reaction is to proceed, and they pass through the metal to be neutralized elsewhere in a *cathodic reaction*, an example of which is the deposition of metal in an electroplating bath.

For each coulomb of electricity that passes from anodic to cathodic regions, one electrochemical equivalent of the metal at the anodic region should corrode.

When two metals are placed in an aqueous solution so that there is no metallic contact between them, as in fig. 16.2, it is found that there will be an electromotive force between them, which would cause a current to flow if they were connected by an electrical conducting path. Under standard conditions, the metals can be arranged in a series such that any metal will be anodic to any metal lower in the series, and cathodic to any metal higher in the series. The commoner metals arranged in the electro-motive series are given in Table 16.1. Thus for the two metals shown in fig. 16.2, zinc would be anodic to copper and if they were connected externally, as in fig. 16.3, a current would flow causing the zinc to corrode.

The potentials of the metals under standard conditions are also given in Table 16.1, these being the potentials at which the element is in equilibrium with its ions in a " normal " solution, i.e. one which contains one gram-equivalent of the ions per litre. The decrease of free energy* $(-\Delta G)$ of a reaction and the potential E are related by

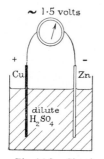

Fig. 16.2.—Simple voltaic cell

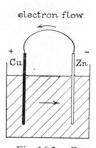

electron flow

Fig. 16.3.—Current flow from cell of fig. 16.2.

$$-\Delta G = n\,EF$$

where n is the valency and F is the Faraday, i.e. the quantity of electricity that will liberate or deposit one gram-equivalent of a substance during electrolysis.

If the electrode is raised above its " normal electrode potential ", the metal will corrode, while if lowered below that value the reaction will be reversed.

The potential of the hydrogen electrode, i.e. hydrogen gas in equilibrium with a " normal " solution of hydrogen ions is taken as the reference voltage. The potential of an electrode is modified if the ion concentration in the solution is not normal, being given quantitatively by

$$E = E_0 + \frac{RT}{nF} \log_e C$$

where E is the potential, E_0 is the standard potential, and C is the concentration in gram-ions per litre. This will give a potential change of $0.059/n$ volts for every change in concentration by a factor of ten.

When a current is flowing, there is also a change of potential due to *polarization*. For example, at a cathode where hydrogen is liberated by the reaction of hydrogen ions in solution with electrons

$$2H^+ + 2e^- \rightarrow H_2$$

* See Appendix II.

the greater the current density, the greater is the potential necessary to continue to produce evolution of hydrogen.

Under any conditions other than the standard conditions described above, the actual potential difference that would be set up between two metals immersed in an aqueous solution will be different from the value given by Table 16.1, and the order of the metals in a *galvanic series* may differ from that in the electromotive series. A galvanic series places metals in order such that each is anodic to those lower in the series under actual conditions, and will therefore differ for different solutions.

TABLE 16.1—ELECTROMOTIVE SERIES OF THE METALS

Metal and ion considered	Normal electrode potential (volts)
Anodic (corroded) end	
Li, Li$^+$	− 3·04
K, K$^+$	− 2·92
Na, Na$^+$	− 2·71
Mg, Mg^{++}	− 2·37
Be, Be^{++}	− 1·85
Al, Al^{+++}	− 1·66
Zn, Zn^{++}	− 0·76
Cr, Cr^{++}	− 0·74
Fe, Fe^{++}	− 0·44
Cd, Cd^{++}	− 0·40
Co, Co^{++}	− 0·28
Ni, Ni^{++}	− 0·25
Sn, Sn^{++}	− 0·14
Pb, Pb^{++}	− 0·13
H$_2$ H$^+$	0·00 (Reference)
Cu, Cu^{++}	+ 0·34
Hg, Hg^{++}	+ 0·79
Ag, Ag$^+$	+ 0·80
Pt, Pt^{++}	+ 1·2
Au, Au^{+++}	+ 1·50
Cathodic (protected) end	

Electrolytic corrosion can occur on a single piece of metal when in contact with an aqueous solution. Owing to slight inhomogeneities in the metal, or varying concentration of ions or molecules in the liquid, particularly dissolved oxygen, local anodic and cathodic regions will form with small potential differences between them, and localized corrosion may occur.

16.7. Anodic and cathodic reactions

Various reactions are possible at the anode and at the cathode. The most probable ones at the anode are:

(a) formation of metal ions in solution

$$M \rightarrow M^{++} + 2e^-$$

(b) oxide formation

$$M + 2\,OH^- \rightarrow MO + H_2O + 2\,e^-$$

(c) hydroxide formation

$$M + 2\,OH^- \rightarrow M(OH)_2 + 2\,e^-$$

(d) formation of an insoluble salt

$$M + 2\,X^- \rightarrow MX_2 + 2\,e^-$$

At the cathode the more probable reactions are:

(e) metal deposition

$$M^{++} + 2\,e^- \rightarrow M$$

(f) hydrogen evolution

$$2\,H^+ + 2\,e^- \rightarrow H_2$$

(g) reduction of anions or cations

$$2\,M^{+++} + 2\,e^- \rightarrow 2\,M^{++}$$
$$2\,X^{--} + 2\,e^- \rightarrow 2\,X^{---}$$

(h) molecular reduction, especially oxygen

$$\tfrac{1}{2}O_2 + H_2O + 2\,e^- \rightarrow 2\,OH^-$$

When metal ions form and pass into solution (reaction a), they may react with other ions present to form a precipitate, which by forming away from the anodic surface does not give protection. Little polarization occurs and the rate of reaction is controlled by the rate at which electrons can be absorbed in the cathodic reaction. The reaction is therefore said to be under cathodic control.

If the anodic reaction produces substances (reactions b, c, and d) which adhere to the surface as a film, protection is given against further corrosion, leading to *passivity*. Unless there is film breakdown, further corrosion is controlled by diffusion as in Section 16.4. The film may fail by dissolving, if soluble, or by undermining or cracking. Oxides are generally more protective than hydroxides.

Metal deposition (reaction e) will occur if the solution contains a sufficient concentration of ions of a more noble metal. Thus copper is deposited on the blade of a steel knife when placed in a solution of copper sulphate.

Hydrogen evolution can occur if the potential anywhere on the metal surface is below the value for equilibrium of the reaction as listed in Table 16.1.

The oxidation or reduction of ions in solution is determined by the potential necessary for their change-of-valency reaction. Examples that can occur are the oxidation of chromium Cr^{+++} ions to chromate ions in which chromium has a valency of six, and the reduction of ferric Fe^{+++} to ferrous Fe^{++} ions.

The reduction of oxygen (reaction *h*) can occur only if there is dissolved oxygen in the solution. Of all processes this is probably the most important. Absence of dissolved oxygen will stifle this reaction and, if potentials are not sufficient to allow one of the other possible cathodic reactions to occur, then, due to cathodic control, corrosion at the anodic area may not occur.

16.8. Forms of metallic corrosion

The general corrosion mechanisms have been described, but each mechanism may make itself apparent in various forms.

Uniform attack is the term applied where all the surface is corroded to the same degree. Under such conditions, the useful life is easily estimated and unexpected failure should not occur.

Pitting and *intergranular corrosion* are non-uniform and can proceed in otherwise undamaged material. Their presence may not be known until failure occurs. Pitting may start as a localized anodic area due to an inhomogeneity. Once started, the solution around the anodic and cathodic areas will have different concentrations and form a concentration cell which accelerates the process. The inhomogeneities may occur in the metal or in the solution. For example, a drop of water on a steel surface will have a somewhat higher concentration of dissolved oxygen near the outside than at the centre. An anodic area would form at the centre. The Fe^{++} ions released would react with OH^- ions to form ferrous hydroxide, thereby decreasing the OH^- concentration, while the cathodic reaction at the edges would increase the OH^- concentration. These two effects will increase the potential difference and hence the corrosion current. The ferrous hydroxide would react with oxygen to form rust, which is a form of ferric hydroxide. The process is shown diagrammatically in fig. 16.4.

Surface inhomogeneities which cause localized anodic and cathodic areas are:

Breaks in a protective layer.

Deposits of foreign matter or loose corrosion products.

Local inhomogeneities in the metal, such as oxide particles.

Localized stressing of the metal, the stress causing a change in the electrochemical potential.

Where any corrosion products are removed mechanically by rapidly moving liquids or gases, corrosion will be accelerated. Local removal may cause pitting due to such corrosion-erosion or *impingement attack*.

Intergranular corrosion occurs where the grain boundaries are much more reactive than the remainder of the alloy. Weld decay in unstabilized stainless steels (Section 15.10) is an example of this.

Two-phase alloys are more prone to corrosion than are similar single-phase alloys, but even in the latter, preferential corrosion of one of the components may occur. *Dezincification* of brasses is an example of this effect. It is more likely to occur with higher zinc contents. In certain environments the brass goes into solution, a concentration cell is formed,

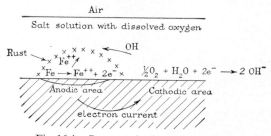

Fig. 16.4.—Processes in the rusting of iron

and the copper is re-deposited as a spongy mass which has no strength. When this occurs generally over the surface, i.e. *uniform attack*, the effect is not serious. When however it is localized, giving *plug*-type dezincification, deep pits filled with spongy copper form and may even lead to perforation of pipe walls, etc.

Stress corrosion is a form of intergranular corrosion that is more pronounced when the material is subjected to a tensile stress. The destructive effect is then concentrated on a limited number of grain boundaries and travels in a general direction perpendicular to the applied stress.

Corrosion fatigue* is the action of corrosion in the presence of repeated stresses and is far more serious than the action of either factor individually. The cracks that develop usually follow the slip bands set up by the plastic deformation.

When two dissimilar metals are used in contact, the rate of corrosion of the anodic material is determined in part by the relative anodic and cathodic areas. When the anodic area is relatively smaller, any cathodic control factors have little effect and corrosion is intense, whereas when the cathodic area is smaller, the corrosion of the anodic part is much less.

* P. T. Gilbert, " Corrosion Fatigue," *Met. Rev.*, Vol. 1, 1956, p. 379.

16.9. Prevention of corrosion

Various methods which can be used to reduce the extent or likelihood of corrosion are discussed in this section.* Some are applicable at the design stage and others during service.

(i) *Treatment of corrosive medium*

In most cases, for example where parts are used in sea-water, this is not practicable.

The variation of the aqueous corrosion of iron and steel with pH-value is shown in fig. 16.5, and may be seen to be least when the solution is of sufficient alkalinity (pH 11–12). Film breakdown does not occur so

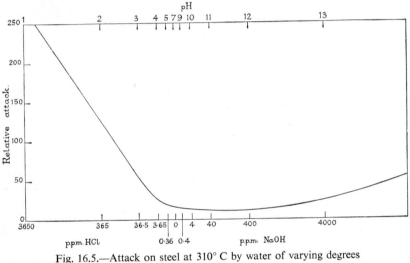

Fig. 16.5.—Attack on steel at 310° C by water of varying degrees
of acidity and alkalinity
[Redrawn from curve by Partridge and Hall—International Nickel]

readily within certain ranges of pH-value and also if the solution contains sufficient inhibitors (chromates, phosphates, etc.) which have an oxidizing effect.

Boiler water is made sufficiently alkaline by dosing the feed water with caustic soda. If, however, a high concentration of alkali is allowed to build up in a boiler, the steel may show a form of stress corrosion known as *caustic embrittlement*.

Paints containing inhibitors reduce the probability of film breakdown under the paint.

● W. D. Clark, " Design from the Viewpoint of Corrosion," *Met. Rev.*, Vol. 3, 1958, p. 279.

(ii) *Choice of metal*

The more noble metals offer better corrosion resistance, but the most inert ones are the most expensive. The most useful ones are those which form a stable protective film.

Stainless steels, containing at least 12% chromium and often some nickel, form a film which depends for its stability on Fe^{+++} and Cr^{+++} ions. Under reducing conditions (low potentials) the Fe^{+++} ions are reduced to soluble Fe^{++} ions and under oxidizing conditions (high potentials) the Cr^{+++} ions are oxidized to soluble Cr^{6+} ions, so that film breakdown can occur under extreme conditions.

Aluminium forms a very thin protective film which is resistant to solutions of pH 5–9. If, however, ions of noble metals are present even in extremely minute quantities, deposition of the metal occurs, followed by rapid corrosion of the aluminium. The Duralumin-type alloys which contain copper have a poor corrosion resistance. Also the film on pure aluminium is easily damaged and if local rubbing continues so that a new protective layer is continuously removed, pits form.

Copper, being a noble metal, has good corrosion resistance and is almost completely passive in water and alkaline solutions.

(iii) *Construction*

Where different metals have to be used in the same structure and are liable to exposure to a corrosive medium, direct contact between the metals should be avoided by insulating layers, such as washers and sleeves at bolted joints, or suitable paints between contacting surfaces.

(iv) *Cathodic protection*

By deliberate use of a metal that is anodic to the main metal, protection can be gained at the expense of corrosion of the sacrificial metal.

Examples are the use of zinc plates in boilers and on the steel hulls of ships near bronze propellors.

(v) *Protective coatings*

The majority of corrosion protection is achieved by the application of additional surface layers.

Organic materials used are oils and greases for temporary use, and paints, varnishes, or lacquers for more permanence. The last three may also contain pigments for decorative purposes.

Inorganic materials used are the vitreous enamels which are basically silicate or borosilicate glasses containing pigments to render the enamel opaque and of suitable colour. Chromates, phosphates, etc., which have been mentioned above as being corrosion inhibitors, act as oxidizing agents and promote the formation of oxide films which give anodic control.

Metallic coatings are widely used to give protection. If the base metal is isolated from the corrosive environment by a metal lower in the galvanic series, as for example by chromium, nickel, or tin on steel, the protection continues as long as the surface metal is self-protected. If the surface layer is scratched, however, the steel will be anodic and corrode where exposed. In the presence of an acid, tin becomes anodic to steel, hence giving protection when tinplate is used as a container for fruit, etc.

Galvanic protection is provided when the surface metal is higher in the galvanic series, e.g. cadmium and zinc on steel. If the surface is scratched, the surface metal is corroded, and a protective layer of cadmium or zinc oxide builds up over the scratch. Zinc and tin are usually applied by hot dipping, i.e. dipping the steel into the molten metal, and chromium, nickel, and cadmium by electroplating.

Thick diffusion coatings can be made by heating a metal in the presence of powdered aluminium (calorizing), chromium (chromizing), zinc (sherardizing), etc. Layers can also be applied by metal spraying, the covering metal being melted and blown on to the base metal as fine drops.

For metal cladding, a thin layer of corrosion-resistant material is made to adhere to sheets or plates of the base metal by rolling or some similar process. Alclad sheet is a Duralumin-type alloy with a thin surface layer of pure aluminium. Stainless steel is employed as a cladding for mild-steel sheets.

CHAPTER 17

Welding

17.1. Nomenclature

Welding is the joining of metal components by means of the inter-atomic forces—as distinct from joining methods like bolting, riveting, etc. A broad classification of welding methods would be into *plastic welding* and *fusion welding*. In *plastic-welding* processes, the parts are brought together under pressure, usually accompanied by heating to a temperature below the melting-point, so that plastic flow can occur and the parts become bonded together. The blacksmith welds steel parts together by the simple expedient of hammering. The main use of this method today is in resistance welding, the heating being due to the passage of a heavy electric current through a small region of contact where the components are brought together under pressure. These methods are *spot welding*, where joining is localized, and *seam welding* where the parts, usually sheet metals, pass between two pressure rollers while the current flows continuously.

Fusion welding is any process in which metal is made molten to make the joint. Either the parent metal or added filler metal is melted by an oxy-acetylene flame or electric arc, or some other means, and the molten metal allowed to solidify without the application of any pressure. Owing to the relative amounts of molten metal and unmelted metal, the weld metal is cooled quickly so that it solidifies in the manner of a chilled casting, that is, with columnar crystals and a dendritic appearance.

The *heat-affected zone* is that metal which is not deformed plastically in plastic welding or melted in fusion welding, but which has its tempera-ture raised sufficiently to cause metallurgical changes.

In the brief survey given here of some of the metallurgical changes that can occur due to welding, only arc welds will be discussed. Similar considerations will apply to welds made by other methods, with due allowance made for differences in temperatures and cooling rates.

17.2. Heat distribution in the vicinity of the weld

In successive regions of the heat-affected zone, metal will have reached all temperatures intermediate from room temperature to the temperature of the molten metal. The rate of cooling will depend upon the method of welding and the size of the specimen. In electric-arc welding, the heat is applied very locally, so that temperature gradients are steep and the heat-affected zone may extend only a fraction of an inch from the weld. In oxy-acetylene welding, on the other hand, the heat is not applied in so localized a manner, so that the heat-affected zone is larger, temperature gradients are not so steep, and the rate of cooling is generally less. Fig. 17.1 shows possible temperature-time curves for various regions in the heat-affected zone of an electric-arc weld.

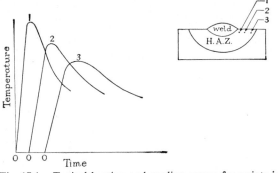

Fig. 17.1.—Typical heating and cooling curves for points in the heat-affected zone of a weld

17.3. Metallurgy of weld metal and heat-affected zone

The metallurgical changes that occur in the heat-affected zone will reflect the whole metallurgical behaviour of the particular alloy, and can be deduced from a knowledge of the equilibrium diagram and the laws of recrystallization and grain growth, together with the top temperature and rate of cooling for each point. Alternatively, the resultant micro-structure would enable the heating and cooling history of any point to be deduced.

If the weld metal is not shielded from the atmosphere, then gases may dissolve in the liquid metal, especially oxygen, nitrogen, and hydrogen (the last is particularly likely if damp electrodes are used). On solidifica-tion, these will not escape and may form pockets of gas or compounds— oxides, etc.—which may have a serious effect upon mechanical properties. As an example, hydrogen causes embrittlement of steel welds.

The flux coating provided on most types of electrodes will help remove oxides that form and also provide a shielding layer to exclude the atmos-phere during welding and the subsequent cooling. The layer of slag can also reduce heat losses and so control the rate of cooling.

Certain welding processes are carried out with an inert gas surrounding the arc to exclude all atmospheric gases.

Weld metal   M.P.   Heat-affected zone

Fig. 17.2.—Fusion we[l]

In alloys there may be a loss of one or other of the elements due to volatilization. This can be compensated by using a filler rod of suitable composition which has an excess of the more volatile element.

Any effects due to previous heat treatment may be partially or completely destroyed, and the effects of previous cold work will be removed, by recovery, recrystallization, and grain growth.

The rate of cooling can influence the grain size and also, when phase

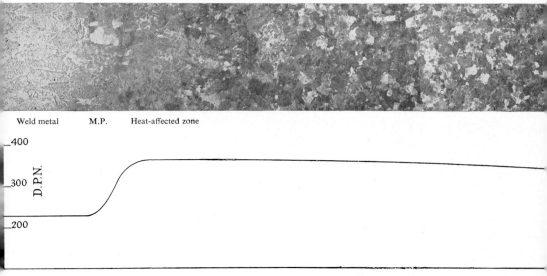

Weld metal   M.P.   Heat-affected zone

Fig. 17.3.—Fusion weld in a 0·5% C stee[l]

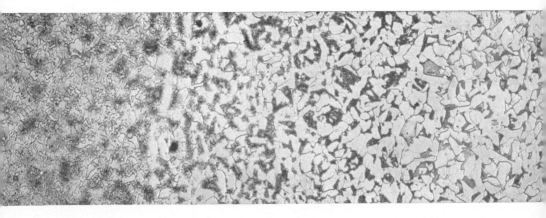

A₃   A₁   Unaffected metal

a 0·15% C steel (× 100).

changes occur on cooling, the final structure. Rapid cooling of steels may give a martensitic structure or a split transformation.

17.4. Welds in steel

A section of a fusion weld in mild steel is shown in fig. 17.2. Various zones are marked and their relationship to the iron-carbon equilibrium diagram shown. The zones are not sharply defined, but blend into one

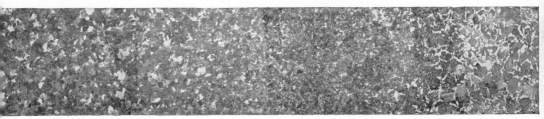

A₁   Unaffected metal

400—

300—

200—

100). Variation of hardness is shown.

another. The unaffected zone, where the base metal has not reached the critical temperature, shows the typical grain structure of a normalized steel. In the transition zone, where the top temperature was between A_1 and A_3, the original pearlite and, towards the weld, increasing amounts of ferrite had changed to austenite on heating. The ferrite and pearlite have reformed on cooling with the pearlite progressively more dispersed towards the weld end. Where the top temperature was above A_3, the metal was entirely austenitic and grain growth occurred as the top temperature became higher. The final structure gives some indication of

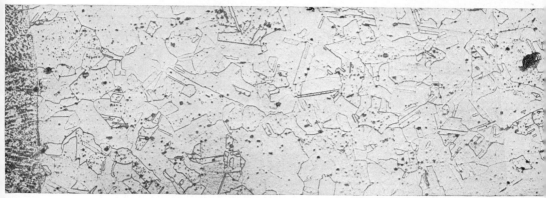

Weld metal   Heat-affected zone

Fig. 17.4.—Fusion weld in work-hardened copper ($\times$ 160).

the size of the austenite grains and shows that there has been grain refining near the A_3-temperature, and a much larger grain size near the weld. The weld metal shows the typical cast-metal structure of columnar grains with a dendritic pattern.

Higher-carbon steels and low-alloy steels have slower critical cooling rates and hence are more prone to form martensite. Any tendency to form martensite is unsatisfactory, as it gives high internal stresses and a brittle structure which may lead to cracking. Fig. 17.3 shows a weld in a medium-carbon steel, together with a graph of the hardness variation.

A metal which when joined by welding will give more satisfactory service is said to possess good *weldability*. In the case of steels, lower carbon contents give better weldability and should be used when possible where welding is to be used as a joining method.

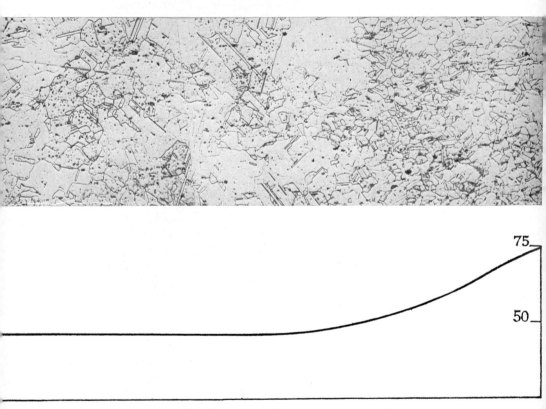

75

50

Decrease in hardness is due to recrystallization and grain growth.

17.5. Welds in non-allotropic materials

Fig. 17.4 shows the heat-affected zone of a weld in work-hardened copper. Progressing through the heat-affected zone towards the weld there are successively, recovery, recrystallization, and grain growth, the effect of which on the mechanical properties is seen in the graph of hardness variation. Any calculation of strength of the article based on the properties of the work-hardened material would not be valid in the vicinity of the weld.

In a precipitation-hardened material, the effect of heating would be to solution-treat the metal and so remove the hardening effects. Depending on the rate of cooling, some subsequent age-hardening might or might not be possible. If the component is small enough to be placed inside any available heat-treatment furnace, the correct heat treatment could be applied to the weld metal and heat-affected zone. Otherwise, as in the case of the cold-worked material, the properties would not be homogeneous throughout the component.

CHAPTER 18

The Nucleus

18.1. The structure of the nucleus

The nucleus of an atom is very small compared with the overall size of the atom (see p. 11). It has a charge $+Ze$ and a mass which is almost an integral multiple of the mass of the hydrogen atom. This integer is known as the mass number A.

Experimental work has shown that the diameter of a nucleus is given by $d = 3 A^{1/3} \times 10^{-15}$ m, i.e. nuclear diameters lie between about 3×10^{-15} m and 19×10^{-15} m.

At one time it was thought that there were only two fundamental particles—the electron and the proton—the proton being the nucleus of the simple hydrogen atom. A nucleus would then be composed of A protons to give the necessary mass and $(A-Z)$ electrons to reduce the total charge to the correct value.

Consideration of the electron in terms of wave mechanics shows that it could exist in the nucleus only if its wavelength were of the same order of magnitude as the nuclear diameter. The energy corresponding to such wavelengths is of the order of hundreds of MeV*, whereas the energies of particles in the nucleus are of a much lower order of magnitude; thus it is reasonable to assume that a nucleus cannot contain an electron and remain stable. The neutron was postulated, being a particle of the same mass as the proton and having zero charge. The existence of the neutron has since been confirmed experimentally. The mass number A is the sum of the number of protons Z and the number of neutrons N.

For the light elements, $N \approx Z$, but as the atomic number increases, N becomes greater than Z.

18.2. Isotopes

Since the chemical properties of an element depend upon the number of electrons which atoms of that element have, and hence on Z, the value of N does not affect the chemical properties. If two nuclei with the same Z but different N existed, then there would be two chemically

---

* MeV = million electron volts. The *electron volt* (eV) is the energy change of a particle with a charge equal to that of an electron when it traverses a potential difference of 1 volt. 1 eV = $1 \cdot 602 \times 10^{-19}$ joule.

identical atoms with different atomic weights. Such atoms do occur, and the two sorts of atoms with the same Z are known as *isotopes*.

Isotopes may be identified and distinguished by writing the Z and A-values together with the symbol for the element as follows: $_ZX^A$. Thus $_1H^1$ is a hydrogen atom. $_2He^4$ is the most common isotope of helium, etc.

Many elements have more than one naturally occurring isotope. The atomic weight of chlorine as determined by chemical methods is 35·5. However, physical tests show that there are two isotopes, $_{17}Cl^{35}$ and $_{17}Cl^{37}$, and there are about three times as many of the former, giving a weighted mean of 35·5. Also many isotopes have been produced in the laboratory by various nuclear reactions.

Fig. 18.1 shows a plot of all the *nuclides*, or types of nuclei that had been reported up to the year 1956. The solid circles represent isotopes with stable nuclei and the crosses are the ones with unstable nuclei (see p. 269). The two terms *isotones* and *isobars* which appear in the diagram refer to nuclei with the same N and same A respectively.

18.3. Mass defect

The standard that has been adopted for expressing the masses of atoms is the *atomic mass unit* (a.m.u.). The unit used by physicists is one-sixteenth of the mass of an atom of the most abundant isotope of oxygen (i.e. this isotope has a mass of 16·000 a.m.u.).* The masses of a hydrogen atom, $_1H^1$, a neutron, $_0n^1$, and a helium atom, $_2He^4$, are respectively 1·00814, 1·00898, and 4·00388 a.m.u. The helium atom is made up of two protons, two neutrons, and two electrons which have a total mass of $2 \times (1·00814 + 1·00898)$, i.e. 4·03424 a.m.u., which is 0·03036 a.m.u. more than the actual mass. This apparent loss of mass is referred to as the *mass defect*.

It has been shown, as a consequence of Einstein's relativity theory, that mass and energy are equivalent, the relation between energy E and mass m being $E = mc^2$, where c is the velocity of light.†

When protons and neutrons are combined to form a helium nucleus, the loss of mass is converted to energy according to this relationship. The mass defect per *nucleon* (proton or neutron) in this case is 0·00759 a.m.u. and is equivalent to 7·06 MeV. This is called the *binding energy* per nucleon and is a measure of the stability of the nucleus. If the atom

---

* The chemists' unit is one-sixteenth of the average mass of the naturally-occurring oxygen atoms. As 0·04% and 0·20% of these atoms are isotopes of mass 17 and 18 respectively, the chemists' unit is about 0·03% greater than the physicists' unit.

† Hence 1 a.m.u. = 931 MeV.

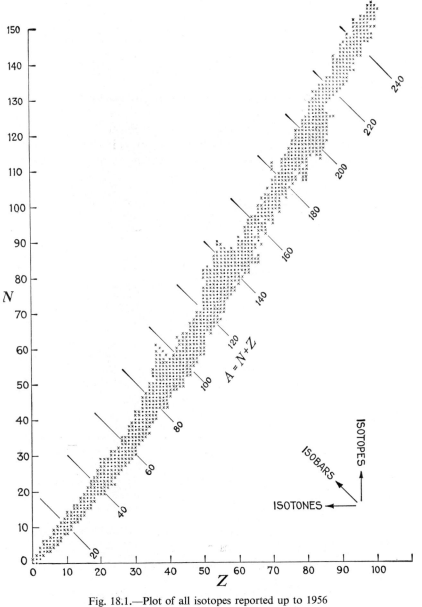

Fig. 18.1.—Plot of all isotopes reported up to 1956

● naturally-occurring or stable isotopes.   × artificially-produced isotopes

were formed from the elementary particles, this energy would be released either as kinetic energy of particles or as electromagnetic radiation.

The binding energy per nucleon is

$$931 \frac{ZM_H + (A-Z)M_N - M}{A} \text{ MeV}$$

where M_H = mass of $_1H^1$ atom, M_N = mass of neutron, M = actual mass of atom in a.m.u.

The manner in which the binding energy per nucleon varies with atomic mass is shown in fig. 18.2. From the curve it may be seen that the nuclei of elements with mass numbers of about 80 are the most stable,

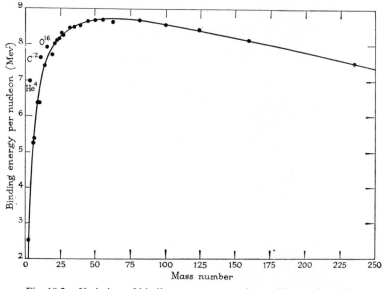

Fig. 18.2.—Variation of binding energy per nucleon with atomic weight
[Glasstone and Edlund]

as energy would have to be supplied to change them into lighter elements.

If nuclei in this middle mass range could be produced either by combining light nuclei or by splitting heavy nuclei, a great deal of energy would be released.

The combination of light elements to form heavier ones is known as *nuclear fusion*. It is the source of energy in the sun, and fusion reactions have been initiated by man, but it has not yet been utilized as a practical source of power.

The splitting of heavy nuclei is known as *nuclear fission*. It may occur spontaneously, but only at a slow rate. The probability of fission is vastly increased if the nucleus is excited, i.e. its energy increased, by some 5 or 6 MeV. In nuclear reactors this excitation is provided by neutron bombardment (see Section 18.5). The excited nucleus may then break down to give two nuclei of mass number about 70–160 and 2 or 3 neutrons. As can be seen from fig. 18.2, the process releases about 1 MeV of energy per nucleon, or approximately 200 MeV per fission. The energy appears mainly as kinetic energy of the fission-product nuclei, some of the re- mainder being kinetic energy of the neutrons and energy of radioactive emission. Most of the energy is converted to heat in the reactor, and this heat is used to provide power. The neutrons present among the fission products can make these processes self-sustaining.

18.4. Nuclear reactions

So far reference has been made primarily to elements whose nuclei do not change spontaneously. These are the ones marked as solid circles in fig. 18.1. Other nuclei are unstable and will tend to change into stable nuclei by one of the several processes listed in Table 18.1. These changes can occur only if the total mass of the products is less than the initial mass, i.e. if there is an increase in the mass defect, which is released as energy. These processes are known as *radioactive decay* processes.

TABLE 18.1—DECAY PROCESSES OF UNSTABLE NUCLEI

Decay mode	Description	Change in atomic number	Change in mass number
α	α-particle ($_2He^4$ nucleus) emitted from nucleus	-2	-4
β^-	electron emitted	$+1$	0
β^+	positron (positive electron) emitted from nucleus	-1	0
K-capture	capture of an orbital electron from the K-shell by the nucleus	-1	0
isomeric transition	nucleus changes from excited to stable or ground state by emission of energy as γ-rays	0	0

α- and β-decay and K·capture may also be accompanied by the emission of energy in the form of γ-rays.

It is plausible that α-particles can emerge from the nucleus, but there are no electrons present to provide a source of β-rays. The electron of

β^- decay can be regarded as being formed from a neutron which changes into a proton and an electron.

$$_0n^1 \rightarrow p + e^-$$

In doing this, there is a change in the binding energy, this energy contributing towards the kinetic energy of the electron and the energy of the accompanying γ-ray.

Positrons are particles of the same mass and magnitude of charge as an electron but of opposite sign. They may be formed in the nucleus by the reaction

$$p \rightarrow _0n^1 + e^+$$

Positrons are short-lived, one becoming annihilated when it meets an electron.

$$e^+ + e^- \rightarrow \gamma\text{-rays}$$

An unstable nucleus can change to a stable one by altering its nuclear charge without changing its mass number. Nuclei with excess neutrons can become stable by β^- emission and those with excess protons by β^+ emission or K-capture.

Each nucleus has a certain probability of undergoing decay in a given time, so that the amount of unchanged material decreases exponentially. The probability of decay is usually expressed in terms of the *half-life*, that is, the time taken for any given quantity of the particular isotope to decrease to half the original quantity. Half-lives as short as 10^{-9} second and as long as 10^{17} years have been observed.

Unstable nuclei do occur in the earth's crust, but the only ones now remaining are those which have a long half-life or are produced by decay of a long-lived " parent " nucleus. All elements with atomic numbers greater than that of lead are unstable.

18.5. Reaction cross-sections

Other unstable nuclei may be produced by bombarding " target " nuclei with " projectiles " which are other nuclei or neutrons. The projectile may be absorbed by the target nucleus forming a new nucleus which will normally be in a highly excited state. It will change rapidly from this state, either losing energy by γ-radiation and reverting to the ground state of the new nucleus, or forming a third type of nucleus or undergoing fission (see Section 18.3). The product nuclei in each case may be stable or also decay in due course.

Two examples of the effect of neutron absorption are:

$$_{27}Co^{59} + _{0}n^{1} \rightarrow _{27}Co^{60} \text{ excited}$$

$$_{27}Co^{60} \text{ excited} \underset{\text{rapid}}{\rightarrow} _{27}Co^{60} \text{ ground state} + \text{energy}$$

$$_{27}Co^{60} \text{ ground state} \underset{\substack{\text{half-life 5·25 years}}}{\rightarrow} _{28}Ni^{60} + \beta + \gamma$$

and

$$_{92}U^{235} + _{0}n^{1} \rightarrow _{92}U^{236} \text{ excited}$$

$$_{92}U^{236} \text{ excited} \begin{cases} \text{either} \nearrow \text{fission} \\ \text{rapid} \\ \text{or} \searrow \\ _{92}U^{236} \text{ ground state} \end{cases}$$

$$_{92}U^{236} \text{ ground state} \underset{\substack{\text{half-life} \\ 2·4 \times 10^{7} \text{ years}}}{\rightarrow} _{90}Th^{232} + \alpha$$

Most fission products are β^{-} radioactive due to being neutron-rich.

The probability of interaction of a moving particle with a nucleus or other target depends on the kind of particle, its energy, and the target involved. It can be expressed quantitatively as the *cross-section* for interaction. In the remainder of this Section, discussion is restricted to the interaction of neutrons with nuclei.

Consider a sheet of material placed in the path of a stream of the moving particles. Suppose that the stream intensity (i.e. number of particles per unit area per second) decreases, on traversing a thickness dx, from I to $I + dI$ due to interactions of some particles with the targets.

If N_0 is the number of atoms per unit volume of the material, then a unit area of thickness dx of the sheet of the material contains $N_0 dx$ atoms. If each nucleus has an effective area σ, i.e. the area within which a neutron must pass if it is to interact with the nucleus, then

$$-\frac{dI}{I} = \sigma N_0 dx$$

σ is known as the nuclear cross-section for the particular reaction involved. The intensity I of a beam after traversing a sheet of thickness x will be given by

$$I = I_0 e^{-\sigma N_0 x}$$

where I_0 is the intensity of the incident stream.

Cross-sections are usually expressed in units of *barns*, one barn equalling 10^{-24} cm^2. The total cross-section for the interaction of a neutron with a particular kind of nucleus may be divided in the proportions of the probabilities of the various types of interaction that may occur, that is into scattering cross-section and absorption cross-section, the latter being further subdivided into capture and fission cross-sections.

Scattering cross-sections are of the order of a few barns for most materials and are largely independent of the neutron energy. Absorption cross-sections vary greatly with the speed or energy of the neutron, being much greater for slow-moving than for fast neutrons, and also vary greatly from element to element.

$\Sigma = N_0\sigma$ is known as the *macroscopic cross-section*. It can be shown that $1/\Sigma$ is the corresponding mean free path (see p. 31) of the moving particle.

A fast neutron, such as one formed in the fission of a $_{92}U^{235}$ nucleus, has an energy of the order of 2 MeV. At each collision which causes scattering, there will be an energy interchange between the neutron and the particle with which it collides, resulting in a decrease of energy of the neutron. When the energy has decreased to the order of the thermal energy of the particles with which it comes in collision its mean energy (of the order of 0·025 eV) will not decrease further. The neutron is then known as a *thermal neutron*.

The fission cross-section of $_{92}U^{235}$ for thermal neutrons is much larger than for high-energy neutrons, whereas $_{92}U^{238}$ will undergo fission only after interaction with high-energy neutrons.

To make a fission process a self-sustaining chain reaction, as is necessary in a nuclear reactor, one of the neutrons produced per fission must be available to promote another fission. Although each fission produces, on average, 2·5 neutrons, capture and loss due to leakage from the system have to be considered.

Natural uranium, consisting of about 99·3% of U^{238} and 0·7% of U^{235}, has a relatively low fission cross-section for high-energy neutrons compared with the cross-sections for non-fission reactions, so that it is impossible to maintain a chain reaction with high-energy neutrons in natural uranium. By using a fuel enriched in U^{235} a chain reaction with fast neutrons can be achieved.

A chain reaction is possible in natural uranium if fission is mainly due to slow neutrons and if the neutrons are slowed down in a *moderator*, which is placed between the various fuel elements. The moderator must be of a material which has a high scattering cross-section and a relatively small absorption cross-section.

18.6. Radiation damage due to scattering

Owing to absorption and to scattering, various effects occur which alter the mechanical and physical properties of the material irradiated, such effects being known as *radiation damage*. A few of those effects which modify the mechanical properties will be discussed here.*

When fast-moving electrons are scattered, the atoms that cause the scattering are knocked out of place by the recoil and move with high energies which become dissipated in further collisions. The scattered atoms are known as *knock-ons*. Thermal neutrons do not have sufficient energy to cause any knock-ons.

Atoms are knocked out of place, leaving vacancies, and go into interstitial positions. The energy of a single vacancy in copper is about 1 eV and of an interstitial atom is about 4 eV, whereas 25 eV are needed to create a vacancy-interstitial pair. A fast-moving neutron can therefore create many such point defects while it is being slowed down. The excess energy between that needed to create a vacancy-interstitial pair and the energy remaining in the defects is released as heat, so that there is also intense heating in the zone in which the neutron is slowed down, a *thermal spike*. The temperature rise is sufficient to cause annihilation of many of the defects by diffusion of the interstitials to vacancies, but a proportion remains.

Metals subjected to neutron irradiation become harder, and if they have a notch ductile-brittle transition (see p. 185), the transition temperature is raised (increases of 80° C in steel and 100° C in molybdenum have been reported). It is thought that the defects migrate to the dislocations already present and have an anchoring effect. There is less hardening due to neutron irradiation in a work-hardened metal, and even softening in a very heavily work-hardened material.

The damage can be restored by annealing, causing the interstitials and vacancies to migrate together and cancel. However, the stored energy is high, sufficient to cause a considerable temperature rise if it were released. In graphite, for example, it could raise the temperature by 200° C.

Atomic rearrangements are also possible which can lead to various effects, such as formation of a ferromagnetic phase in austenitic stainless steel.

18.7. Radiation damage due to absorption

The various reactions possible when a neutron is absorbed by a nucleus have been discussed in Section 18.5.

The new elements formed may alloy with or combine chemically with the original element giving dimensional changes and hence internal stressing, among other effects, or may set up conditions where corrosion

---

* For a review, see A. H. Cottrell, " Effects of Neutron Irradiation on Metals and Alloys," *Met. Rev.*, Vol. 1, 1956, p. 479. Also A. H. Cottrell, Thomas Hawkesley Memorial Lecture, 1959, Inst. Mech. Engrs.

is possible, whereas the original material was corrosion-resistant in its surroundings.

The transmutation products may be inert gases, such as krypton or xenon which do not combine chemically with the parent material. Initially the gas molecules will migrate to vacancies, which will then diffuse together so that pockets of gas are formed, the pressure becoming so great that the metal swells.

18.8. Conclusion

It is obvious from this extremely brief survey that in the application of materials in the nuclear-energy field a number of new factors appear, and the problem of selection of materials is no longer governed solely by the consideration of the straightforward factors such as strength, corrosion resistance, and weldability.

Features such as adequately large or small cross-sections and the effects of irradiation may severely restrict the choice for certain applications, and adequate corrosion resistance, etc., may then reduce the possibilities still further. Many of the rarer elements, which had no previous engineering applications because of their scarcity and cost, are found to have favourable properties in some of the cases where choice is severely restricted and are emerging to an era of popularity.

QUESTIONS

1. Describe the structure of the rubidium atom of mass number 87 (Rb^{87}) in terms of the elementary particles.

This naturally-occurring isotope is radioactive, exhibiting β-decay and having a half-life of 6×10^{10} years. Explain this statement. What is the element formed in the decay process? [MST]

2. What isotope does $_6C^{14}$ become after radioactive emission of a β-particle? What isotope does $_{92}U^{238}$ become after emission of an a-particle?

3. $_{92}U^{238}$ will absorb a neutron and then emit a β-particle. What isotope does it become? If $_{92}U^{235}$ absorbs a neutron and then undergoes fission to form two atoms of the same isotope and two neutrons, what is the isotope?

4. Calculate the binding energy per nucleon of (a) $_{92}U^{238}$, and (b) $_{45}Rh^{103}$. These are the abundant isotopes and the atomic weights may be considered to be entirely due to them. (The atomic weights given in Table 2.1 are quoted in terms of the chemists' mass unit.)

5. What energy is released by 1 gm of $_{92}U^{235}$ undergoing fission into two approximately equal parts? (Binding energies change little for small changes in atomic number, and the results of question 4 should be used.)

APPENDIX I

Some Equilibrium Diagrams of Interest and Importance*

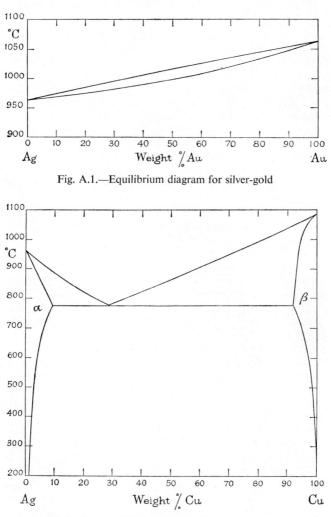

Fig. A.1.—Equilibrium diagram for silver-gold

Fig. A.2.—Equilibrium diagram for silver-copper

* These are based on diagrams in the *Metals Reference Book*, second edition edited by Smithells. Butterworth.

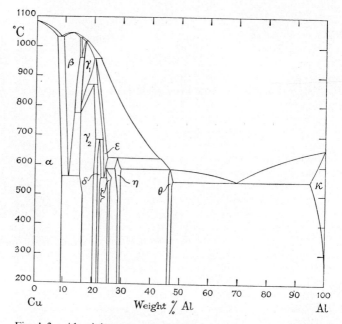

Fig. A.3.—Aluminium-copper. (Aluminium bronze up to 15% Cu.)

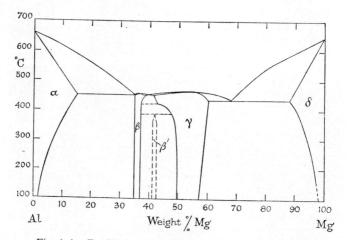

Fig. A.4.—Equilibrium diagram for aluminium-magnesium

276

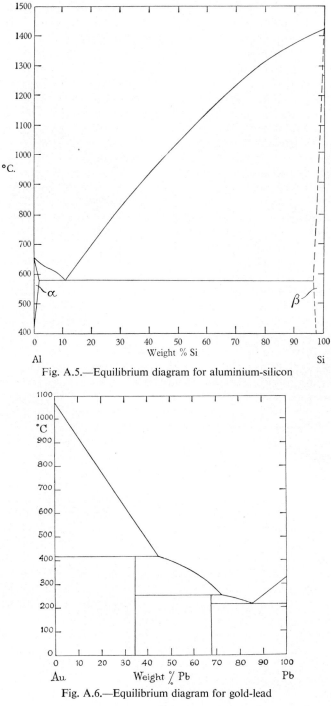

Fig. A.5.—Equilibrium diagram for aluminium-silicon

Fig. A.6.—Equilibrium diagram for gold-lead

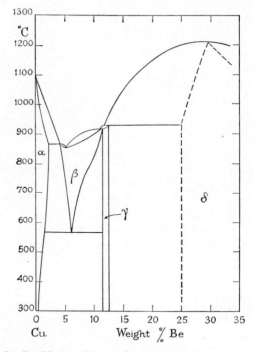

Fig. A.7.—Equilibrium diagram for copper-berryllium, copper-rich
end (beryllium bronze)

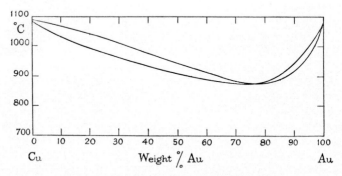

Fig. A.8.—Equilibrium diagram for copper-gold

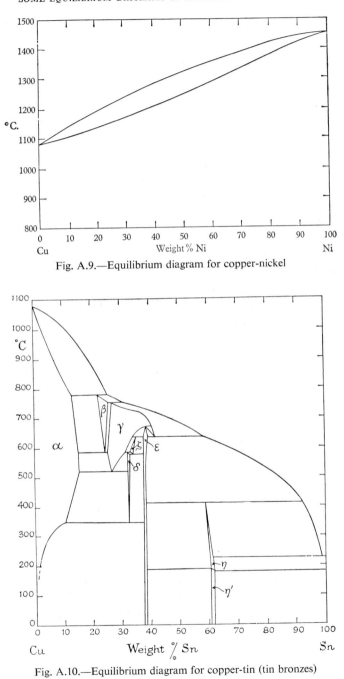

Fig. A.9.—Equilibrium diagram for copper-nickel

Fig. A.10.—Equilibrium diagram for copper-tin (tin bronzes)

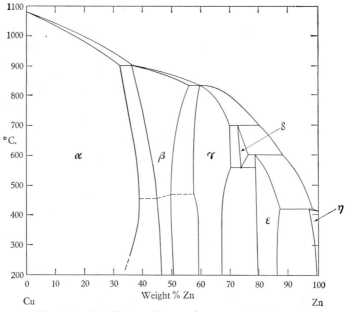

Fig. A.11.—Equilibrium diagram for copper-zinc (brasses)

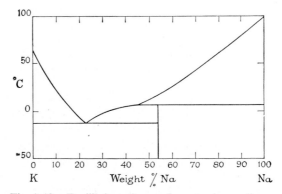

Fig. A.12.—Equilibrium diagram for potassium-sodium

280

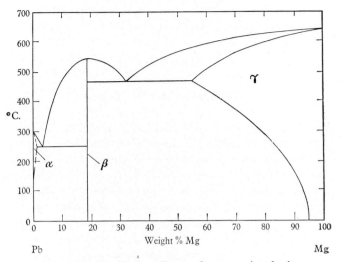

Fig. A.13.—Equilibrium diagram for magnesium-lead

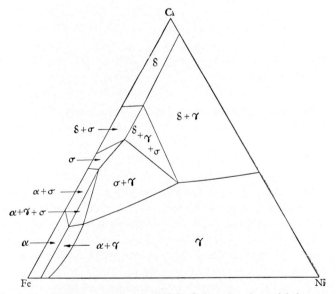

Fig. A.14.—Isothermal section at 650° C of chromium-iron-nickel system

APPENDIX II

Equilibrium and Free Energy

As has been shown in various chapters in this book, materials can change their structure, phase or state due to changes in temperature and pressure. For any given values of these variables there will be a particular configuration which is the stable form, and at certain values two forms may exist in equilibrium. Of the forms possible for a system the stable one is that for which the free energy is least, and when two forms exist in equilibrium, their free energies are equal.

The concept of free energy will be outlined briefly here, but for a more complete treatment and proofs of the statements made, the reader is referred to textbooks on thermodynamics.

If a system, that is a portion of matter around which a hypothetical control surface may be drawn, has the following properties:

volume V

pressure p

absolute temperature T

internal energy U

entropy S

then the *Helmoltz free energy* F and the *Gibbs free energy* G are respectively

$$F = U - TS$$

and
$$G = U + pV - TS$$

The internal energy of a system is the sum of the energies of all the particles which make up the system, that is the kinetic energies of the particles which depend on their vibrational motions, etc., and the potential energies which are due to the forces between the particles (e.g. the electrostatic forces between ions and the Van der Waals forces between atoms and molecules).

Entropy is defined as follows: If a system absorbs an infinitesimal quantity of heat dQ in a reversible manner, when at an absolute temperature T, then the increase of entropy of the system is

$$dS = dQ/T$$

If the change is irreversible, then

$$dS > dQ/T$$

By the principle of conservation of energy, the internal energy of a system can be altered only by giving or receiving energy in the form of heat or work. The First Law of Thermodynamics states that the change of internal energy dU is the sum of dQ, the heat supplied to the system, and dW, the work done on the system, i.e.

$$dU = dQ + dW$$

If in any small change, the system changes its volume by dV, then it does an amount of work pdV against the surroundings:

$$dW = -pdV$$

Hence by the First Law

$$dU = dQ - pdV$$

But by the definition of entropy

$$TdS \geq dQ$$

the equality applying to reversible changes, i.e. changes under conditions of equilibrium.

$$TdS \geq dU + pdV$$

or

$$dU + pdV - TdS \leq 0$$

If the system is in equilibrium

$$dU + pdV - TdS = 0$$

For equilibrium under conditions of constant temperature and volume, $pdV = 0$, so that

$$dU - TdS = 0$$

or

$$\begin{aligned} dF &= d(U - TS) \\ &= dU - TdS - SdT \\ &= dU - TdS \quad (\text{since } dT = 0) \\ &= 0 \end{aligned}$$

For equilibrium under conditions of constant temperature and pressure,

$$\begin{aligned} dG &= d(U + pV - TS) \\ &= dU + pdV + Vdp - TdS - SdT \\ &= dU + pdV - TdS \quad (\text{since } dT = 0 \text{ and } dp = 0) \\ &= 0 \end{aligned}$$

Thus for equilibrium under these conditions either the Helmholtz free energy or the Gibbs free energy will remain constant for small changes of the remaining variables, and it can be shown that the actual value of F or G will be a minimum under such conditions.

The form of free energy to be considered is related to the conditions for equilibrium. In solids and liquids at atmospheric pressure, the pV term is sufficiently small compared with U and TS to be neglected, so that a condition of minimum F is adequate to define all equilibrium changes in these states.

ANSWERS TO NUMERICAL QUESTIONS

Chapter 2

1. 2, 4, 2, 3, 5, 3, 2, 3, 6, 7
4. 1215 Å; 18720 Å
6. 1.82×10^6 m/sec; 9.36 eV
7. 1.10×10^{-33} m

Chapter 3

1. 86.5
2. 6.15×10^2 m/sec
3. 1.535 newton/m^2
5. 37.4

Chapter 4

3. 2.49 Å; 8.96 gm/cm^3
4. 2.039 Å; 1.442 Å; 2.355 Å

Chapter 6

4. $LaSn_3$, La_2Sn_3, La_2Sn
5. 8.15

Chapter 7

1. Liquid (22% Ni) 47%; solid (37% Ni) 53%
2. $PbMg_2$; at 500° C: 30Pb/70Mg solid solution;
          at 300° C: β-phase ($PbMg_2$) 21%
                      γ-phase (82% Mg) 79%
3. Na_2K; Liquid (33% Na) 13%, Na_2K 87%
6. 320°C, 465°C; Solid solution (11.3% A in B) 22%,
   A_2B 78% divided as follows:
       primary A_2B 34.5%
       eutectic A_2B 32.2%
   precipitated from eutectic solid solution   11.3%
9. (a) One phase   30 Cr 30 Fe 40 Ni
   (b) Two phases   γ   38 Cr 10 Fe 52 Ni 30%
                      δ   83 Cr 10 Fe   7 Ni 70%
   (c) Three phases γ   35 Cr 30 Fe 35 Ni 45%
                      δ   65 Cr 26 Fe   8 Ni 38%
                      σ   53 Cr 39 Fe   8 Ni 17%

Chapter 8

1. $-2 \cdot 73\%$
2. $+2 \cdot 97\%$ assuming true close packing [i.e. $c/a = \sqrt{(2/3)}$]
   $+3 \cdot 6\%$ from actual c/a ratio
3. $1 \cdot 24$ Å; $3 \cdot 50$ Å
5. $0 \cdot 41$

Chapter 9

2. $3 \cdot 8 \times 10^{-19}$ joule/atom
4. (a) $0 \cdot 0937$; (b) $0 \cdot 107$
5. 10^4 cal/gm mole $= 6 \cdot 9 \times 10^{-20}$ joule/molecule

Chapter 10

2. (a) 110 Lb/in^2
   (b) $25°\ 10'$; $16°\ 29'$
   (c) 172 Lb/in^2
3. $120 \cdot 4$ Lb/in^2
5. 6680

Chapter 12

1. (a) $10 \cdot 2$ Tons/in^2
   (b) $8 \cdot 4$ Tons/in^2; 13%; 64%
2. 50 Tons/in^2; $0 \cdot 22$; $29 \cdot 5$ Tons/in^2
3. $\sigma_t = 8 \cdot 8\ \varepsilon^{0 \cdot 215}$ Tons/in^2; $5 \cdot 23$ Tons/in^2
4. $15 \cdot 4$
5. $22 \cdot 6$
6. (a) $0 \cdot 122$; (b) $7 \cdot 03$ Tons
7. $51 \cdot 6\%$; $0 \cdot 845$ in
8. $0 \cdot 415\ H_D$

Chapter 14

4. (a) 100% austenite
   (b) 8% ferrite, 92% austenite
   (c) 50% ferrite and pearlite, 50% austenite
   (d) 50% ferrite and pearlite, 50% martensite
   (e) 50% ferrite and pearlite, 50% tempered martensite
7. $0 \cdot 65$ in; $474\ H_D$

Chapter 15

3. 360, 470. No
4. $1 \cdot 9$ in, $3 \cdot 7$ in

Chapter 18

1. $_{38}Sr^{87}$
2. $_{7}N^{14}$, $_{90}Th^{234}$
3. $_{93}Np^{239}$, $_{46}Pd^{117}$
4. (a) $12 \cdot 1 \times 10^{-13}$ joule = $7 \cdot 5$ MeV
   (b) $13 \cdot 6 \times 10^{-13}$ joule = $8 \cdot 5$ MeV
5. 9×10^{10} joule

INDEX